Engineering & Construction
Project
Management

Engineering & Construction
Project Management

Arthur E. Kerridge
and
Charles H. Vervalin
Editors

Gulf Publishing Company
Book Division
Houston, London, Paris, Tokyo

Engineering & Construction
Project
Management

Library of Congress Cataloging in Publication Data
Main entry under title:

Engineering & construction project management.

Includes bibliographies and index.
1. Engineering—Management—Addresses, essays, lectures. 2. Construction industry—Management—Addresses, essays, lectures. 3. Industrial project management—Addresses, essays, lectures. I. Kerridge, Arthur, II. Vervalin, Charles H. III. Title. IV. Title: Engineering and construction project management.

TA190.E52 M 1986   624′.068   85-24799
ISBN 0-87201-745-1

Contents

Chapter 18 – Contingency, Risk, and Sensitivity Analysis, 239
A. E. Kerridge

Types of project estimates. Fixed capital cost estimation. Estimate accuracy. The need for a contingency. Determining contingency. Maximum risk contingency. Other methods. Sensitivity. Judgment factor.

PART VI: COST CONTROL, 253

Chapter 19 – Control the Cost of New Plants, 255
John H. Hanna

Execution plan. Design philosophy. Principles of cost control. Detail procedures.

Chapter 20 – Control Project Costs Effectively, 261
A. E. Kerridge

The estimate—variations, procedures. Basic engineering—cost influence. Equipment—control equipment costs. Commodities—document review, commodity price control. Home office—home office costs, reduce HO manhours. Construction—detailed estimate, control field manhours, construction supervision. Field subcontracts. Schedule—optimization. Project changes.

PART VII: TRACKING AND TRENDING, 275

Chapter 21 – Check Project Progress with Bell and "S" Curves, 277
A. E. Kerridge

The curve applications. Engineering curves. Individual discipline curves. Unsuitable curves. Plan, measure, report. Periodic recording. Manpower forecasting. Master project schedule. Narrow band. Construction curves. Plan and track.

Chapter 22 – Predict Project Results with Trending Methods, 291
A. E. Kerridge

Applications. Limitations. Benefits. Projected deviations. Trend projection. Performance trending. Schedule trending. Cost trending. Material trending. Simplicity.

PART VIII: PROCUREMENT, 311

Preface

An old saying goes, "Those who can, do—those who can't, write about it." Fortunately, some skilled *doers* are also good writers. And that's good, because communication is an essential part of project management. A project manager cannot manage if he can't communicate his ideas to others. Verbal communication alone is not adequate. Written directions and procedures are essential for effective execution.

This book comprises 25 project management articles by 13 different "doer" authors who have published in HYDROCARBON PROCESSING Magazine since 1975. The articles all have lasting information that has stood the test of time. The management methods described are good for today and tomorrow as well.

Today a plethora of computer programs claim to be able to "project manage your job." The question may be asked, "Why doesn't this book discuss up-to-date computer techniques?" The fact is that the computer is only a tool. The programs are skillful conversions of age-old principles into coded statements that can be interpreted electronically. Newer, faster, and more "user friendly" computer programs will continue to be marketed, but they will still all be based upon the same fundamental principles of project management and control that have been developed and tested over the years. The articles in this book describe practical approaches to project management problems that have been found to work by experienced practitioners. Anyone using a convenient computer program as a tool will be that much more effective if he understands the underlying project management principles.

Readers who seek a current view of computer systems should contact the Project Management Institute, Drexel Hill, Pa. PMI, in its literature and activities, has long tracked the computer's evolution in project management.

Most articles in this book describe management styles or communication techniques for which there never will be an electronic replacement. All projects require the expenditure of human hours and management can only be applied to the human interface.

A book that is a collection of articles by different authors over a ten-year period has both strengths and weaknesses. Clearly, the book will not have the same continuity and logical development of subject matter compared with one on the subject by a single author. On the other hand, one strength of the book is that it offers diverse opinions and proves that successful projects can be run with many different styles of project management.

The execution of a project from concept through to full on-stream operation involves many different people in project managerial positions. There is the owner's product line manager who is the project economic manager and project sponsor, the owner's project manager who is responsible for engineering, procurement and construction, and one or more contractor project managers who are responsible for different aspects of a project. The project will pass through the phases of economic feasibility, process design, engineering, procurement, construction and start-up. And each phase is a separate mini-project. At each phase, different managers will be responsible. At the completion of every project, several people will claim with honesty that they were the "project manager" on that project. And all may be correct. They will have been the project manager responsible for a specific area or phase. In the end, a team effort builds a successful project.

The articles have been grouped under section titles that match the main message contained in the article. Many articles discuss other topics, and to cover this an additional cross-reference index has been provided.

Most of the information in this book was developed in the late '70s and early '80s when engineering and construction work for energy projects was at its peak. There was unbounded optimism and belief in the continued demand for mega-projects in energy and related industries. The optimistic forecasts and projections have changed drastically. Both owners and E/C contractors are having to remain flexible to react to an unknown future. To some extent, there has been a reaction of retrenchment and a return to the less complicated and more streamlined methods of earlier times. Project management, which has learned to become sophisticated and complex, may re-learn some of the simpler and more direct methods used in the past, before the era of the mega-projects. This book will benefit project managers who work toward that end.

Arthur E. Kerridge
Charles H. Vervalin

Part 1: Project Financing

Chapter 1

Make Your Own Econometric Model

SUBJECT-PROJECT PHASE MATRIX

SUBJECTS		PREAWARD 1	INITIATION 2	ENGINEERING 3	PROCUREMENT 4	CONSTRUCTION 5
A	FINANCIAL/CONTRACTUAL	●				
B	ORGANIZATION/EXECUTION PLANNING					
C	MANAGING PEOPLE/COMMUNICATION					
D	ESTIMATING/COST CONTROL	●				
E	RISK ANALYSIS	●				
F	SCHEDULING	●				
G	TRACKING/TRENDING					
H	PROGRESS/PRODUCTIVITY MEASUREMENT					
I	MATERIAL MANAGEMENT					

A. E. Kerridge

The factors affecting the feasibility and the potential profitability of a new project are of concern to marketers, developers, and investors (Fig. 1). Complex econometric models which analyze these variables have been developed to run on large computers. (Econometrics is the use of mathematical and statistical methods to verify and develop economic theories.) Now, a personal computer will suffice.

In creating the PC econometric model, six factors must be considered:

1. Capital costs. The capital costs of a new project can usually be estimated with reasonable accuracy (say, within ± 15 percent). The capital cost does not have a great effect on the overall return, but nevertheless is an extremely important number for two reasons: First, the capital is required "up front." The money has to be found and be spent many years before there is a payout. It is always embarassing and more difficult to raise additional funds after a project has started. Second, the overall profitability of a project is usually measured in terms of Return on Investment (ROI). Many operating concerns or investors set goals on ROI (say, a minimum of 20 percent per annum pretax). The average annual ROI is the total earnings divided by the specified project life times the total investment. A 10% increase in the capital cost will cause a corresponding 10% drop in the ROI for a project with a 10-year life. A 20% ROI on a project with a 10-year life means that the project will earn 20 percent for 10 years, which is 200 percent over the life of the project or 100 percent over five years. This is equivalent to a payout period of five years.

FACTOR	PROBABLE ACCURACY OF ESTIMATE/ PREDICTION	POSSIBLE EFFECT ON PROJECT PROFITABILITY
1. LAND & SITE COSTS	GOOD	MINOR
2. ENGINEERING COSTS	GOOD	MINOR
3. EQUIPMENT & MATERIAL COSTS	GOOD	MAJOR
4. CONSTRUCTION COSTS	FAIR	MAJOR
5. INITIAL START UP COSTS	FAIR	INTERMEDIATE
6. CONSTRUCTION DURATION	GOOD	MINOR
7. WORKING CAPITAL	FAIR	MAJOR
8. OPERATING COSTS	FAIR	MAJOR
9. PLANT LABOR RATES	POOR	MAJOR
10. COST OF FEEDSTOCKS	POOR	MAJOR
11. COST OF UTILITIES	POOR	MAJOR
12. PRODUCT SALES VOLUME	POOR	MAJOR
13. PRODUCT SALES PRICE	POOR	MAJOR
14. RESIDUAL PLANT VALUE	POOR	MINOR
15. TAXATION RATES	POOR	MAJOR
16. RATES OF INFLATION	POOR	MAJOR
17. INTEREST RATES	POOR	MAJOR
18. CURRENCY EXCHANGE RATES	POOR	MAJOR
19. GENERAL ECONOMIC CLIMATE	POOR	INTERMEDIATE
20. GOVERNMENT INFLUENCES	POOR	MAJOR

Figure 1—Major factors affecting the project's profitability.

The need to maintain a high ROI to attract investors explains why there is so much pressure to keep the initial capital investment to a minimum. Frequently, desirable options and expansion items are deferred. Features that will improve yields and increase efficiency are carefully scrutinized if they add to the cost.

Fig. 2 is a checklist of typical items that make up the capital cost of a new project. Major elements in the capital cost estimate are 1. land and site development costs, 2. engineering, procurement and construction costs, and 3. startup costs.

The land or site costs should be noted separately, since these will have residual value at the end of the project life. For all projects there should be a substantial sum set aside for startup (say 15 percent to 20 percent). This sum may need to be higher for new unproven projects and could be less for established projects. A suitable contingency or management reserve should also be included in the capital cost estimate.

"If ROI is so important, why not increase the plant life from 10 to 15 years or longer?" The answer is that few HPI projects can be considered

MAJOR CLASSIFICATION	DETAIL ITEMS
1. SITE	PROPERTY COST, FEES, SURVEYS, CLEARING AND GRADING, ROADS, RAILROADS, FENCES, PAVED AREAS, LANDSCAPING.
2. BUILDINGS FOUNDATIONS & STRUCTURES	PROCESS, AUXILIARY, AND ADMINISTRATION BUILDINGS, PROCESS STRUCTURES, PIPE RACKS, PLATFORMS, LADDERS, MAINTENANCE/HANDLING FACILITIES AND FOUNDATIONS.
3. BUILDING SERVICES	PLUMBING, HEATING, VENTILATION, AIR CONDITIONING, FIRE FIGHTING, LIGHTING, ALARMS AND COMMUNICATIONS.
4. PROCESS EQUIPMENT	AN ITEMIZED PROCESS EQUIPMENT LIST PREPARED FROM CHECKED PROCESS FLOW SHEETS.
5. NON PROCESS EQUIPMENT	FIRE FIGHTING, MAINTENANCE, STORAGE, AND OTHER MOBILE EQUIPMENT. FURNITURE, LOCKERS, OFFICE, LABORATORY, AND HOUSEKEEPING EQUIPMENT, TOOLS.
6. PROCESS AUXILIARIES	PROCESS PIPING AND SUPPORTS, INSTRUMENTATION, INSULATION, ELECTRIC WIRING, SWITCHGEAR, GROUNDING AND CONTROLS.
7. UTILITIES	STEAM PLANT, POWER SUPPLY AND GENERATION, AIR PLANT, REFRIGERATION, WATER SUPPLY AND TREATMENT, EFFLUENT OUTFALL AND TREATMENT, SEWERS AND DRAINS, INERT GAS.
8. OFFSITE FACILITIES	DISTRIBUTION PIPELINES FOR STEAM, CONDENSATE, WATER, GAS, AIR, FUEL, ELECTRICAL SUPPLY LINES, FEEDSTOCKS AND FINISHED PRODUCTS HANDLING AND STORAGE, TANKS, SPHERES, DRUMS, BINS, SILOS, RAILCAR AND TRUCK SCALES, BLOWDOWN AND FLARE FACILITIES.
9. ENGINEERING COSTS	ADMINISTRATION, PROCESS, PROJECT, AND DESIGN ENGINEERING, PROCUREMENT, EXPEDITING, INSPECTION, REPRODUCTION, COMPUTERS, COMMUNICATIONS, FEES.
10. CONSTRUCTION COSTS	CONSTRUCTION LABOR, SUPERVISION, EQUIPMENT, TOOLS, TEMPORARY FACILITIES, CONSUMABLES, TESTING.
11. MISCELLANEOUS ITEMS	CATALYSTS AND CHEMICALS, SPARE PARTS, SURPLUS EQUIPMENT, CONSTRUCTION SPARES, SHIPPING CHARGES, TAXES AND INSURANCE, DUTIES, START-UP EXPENSES, AND INITIAL CHARGES, ERRORS AND OMISSIONS, MANAGEMENT RESERVE.

Figure 2—General checklist of items in the capital cost estimate.

secure after 10 years of operation. There are the possibilities of obsolescence due to new technology or changed market conditions. Most investors would like to see a project life of not more than 10 years, after which time the plant can be scrapped, rebuilt or undergo a major revamp and modernization.

2. Working capital. Fig. 3 is a checklist of typical items that are considered working capital. Working capital is also needed "up front." There must be enough capital available to build up inventories, operate the plant, and continue to pay debtor's bills before payments from clients and creditors are received.

A major component of working capital is the cost of maintaining inventories of feedstocks, products, and other consumables. Fig. 3 also shows typical inventory levels considered necessary. Working capital, although required "up front," also has a residual value at the end. Inventory can be sold off and the cash value realized on completion of the plant life.

ACCOUNT	PERIOD MONTHS
1. FEEDSTOCK ACCOUNTS PAYABLE	0 - 1
2. FEEDSTOCKS INVENTORIES	0.5 - 1
3. STAFF AND LABOR PAYROLL	0.5 - 1
4. UTILITIES	1 - 2
5. MANUFACTURING CONSUMABLES	1 - 2
6. PRODUCT INVENTORIES	1 - 3
7. PRODUCT ACCOUNTS RECEIVABLE	1 - 2
8. TAXES PAYABLE	4 - 6
7. FREIGHT PAYABLE	0.5 - 1

Figure 3—Working capital items and periods.

MAJOR CLASSIFICATION	DETAIL ITEMS
1. MATERIALS	FEEDSTOCK MATERIALS, PROCESSING CHEMICALS AND CATALYSTS, UTILITIES, MAINTENANCE MATERIALS, OPERATING SUPPLIES AND CONSUMABLES.
2. LABOR	PLANT LABOR AND SUPERVISION, MAINTENANCE LABOR AND SUPERVISION, PAYROLL ADDITIVES.
3. PLANT OVERHEADS	ADMINISTRATION, LABORATORY, TECHNICAL, PURCHASING, INSPECTION, SHIPPING, PERSONNEL, SAFETY, ACCOUNTING, CLERICAL, SHOPS AND REPAIR FACILITIES, CAFETERIA, COMMUNICATIONS, TAXES AND INSURANCE.
4. MARKETING	SALEMEN'S SALARIES AND COMMISSIONS, ADVERTISING, PUBLICITY, SAMPLES, TRAVEL AND ENTERTAINMENT, MARKET RESEARCH.
5. DISTRIBUTION	CONTAINERS AND PACKAGES, TRANSPORTATION AND SHIPPING, TERMINALS AND WAREHOUSES.
6. GENERAL OVERHEAD & ADMINISTRATION	GENERAL MANAGEMENT AND CENTRAL TECHNICAL, MARKETING AND OTHER ACTIVITIES, LEGAL AND PATENT, RESEARCH AND DEVELOPMENT, PUBLIC RELATIONS.
7. FINANCIAL	DEPRECIATION, DEBT MANAGEMENT, MAINTENANCE OF WORKING CAPITAL, CREDIT FUNCTIONS, INTEREST PAYMENTS.

Figure 4—Checklist of items for operating cost estimate.

3. Operating costs. Fig. 4 lists the typical elements that go into the makeup of operating costs. These are costs which, in general, are proportional to the plant thruput. They are necessary to run the plant.

Usually the major operating costs of a process plant are the costs of feedstocks, raw materials, utilities and other consumables. It is not unusual for the annual cost of feedstocks and utilities for an HPI plant to exceed the capital cost by a significant factor. This is often recognized by the fact that a major reason for considering a new plant is the availability of feedstock, raw materials, or a key utility at an especially advantageous price. In many cases, the physical location of the plant may be dictated by the location of the available feedstock or utility.

Normally, an investor or potential developer will want to make sure that there is a guaranteed source of feedstock and supplies of key utilities at fixed prices. Long-term contracts may be signed in advance for the supply of feedstock and utilities. Such a move can go a long way to reducing the major part of the risk in a new project venture.

4. Product revenues. The key objective of the project is to earn revenue from the sale of the products. For the project to be successful there must be a secure market. The main features that marketers will attempt to establish are: 1. Is there a demand for the products and will this continue and preferentially increase over the life of the project?, and 2. Will the price of the products remain stable or increase over the life of the project?

The total profitability of the project is set by the margin between the cost of production and the selling price of the product. The selling price must be competitive initially and so far as can be seen remain competitive over the life of the project. The potential markets should be identified and the ability of the buyers to pay must also be evaluated. Many a project has failed because although there was a need for the product, the buyers did not have the wherewithall to pay. The ultimate retail consumer is the one who pays in the end. Most astute developers will attempt to negotiate long-term "base load" sales contracts at preferential prices. They will find a financially sound buyer who will take a substantial portion of the product at a rate that is attractive and guaranteed over a period of five or more years. This establishes a base operating level and a base income for the project.

The operating level is also key to the project success. Large plants are said to benefit from the "economy of scale." A large thruput achieves higher operating efficiencies and also allows many fixed or semi-fixed costs to be distributed over a higher volume of product resulting in a lower unit cost. The theory of economy of scale is admirable provided there is a demand for the volume of product produced. Large plants can be big money losers when not running at full capacity. In any feasibility study, the level of plant operation is a major contributor to the overall profitability.

5. Economic factors. Economic factors cannot, in general, be predicted over a long period. These are such things as the rate of inflation, interest levels, foreign currency exchange rates, and the general business climate. Inflation, interest and foreign currency exchange rates can all be built into the econometric model to see the effect on profitability. Different high/low rates may be selected over the life of the project to determine the best and the worst that could happen. From this the profitability risk can be assessed. In some cases it may be possible to hedge against adverse conditions by buying forward or by incorporating adjustment or escalation clauses in contracts.

6. Government influences. City, state, and federal governments can have a major impact on a project. New taxes may be introduced or existing rates may be changed. Regulations may be passed that require capital expenditures and add to the operating cost. Tax incentives may be made available to competitors in another location.

Nothing can be done about future government influences that may arise. The best that can be done is to pick an area where the government seems stable. Look carefully at the history and check out all pending legislation that might have an effect on the plant operation in the future. If the plant is being built in a foreign location, this historical checking and review is doubly important. Many of the overseas projects built in the last three decades have suffered through nationalization or discriminatory legislation against foreign investment.

THE OPPORTUNITY

Now that we have discussed the factors, let us consider a particular opportunity. The ABC Co., a large independent chemical producer, is planning a major expansion to a product line. To support this expansion, ABC is looking to secure a long-term supply contract for the necessary raw materials, a specification hydrocarbon product.

XYZ is a development investment group looking at the possibility of supplying ABC's needs. XYZ has obtained an option to purchase a hydrocarbon byproduct on a long-term contract at advantageous terms. XYZ also has access to a new process that will produce product to ABC's feedstock specification from the hydrocarbon byproduct. This new process employs features which give higher yields and increased efficiencies, resulting in lower unit costs than current conventional processes.

A major E/C contractor has provided a preliminary scoping study giving material and utility balances, and estimated costs for this new process. Fig. 5 is a simplified block flow diagram of the proposed plant known as the Thermal Cracking Conversion Unit (TCCU).

ABC has indicated a need for 15,000 bpsd of product "A" for which they will enter into a five-year take-or-pay supply contract. ABC's draft contract also contains options to extend this contract for another five years and increase the quantity to 25,000 bpsd. The product price is to

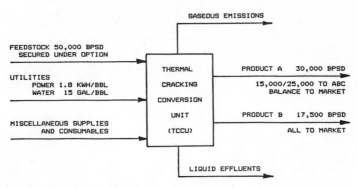

Figure 5—Project block flow diagram.

be initially agreed upon and will be subject to a fixed annual escalation rate. The five-year extension will continue at the same escalation rate.

XYZ's byproduct supply option is for 50,000 bpsd over a five-year period with an option to renew for a further five years. The price will be governed by the same escalation clause used in ABC's purchase contract. As can be seen, 50,000 bpsd of feed provides more product than ABC requires both initially and finally. However, the XYZ group believe that they can dispose of excess product "A" and all of product "B" in the local market.

The E/C contractor's scoping study provides consumption figures for utilities and estimated capital and operating costs. The question now is, does the XYZ group have the right ingredients for a profitable new project venture?

THE ECONOMETRIC MODEL

The first step in preparing the econometric model is to set up the columns and rows required. The operating life of the plant will be ten years, with a three-year construction period. A column of values will be required for each year. An initial design value and a final value are also needed. A reference column and a description column complete the picture resulting in 17 columns overall. These are labeled A through Q.

The rows under the columns now deal in sequence with the factors already described to give the financial picture. Reference should be made to the econometric model in Fig. 6. This model is an example to illustrate method and technique. The actual values are not necessarily in line with commercial practice.

A Ref	B	C Design Value	D 1 1986	E 2 1987	F 3 1988	G 4 1989	H 5 1990	I 6 1991	J 7 1992	K 8 1993	L 9 1994	M 10 1995	N 11 1996	O 12 1997	P 13 1998	Q Final Value
	GENERAL FACTORS															
1	Average Inflation Rate %	—	6.0%	6.0%	7.5%	8.0%	8.5%	9.0%	9.5%	10.0%	10.5%	11.0%	10.5%	10.0%	9.5%	9.5%
2	Compounded Escalation Factor	1.000	1.030	1.061	1.101	1.145	1.193	1.247	1.306	1.372	1.444	1.523	1.603	1.683	1.763	1.847
3	Plant Operating Rate %	100%	0.0%	0.0%	0.0%	60.0%	70.0%	80.0%	90.0%	100.0%	100.0%	100.0%	100.0%	100.0%	100.0%	—
	CAPITAL COST															
4	Land Cost $MM	20.00	20.60													35.26
5	Plant Cost $MM	250.00	51.50	79.57	110.07	28.62										44.08
6	Working Capital $MM	186.15	0.00	0.00	0.00	125.42	23.25	25.31	27.58	30.10	14.60	12.75	13.18	13.61	14.04	299.83
7	Total Capital Cost $MM	456.15	72.10	79.57	110.07	154.04	23.25	25.31	27.58	30.10	14.60	12.75	13.18	13.61	14.04	379.17
	OPERATING COSTS															
8	Feed Unit Cost $/BBL	26.00	0.00	0.00	0.00	26.00	27.30	28.67	30.10	31.60	33.18	34.84	36.58	38.41	40.33	40.33
9	Cost of Feed $MM	455.00	0.00	0.00	0.00	455.00	477.75	501.64	526.72	553.06	580.71	609.74	640.23	672.24	705.85	705.85
10	Utilities Power $MM	2.52	0.00	0.00	0.00	2.12	2.43	2.75	3.09	3.46	3.64	3.84	4.04	4.24	4.44	4.44
11	Utilities Water $MM	0.53	0.00	0.00	0.00	0.44	0.51	0.57	0.64	0.72	0.76	0.80	0.84	0.88	0.93	0.93
12	Maintenance $MM	10.00	0.00	0.00	0.00	8.43	9.63	10.91	12.26	13.72	14.44	15.23	16.03	16.83	17.63	17.63
13	Miscellaneous Materials $MM	15.00	0.00	0.00	0.00	12.64	14.45	16.36	18.39	20.57	21.65	22.85	24.04	25.25	26.45	26.45
14	Plant Labor $MM	3.00	0.00	0.00	0.00	2.28	2.69	3.13	3.60	4.11	4.33	4.57	4.81	5.05	5.29	5.29
15	Administration $MM	8.00	0.00	0.00	0.00	9.16	9.55	9.98	10.45	10.97	11.55	12.18	12.82	13.47	14.10	14.10
16	Total Operating Cost $MM	520.05	0.00	0.00	0.00	516.07	544.31	574.00	605.26	638.21	670.26	704.05	739.40	776.37	815.03	815.03
	REVENUES															
17	Product A Base Price $/BBL	33.50	0.00	0.00	0.00	33.50	35.18	36.93	38.78	40.72	42.76	44.89	47.14	49.49	51.97	51.97
18	Product A Extra Price $/BBL	30.15	0.00	0.00	0.00	30.15	31.43	32.85	34.41	36.13	38.02	40.11	42.22	44.33	46.44	46.44
19	Product A Revenue $MM	345.89	0.00	0.00	0.00	207.53	250.67	297.37	348.10	403.44	440.65	463.02	486.34	510.66	536.00	536.00
20	Product B Price $/BBL	32.00	0.00	0.00	0.00	36.63	38.19	39.91	41.80	43.89	46.20	48.74	51.30	53.86	56.42	56.42
21	Product B Revenue $MM	196.00	0.00	0.00	0.00	134.62	163.73	195.54	230.43	268.84	282.95	298.51	314.18	329.89	345.56	345.56
22	Excess Feed Revenue $MM	0.00	0.00	0.00	0.00	163.80	128.99	90.29	47.40	0.00	0.00	0.00	0.00	0.00	0.00	0.00
23	Total Revenue $MM	637.54	0.00	0.00	0.00	606.23	648.19	692.89	740.93	793.01	850.57	895.27	941.18	988.24	1036.39	1036.39
	FINANCIAL PICTURE															
24	Cumulative Cash Flow $MM	—	-72.10	-151.67	-261.74	-325.61	-244.98	-151.40	-43.31	81.39	247.10	425.57	614.17	812.42	1019.74	1398.91
25	Discounted Cash Flow $MM	—	-70.00	-142.96	-237.79	-284.45	-205.29	-121.41	-33.16	59.34	171.17	279.43	383.14	482.69	578.39	757.47
26	Annual Depreciation $MM	22.50	0.00	0.00	0.00	22.50	22.50	22.50	22.50	22.50	22.50	22.50	22.50	22.50	22.50	0.00
27	Depreciatd Book Value $MM	250.00	250.00	250.00	250.00	227.50	205.00	182.50	160.00	137.50	115.00	92.50	70.00	47.50	25.00	25.00
28	Actual Annual Profit $MM	94.99	0.00	0.00	0.00	67.66	81.38	96.39	113.16	132.30	157.82	168.72	179.28	189.36	198.86	1384.93
29	Discounted Annual Profit $MM	94.99	0.00	0.00	0.00	59.11	68.20	77.29	86.63	96.46	109.32	110.78	111.84	112.51	112.79	944.92
30	Discounted Annual R.O.I. %	20.82%	0.00%	0.00%	0.00%	12.96%	14.95%	16.94%	18.99%	21.15%	23.97%	24.29%	24.52%	24.66%	24.73%	20.72%
	LOAN ALTERNATIVE ($MM 125.00 CAPITAL + $MM 250.00 LOAN)															
31	Loan Interest/Repayment $MM	45.00	45.00	45.00	45.00	45.00	45.00	45.00	45.00	45.00	45.00	45.00	45.00	45.00	45.00	250.00
32	Cumulative Cash Flow $MM	—	-257.90	193.81	79.89	10.38	85.85	181.15	292.09	420.89	592.10	777.62	971.67	1172.87	1381.74	1760.91
33	Cash Retained $MM	375.00	257.90	193.81	79.89	10.38	30.00	60.00	100.00	150.00	210.00	250.00	290.00	320.00	342.47	375.00
34	Interest on Cash in Hand $MM		15.47	11.63	5.99	0.83	2.55	5.40	9.50	15.00	22.05	27.50	30.45	32.00	32.53	210.91
35	Declared Annual Profit $MM		0.00	0.00	0.00	0.00	55.85	65.30	70.94	78.80	111.21	145.52	154.05	171.20	186.40	1039.27
36	Discounted Annual Profit $MM		0.00	0.00	0.00	0.00	46.80	52.36	54.30	57.45	77.04	95.53	96.10	101.72	105.73	687.05
37	Discounted Annual R.O.I %		0.00%	0.00%	0.00%	0.00%	37.44%	41.89%	43.44%	45.96%	61.63%	76.44%	76.88%	81.37%	84.58%	54.96%

Figure 6—The econometric model.

Column headings.
Columns are identified with their headings and year numbers.

General factors

- **Row 1. Average inflation-rate percent.** This row shows the predicted rate of annual inflation for the whole project life of 13 years.
- **Row 2. Compounded escalation factor (CEF).** Row 2 converts Row 1 to a compounded multiplier. CEF for year $N = (1 + I1/100) * (1 + I2/100) * . . * (1 + IN/2/100)$. For year N, the average inflation rate is taken at the midyear point, hence $N/2$.

- **Row 3. Plant operating rate percent (POR).** The plant operating rate is a key variable in the profitability study. A 60% operating rate is assumed for year 1, increasing to 100 percent over the first five years.

Capital cost

- **Row 4. Land cost, $MM.** The land cost of $20MM is expended in year 1 and is also available as a final recoverable sum. The initial and final values are both multiplied by the compounded escalation factor.
- **Row 5. Plant cost, $MM.** The plant cost is estimated at $250MM, which will be expended at the rate of 20 percent in year 1, 30 percent in year 2, 40 percent in year 3, with a final 10% payment in year 4. Expenditures in each year are multiplied by the CEF. The equation for the expenditure in year 3 (for example) is 250 * 0.4 * CEF. The final cost is the residual scrap value, assumed to be 10 percent. The final value is also multiplied by the CEF.
- **Row 6. Working capital, $MM.** The working capital is estimated at $20MM plus two months of feedstock and product inventories. The working capital is generated by an equation which escalates the $20MM and adds 2/12ths of the design feedstock/product quantities times the operating rate times the feedstock/product prices for the year in question. Additional working capital is needed each year to allow for escalation and increased operating rates. The final residual value is the cumulative value of all of the working capital expended.
- **Row 7. Total capital cost, $MM.** This is the sum of Rows 4 through 6.

Operating costs

- **Row 8. Feed unit cost, $MM.** This is the contractual feed cost for the 10-year period. The initial price is $26/bbl subject to a 5% increase each year. The cost in year N is $26 * 1.05 ^ N.
- **Row 9. Cost of feed, $MM.** This value is the barrels per day (50,000) times the number of operating days in the year (350) times the feed unit cost. Since the contract requires that the whole 50,000 barrels be taken, this number is not multiplied by the operating rate.
- **Row 10. Utilities power, $MM.** Power requirements have been estimated at 1.8 kWh/bbl of feed at design thruput. At lower plant operating rates, the power usage per barrel will increase by the 0.6 power. Electricity rates are initially at $0.08 per kWh and are subject to escalation. The equation for power costs thus becomes 50,000 * 350 * 1.8 * 0.08 * CEF * (POR/1) ^ 0.6.
- **Row 11. Utilities water, $MM.** Water requirements have been estimated at 15 gallons per barrel. Water costs at $2.00 per 1,000 gallons

initially are subject to escalation. As with power, water consumption per barrel increases to the 0.6 power at lower operating rates. The equation for water costs is similar to the equation for power costs 50,000 * 350 * 15 * 2.0 / 1000 * CEF * (POR) ^ 0.6.

- **Row 12. Maintenance, $MM.** Annual maintenance has been estimated at $10MM. This value is subject to escalation. Maintenance costs are reduced at lower plant operating rates and again the 0.6 power rule applies. The equation is 10 * CEF * (POR) ^ 0.6.
- **Row 13. Miscellaneous materials, $MM.** Miscellaneous materials are estimated at $15MM. The same equation applies as for maintenance.
- **Row 14. Plant labor, $MM.** Plant labor has been estimated at 100 persons overall at an average cost of $30,000 per year. Plant labor is subject to escalation. At lower plant operating rates, plant labor can be reduced slightly by the 0.8 power. The equation is 100 * 30,000 * CEF * (POR/1) ^ 0.8.
- **Row 15. Administration, $MM.** General administrative and overhead costs have been estimated at $15MM per year. This value is subject to escalation and is not changed by plant operating rate.
- **Row 16. Total operating cost, $MM.** This is the sum of Rows 8 through 15.

Revenues

- **Row 17. Product A base price, $/bbl.** This is the contractual price to be agreed with the ABC Co. A value of $33.50/bbl is selected for the base case. This price will be subject to an increase of 5 percent per year by contract. The price in year N is 33.50 * 1.05 ^ N.
- **Row 18. Product A extra price, $/bbl.** Any product produced over and above that required to meet the ABC contract level will be sold on the open market. It is assumed that initially this extra product may be sold at 90 percent of ABC's price but that this price will strengthen over the years in line with the inflation rate. The price equation will therefore be 33.50 * 0.9 * CEF.
- **Row 19. Product revenue, $MM.** This value is the total product A multiplied by the above prices. For years 1 to 5 = 15,000 * ABC price + (30,000 * POR − 15,000) * Extra price. For years 6 to 10 = 25,000 * ABC price + (30,000 * POR − 25,000) * extra price.
- **Row 20. Product B price, $/bbl.** It is assumed that product B can be sold on the open market. The initial market price is $30/bbl. This value will be increased annually in line with the compounded escalation factor.
- **Row 21. Product B revenue, $MM.** Product B revenue will be the production (17,500) times the POR times the price in Row 20.

- **Row 22. Excess feed revenue, $MM.** Since XYZ is contractually required to buy 50,000 bbls of feed regardless of the plant operating rate, the excess feed must be sold on the open market. It is assumed that the excess feed can be disposed of at 90 percent of the purchase price. The revenue value will be 50,000 * (100 − POR)/100 * 0.9 * feed price.
- **Row 23. Total revenue, $MM.** This is the sum of Rows 17 through 22.

Financial picture

- **Row 24. Cumulative cash flow, $MM.** This value is the cumulative sum of the total revenues (Row 23) minus the total expenditures, Total capital costs (Row 7) and Total operating costs (Row 16). Initially the cash flow is negative due to initial capital outlays.
- **Row 25. Discounted cash flow, $MM.** The discounted cash flow is the actual cash flow in Row 24 converted to present day values. The annual values in Row 24 are divided by the compounded escalation factor.
- **Row 26. Annual depreciation, $MM.** This value is the total capital cost minus the residual cost divided by the plant life. Since both land cost and working capital are residual this value equates to plant cost minus scrap value divided by plant life. There are different methods of calculating depreciation. This is the straight line method.
- **Row 27. Depreciated book value, $MM.** This is an accounting figure and is equal to the capital cost minus the residual value minus the annual depreciation to date.
- **Row 28. Actual profit, $MM.** This value is the total annual revenues (Row 23) minus the total annual operating costs (Row 16) and minus the annual depreciation (Row 26).
- **Row 29. Discounted annual profit, $MM.** This converts the actual annual profit in Row 28 to the present day value by dividing the actual annual profit by the compounded escalation factor. (Row 2).
- **Row 30. Discounted annual ROI percent.** This row gives the value which is of prime interest to investors. The discounted annual profit (Row 29) is divided by the total initial design capital cost to give the ROI (Row 7). The final value gives the average over the plant life.

Loan alternative

The econometric model up until now has assumed that all the capital will be provided by the XYZ Co. An alternative to this is to raise a loan with a fixed interest over the total project life including construction. The loan repayments will be fixed and can be considered an operating cost. The balance of any profit plus the residual costs are then available to the company and can be related to a lower investment cost.

To check out the economics of this alternative, a case is assumed such that $250 MM is taken out as a loan over 13 years. An additional $125 MM is raised as capital by the XYZ shareholders.

- **Row 31. Loan interest/repayment, $MM.** This shows the annual interest due on the $250 MM loan at 18 percent simple interest.
- **Row 32. Cumulative cash flow, $MM.** This is the same as Row 24, except the project starts with $375 MM in hand and $45 MM in interest is paid out each year.
- **Row 33. Cash retained, $MM.** Available cash initially exceeds requirements. Later excess cash is retained to build up capital to pay off the loan. To compare the loan alternative with the base case, the final cash retained equals the loan plus investment capital, leaving the residual value the same as the base case.
- **Row 34. Interest on cash in hand, $MM.** The excess cash in hand will earn interest. It is assumed that interest will be earned at the annual inflation rate in Row 1.
- **Row 35. Declared annual profit, $MM.** In this case, profit can be declared at any level supported by the cash flow less the cash retained.
- **Row 36. Discounted annual profit, $MM.** This is the present or discounted value of the annual profit. Row 35 is divided by the CEF.
- **Row 37. Discounted annual ROI percent.** In the loan alternative, the profit is divided by the shareholders' capital of $125 MM only, since this is the shareholders' total investment. As can be seen, although the total profit earned is lower, the ROI is considerably higher due to the reduced investment.

Analyzing the financial picture. Now that the econometric model is complete, it is possible to examine the profitability of the venture. The base case yields an average annual ROI of 20.72 percent over the 10 years which is at the desired target level. Actually the profitability may be higher than shown, since not all of the working capital is expended initially and some interest could be earned on excess cash in hand. Also the residual value plus the depreciated values exceeds the initial investment. If desired, the econometric model could be adjusted to show these details, however, the base case results shown are probably close enough for analysis and decision-making.

Modifying the variables. Now that the econometric model has been set up, unlimited "What If?" simulations may be carried out to see the effect on the bottom line. The inter-meshing equations in the spread sheet instantly adjust all related values in the columns and rows to show the new picture. To illustrate this, the following five "What If's" are simulated:

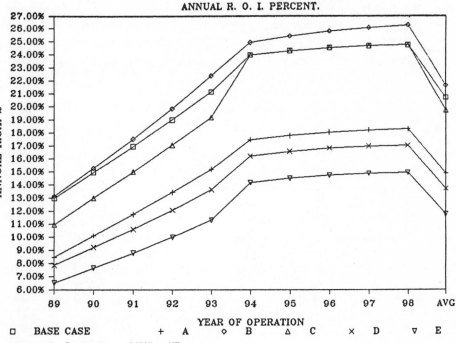

Figure 7—Comparison of "What If" cases.

- **Case A.** Project capital cost overruns by 50 percent.
- **Case B.** Annual inflation rate runs 15 percent higher than predicted.
- **Case C.** Operating rate runs 10 percent lower than hoped for in first five years.
- **Case D.** Due to competitive market, proposed price of product A to ABC Co. must be reduced by 10 percent.
- **Case E.** Market for product B is less buoyant than anticipated, cut by 20 percent.

All of these changes can be entered singly or in combination and the spread sheet will instantly adjust. Fig. 7 shows the effect on the discounted annual ROI percent of each of the above "What If's" and compares the changes against the base case.

Simplicity and flexibility. The personal computer with a spread sheet can be used to create a tailor-made econometric model that can be as complex as you want it to be. Something like this would have been the strict preserve of the main frame or minicomputer a few years ago. Even then, it would not have been so individualized or flexible.

Chapter 2

Major Factors to Consider in Project Financing

SUBJECTS	1 PREAWARD	2 INITIATION	3 ENGINEERING	4 PROCUREMENT	5 CONSTRUCTION
A FINANCIAL/CONTRACTUAL	●				
B ORGANIZATION/EXECUTION PLANNING					
C MANAGING PEOPLE/COMMUNICATION					
D ESTIMATING/COST CONTROL					
E RISK ANALYSIS	●				
F SCHEDULING					
G TRACKING/TRENDING					
H PROGRESS/PRODUCTIVITY MEASUREMENT					
I MATERIAL MANAGEMENT					

C. H. Vervalin

Project financing—broadly defined—is any financing based on the project's viability rather than on the general funds or credit of the equity participants. In other words, the cash flow and credit worthiness of the project are sufficient to induce lenders to loan money . . . The project must meet the cost/risk/return analysis of all parties—owners and lenders.[1]

In the process of seeking lenders, the borrower must consider a number of factors that the lender will fully access before participating in financing arrangements (See Table 1). Banks ordinarily require a detailed appraisal of such elements. Moreover, technical professionals involved in the financing aspects of project development or management should be fully familiar with terms and concepts used by banks and other lending institutions (See Table 2).

The contracts. How do lenders assess credit risk? The project credit structure attempted most frequently incorporates a number of key contracts between sponsors, lenders, suppliers of raw materials, and purchasers of end products designed to address the principal risk.[2] Key contracts that make up this package include:

1. The Joint Venture Formation Agreement between the various partners establishes the percentage ownership, rights and obligations of each party. It spells out the way decisions will be reached and disputes settled. It must be equitable to all parties particularly in the event of changed or adverse circumstances.

TABLE 1—International financing of HPI projects: Major factors to consider

Initial product marketing research
- Locating the market
- Selecting product to fill the market
- Selecting product form to fill the market
- Export-domestic market ratio to justify project
- Marketing assistance when product becomes available
- Test marketing studies in areas selected
- Nontariff trade barriers important in product marketing
- Terminals necessary for successful product marketing

Financing for process evaluation and process selection
- Locally available materials—quality, quantity, price—which affect process selection
- Locally available skills—quality, quantity, price—which affect process selection
- Locally available equipment—quality, quantity, price—which affect process selection
- Tariff barriers for imported materials, equipment, skilled labor and process technology
- National and political policies affecting imports
- Currency transfer restrictions affecting available financing
- Currency restrictions affecting export of products
- Technology uses that affect export of products

Financing construction of the process plant
- When technology is imported
- When equipment is imported
- When materials are imported
- Original catalysts and materials charge to process
- Spare equipment, parts and supplies
- Initial operation of the project

Purchasing and expediting project equipment, materials and skilled labor
- Third country purchases
- Technology-equipment exchanges
- Raw materials-product exchanges
- Investment insurance
- Post products exports for equipment supplied (imported)
- Barter of products for credits

Eventual ownership of project as determined by financing
- Ownership retained by engineer-contractor
- Finance source retains ownership
- Liens on production held by equipment and/or materials suppliers
- Governmental ownership—partial or total
- Ownership retained by third party

Cost Control
- Initial studies
- Engineering and design
- Construction, and initial operation
- Continuing maintenance and operation

Selection of appropriate engineering construction company
- Experience in project type under consideration
- Evaluation of personnel
- Assessment of over-all performance record
- Evaluation of E/C's size and scope

TABLE 2—Glossary of project financing terms

- Balance sheet items—amounts explicitly listed on a company's balance sheet in either the assets or the liabilities column.
- Cash flow—for lending purposes, net profit before taxes plus depreciation, amortization and interest due.
- Central Bank undertakings—usually a guarantee to convert local currency into freely convertible currencies either at fixed exchange rates or at the free market rate.
- Completion delays—delays in completion of construction and/or acceptance testing of a facility beyond the originally specified target date.
- Commitment fees—fees paid to lenders for firmly agreeing to make loans at a future date. Usually stated as a percent per annum applicable on the undrawn amount of the loans.
- Contingent liability—a possible, as opposed to a certain, future liability normally listed in the explanatory footnotes accompanying a corporate balance sheet.
- Cost overrun—cost incurred to complete a facility in excess of the originally specified price.
- Deliver-it-or-pay—term supply agreements which are a financial commitment to pay cash instead if the supplies are not forthcoming in accordance with contract specifications.
- Demand loans—loans payable immediately at the option of the lender on any date.
- Drawing on L/Cs—getting paid from a letter of credit by presenting to the advising bank your draft plus the supporting documentation specified in the L/C.
- Drawing unilaterally—L/Cs that do not specify that any or all the supporting documentation accompanying your draft has to be countersigned by the opening party or its representatives.
- First demand provisions—a clause in performance standby L/Cs enabling the beneficiary to get paid immediately at any time against his simple written statement that he is drawing on the L/C.
- Fixed price contracts—suppliers or contractors agree to provide equipment or an entire facility at a stated fixed price. A fixed price contract is often in effect a cost reimbursable contract if it includes clauses allowing for cost escalation, reopening because of changes in scope, etc.
- Fixed rate loans—loans at a stated fixed interest rate.
- Floating rate loans—loans at an interest rate equivalent to a fixed margin above a variable base interest rate such as the U.S. bankers prime loan rate or the six month London Interbank Eurodollar Deposit Offered Rate (LIBOR).
- Footnote item—assets or contingent liabilities listed in the explanatory footnotes accompanying a corporate balance sheet.
- Foreign currency translation adjustments (FASB rule 8)—nominal foreign exchange losses resulting from exchange fluctuations on items valued in foreign currencies included in US corporate consolidated balance sheets now have to be charged off against quarterly consolidated earnings. *Text continued*

Table 2 (continued)

- Formula prices—variable prices for supplies or products determined by a formula including such factors as cost of production, international market prices, loan agreement operating margin provisions, etc.
- Full recourse—direct or indirect guarantee of a financial obligation.
- Lead commercial bank—the bank which acts as coordinator for the financing package for a project, including acting as manager for any lenders' syndicates that may have to be assembled.
- Letter of credit documentation—the supporting documentation (invoices, shipping documents, etc.) that in order to get paid must accompany your drafts as specified in the L/C.
- Loan disbursement procedure—procedure to get the loan proceeds transferred to the account of the borrower or into an L/C from which the beneficiaries get paid.
- Lump sum contract—see fixed price contracts.
- Offtakers—purchasers of the output of a plant.
- Offtake agreements—product purchasing agreements.
- Operating profit margin—profits from operations, generally net sales less cost of sales before general overhead charges, interest, etc.
- Performance bonds—a promise to pay issued by an insurance company or commercial bank guaranteeing the performance of a contractor or supplier in accordance with contract specifications.
- Permanent financing—financing with a maturity schedule that can be repaid from the cashflow of the facility.
- Price/earnings ratio—market price of a company's common shares divided by annual earnings per share.
- Progress payments—partial payments to a supplier or contractor against work progress certificates.
- Segregation of export revenues—proceeds from exports flow directly from purchasers into a special account at the lending bank rather than into the Central Bank's general foreign currency reserves.
- Sponsors—parties such as suppliers or purchasers who are not necessarily shareholders in a project.
- Standby L/C—guarantee from a commercial bank to pay if the bank's client does not pay.
- Take-and-pay agreement—a simple term purchasing agreement promising to pay against delivery of products.
- Take-or-pay agreement—term purchasing agreements which are financial commitments to pay whether the products are or are not delivered.
- Take-out commitment—undertaking to repay lenders by a certain date, usually from the proceeds of other financing.
- Vendors—suppliers of materials and equipment.
- Working capital balance—current assets less current liabilities.

2. The Completion Agreement requires the partners to put general credit behind the funds borrowed by the Joint Venture until predetermined operating and financial criteria have been met. Such obligation is generally satisfied by a financial guarantee of principal and interest or a purchase of assets agreement. This covers the risk that the investors for unseen circumstances may wish to abandon the project. This would leave the lender with a half complete plant, and no way to get his money back.

3. The Raw Material Supply Contract assures that the raw materials for operation are available to the Joint Venture and in sufficient quantity and quality. The risk of facilities remaining idle is not one lenders are anxious to assume.

4. The Plant Operation/Management Contract, generally exists between the new joint venture and the principal commercial joint venturer who has both the experience and the technology to manage and operate the facilities within projected cost parameters. Without this risk covered, the lenders would have no assurance the facilities would continue to be run and operated by experienced and trained personnel.

5. The Product Sale and Purchase Agreement is to assure that the end product will be sold. It generally involves the various commercial joint venture sponsors buying their pro-rata share from the Joint Venture at market or formula price, whichever is higher. Aim: to assure economic viability and meet debt service requirements. Without such assurance, the lenders will face adverse market conditions which could limit debt service ability.

6. The Loan Agreement is between the Joint Venture as borrower and the lenders. It follows the pattern of domestic term credits and establishes interest rate, repayment terms, borrower covenants as well as events of default.

The risks. Mention was made that the above contracts are to deal with the issue of risks. Three fundamental risks are associated with a major HPI capital project investment:[3]

- **Commercial risks**—Price and supply/demand relationships of the feedstocks and products as projected for the life of the project may fail to follow the projections. This may result in the forecast cash flows being inadequate to pay off the loan.

- **Political/economic risks**—The Iranian revolution makes these risks easy to understand. However, don't assume that these risks are confined to less developed countries. Any country can cause difficulties for a project. Examples: currency devaluations, raising tariff barriers, changing environmental regulations or nationalizing a whole industry.
- **Technical risks**—These risks are associated with the physical plant itself. In the absence of the other two risks, they determine whether or not the project can generate income by producing product at a competitive price throughout its whole life.

Project financing lenders are not risk takers. They seek to protect themselves from non-repayment of their loans by suitable contracts and insurances.

Unfortunately, contractual arrangements are not guarantees against project failure. They must be combined with sound planning and skillful implementation to reduce lender exposure to unforeseen, unpleasant surprises.

Technical risks. Lenders look carefully at a project's technical and economic viability. Major factors examined include (1) selection of a competitive process, (2) estimation of capital requirements, (3) contractor selection, (4) engineering and construction practices and procedures and (5) plant startup factors, such as potential for delays.

Engineer/constructor's role. Today, there is a premium on the contractor's ability to locate capital investors and match them with client requirements for construction of large HPI projects.[4] This market has become so competitive, particularly foreign projects, that the contractor who can offer the best financing often gets the job. A potential contractor for a major project enters the financing picture at two stages,

1. Preparation of bid packages
2. Providing financial assistance to the client.

Contractor responsibility. The contractor has various financial responsibilities. Intitially, he must often help his client obtain financing to get the project "off the ground." Then, during the entire construction program, there must be a continuous effort to assure that the contractor's working capital position is not weakened. The tools for this are cash management, letters of credit, and foreign exchange control.

Project loan structure. How does a lender expect a project loan to be structured? A project loan is a credit to a capital intensive facility having no historical operating record itself. The lender seeks repayment from operations of the project after it is built. Such a credit is divided into two phases:[5]

1. The Construction Loan Period during which time the plant is built by funds advanced from the lender and operations commence.

2. The Permanent Loan Period during which time the plant operates, generating cash flow to retire the debt to the lender and return equity to the sponsors.

This division is helpful because the risks involved in each stage are different. In many cases, the lender during construction is different from the long term lender. A loan for the construction phase must be repaid from permanent financing.

Multiple parties. Apart from the "mechanics" of project financing discussed thus far is the matter of parties involved—their contribution and their knowhow. Projects have become so large and so complex that mutual understanding of the over-all picture is needed by bankers (lenders), lawyers, economists, engineers, financial analysts and even politicians, legislators and government bureaucrats. A broad-brush comprehension is necessary for all of these.[6]

Project cash flow. Technical professionals concerned with project financing matters should understand the ramifications of project cash flow. This includes comprehending a description and interpretation of the concept, the refinancing of existing plants, how bankers view cash flow matters, and how money is managed from project concept to completion. HP has produced a special report to cover this important subject.[7]

New energy sources. Finally, a new dimension has been added to international finance matters—the synthetic fuel facility. In the U.S., especially, which has new legislation relevant to creation of a synfuels industry, financing alternatives must be understood.

Financing options to be considered include (1) municipal financing (of coal gasification plants), (2) utility financing, and (3) industrial financing. Financial analysts who are looking closely at development of solid fuels say that to offset the effects of inflation these sources must get into operation. Once the capital has been spent, escalation on that element of the energy price is established for the life of the project.[8]

Money availability. What about the capital "crunch" we have heard about in some quarters? The best thinking is that credit needs for the equity portion of the private sector will be met by the market mechanism of today. The market mechanism of cash flow and equity and debt offerings will grow at a rate sufficient to meet HPI needs in the future. On an absolute basis, there will be a capital shortage, although the interface of market dynamics will dictate higher returns due to the continuing inflationary spiral.[9]

LITERATURE CITED

[1] Jones, T. D., "Financial Considerations of Major Fuel and Petrochemical Projects" AIChE National Meeting, March 1977.

[2] Swett, J. C., "International Projects: Risks and Sources of Funds," *Hydrocarbon Processing,* January 1980.

[3] Whitehead, R. T., "The Importance of Technical Evaluation in Project Financing," AIChE National Meeting, Houston, April 3, 1979.

[4] Jacobson, H. M., "A Contractor's View of Financing Petrochemical Projects," AIChE National Meeting, March 1977.

[5] Shannon, D. C., "Project Lending: A Lender's Point of View," *Hydrocarbon Processing,* January 1980.

[6] Maples, R. E. and Hyland, M. J., "Developing Major Ventures," AIChE National Meeting, Houston, April 3, 1979.

[7] Project Cash Flow, A Special Report, (multiple authors) *Hydrocarbon Processing,* March 1978 issue, pages 77–98.

[8] Moon, R., French, C. and Bvington, B., "Financing New Sources of Energy," AIChE National Meeting, Houston, April 3, 1979.

[9] Mazzuto, J. D., "Project Finance," *Hydrocarbon Processing,* January 1980.

Chapter 3

Know
Finance
Scope and
Structure

SUBJECTS	1 PREAWARD	2 INITIATION	3 ENGINEERING	4 PROCUREMENT	5 CONSTRUCTION
A FINANCIAL/CONTRACTUAL	●				
B ORGANIZATION/EXECUTION PLANNING					
C MANAGING PEOPLE/COMMUNICATION					
D ESTIMATING/COST CONTROL					
E RISK ANALYSIS	●				
F SCHEDULING					
G TRACKING/TRENDING					
H PROGRESS/PRODUCTIVITY MEASUREMENT					
I MATERIAL MANAGEMENT					

PROJECT PHASE

SUBJECT-PROJECT PHASE MATRIX

E. A. Tondu

In the international field the proportion of "true" project financing—projects financed by lenders without full recourse to the project's shareholders or other sponsors—is small, but growing rapidly. Even in the Third World and Socialist Bloc countries where projects are normally financed against government guarantees on the corresponding loans, there is emerging a growing interest in financing plants—including those that do not have a foreign joint venture partner/offtaker—with only supplemental host country financial support in the form of certain undertakings.

Some of the following comments may only be partially relevant to cases where the owner, often a Third World government agency, wants to build a project regardless of economics or cost, and has the creditworthiness to do so.

Protection sought. If the debt financing of a project relies for repayment primarily on the cash flow of the project itself, in addition to proven technology, owners/sponsors with acceptable credit standing and a hospitable political environment, potential lenders will insist on protection against:

1. Supply and sales risks.
2. Construction period risks.
3. Operating risks.
4. Operating profit margin risks.
5. Political and exchange inconvertibility risks.

Supply and sales risks. After analyzing the project's economic feasibility study, potential lenders will next verify long-term raw material/energy supply and product offtake agreements. Ideally these agreements should include deliver-it-or-pay (i.e., if you don't deliver, you pay instead) and take-or-pay (i.e., you pay regardless of whether the product is available for delivery or whether you take delivery) provisions, preferably with specific starting dates.

U.S. suppliers/offtakers, in particular, are reluctant to agree to these types of clauses. They represent a direct rather than a contingent financial obligation. They are thus classified as such by their auditors.

Primary considerations. When arranging the financing package with private-sector owners/sponsors, structure their various undertakings so that their auditors will classify them as footnote contingent liabilities rather than direct liabilities shown on their balance sheets.

The price provisions specified in supply-offtake agreements are usually a major bone of contention. Offtakers aim either for a predictable price structure or for a tie to international market prices for the product. Suppliers naturally want to maximize their revenues and at least cover their costs by an adequate margin. Lenders wish to see the relation of supply to offtake prices structured so that an adequate project company operating profit margin and cash flow are assured.

Construction period risks. Cost overruns, completion delays and plant operability in accordance with contract specifications are the principal risk areas.

- **Cost overruns** often are provided for by a cost overrun standby agreement (i.e., if costs exceed a predetermined target, the owners/sponsors agree to inject more equity capital or subordinated debt into the project company to cover the additional costs).

  More unusual is a formula price offtake agreement which includes a factor to cover amortization of the additional financing required for cost overruns.

  Lump sum/fixed price turnkey contracts are another possible solution. However, the contractor may be bidding in an inflationary environment. The plant location may be in an area where historical construction costs are not available or imprecise. Thus, the contingency margin the contractor has to include in his bid price may make the project economically unfeasible.

  Lenders generally insist on cost overrun standby agreements from the owners/sponsors even if a lump sum turnkey contract for the facility is awarded. This is because of the risk that the contractor may walk away from his contract. It has happened in the international field more than once in recent years. Recovering from the contractor sufficient funds to complete the facility has proven difficult.

If a project has in effect only one owner/sponsor with an impeccable credit rating, it is possible to finance a project during the construction period against a firm take out commitment. And this includes funding of cost overruns. There need be no additional financing agreements. A firm take-out commitment states that the owner/sponsor will:

(a) either arrange permanent financing by a certain date, or

(b) pay out the short-term note holders by a certain date.

• **Completion delays** can be covered by completion agreements. Here, the owners/sponsors undertake to guarantee the project company's debt if completion delays beyond agreed-upon allowances occur.

Take-or-pay, deliver-or-pay and take-out commitments with specific starting dates may be a satisfactory substitute to lenders depending on the project concerned.

• **Plant operability** in accordance with specifications is often guaranteed by the turnkey contractor. His guarantee is normally limited, however, to a specified liability amount which may not cover the funds required to bring plant production up to agreed-upon standards. Therefore lenders will often ask for the owners/sponsors to directly guarantee the project company's debt if specified amounts of production at specified costs are not achieved during the plant testing period.

Again, certain other overlapping undertakings may be a satisfactory substitute to lenders.

Operating profit margin risks. Adequate operating profit margins could be covered by factors in the formula product price allowing for cost of raw materials, power, labor, etc. Lenders usually ask, however, for a more encompassing working capital maintenance agreement, Under this agreement, owners/sponsors are to maintain the working capital balances in the project company at a certain minimum level. This is to protect lenders after the plant commissioning date against all unforeseen events not covered by catastrophe insurance.

Note that a working capital maintenance agreement may obviate the need for certain other owners'/sponsors' key undertakings such as deliver-or-pay supply provisions, take-or-pay offtake contracts and plant operability guarantees. However, auditors may want to classify working capital maintenance agreements as a financial guarantee of all the project company's obligations.

Political and exchange inconvertibility risks. In areas of the world where these risks are significant, lenders may ask for an insurance policy issued by Overseas Private Investment Corp. or private insurers such as Lloyds of London.

The definition of events under which political risk claims are paid are subject to interpretation at the time claims are filed. Lenders therefore often prefer to rely on other owners'/sponsors' undertakings that already are included in the project financing structure. In particular if one of the owners/sponsors is a host country government agency, the value of the rather expensive political risk insurance is often questionable.

An exchange inconvertibility event is easier to demonstrate to the insurer. Therefore additional owners'/sponsors' undertakings are normally not required by lenders to cover this contingency.

Increasingly, where an international agency participates in the project as owner or lender, other sources of financing insist on a cross default clause in their loan agreements, tying automatic default on the international agency financing directly to default on their loans.

IMPLEMENTATION

In particular, when export credit/procurement agreements with several supplier countries form part of a project's financing structure, implementation of the various financing agreements deserves close attention.

More than once both contractors and owners/sponsors have found they have signed commercial contract conditions that cannot be implemented because of the terms of the financing—in particular export credit agreements.

Look carefully at these areas:

Vendor guarantees. Is the project owner or the contractor the direct beneficiary? In the case of all lump sum contracts plus certain cost reimbursable contracts, the contractor is required to order in his own name, not as purchasing agent for his client. In such cases, the client recovers for latent defects, etc., from the contractor. The contractor incurs the contingent liability of having to attempt to recover in turn from the relevant vendors, i.e., "Standing in front of the vendors."

In the case of exports to Third World countries, especially, government export credit agencies often try to include a provision in their credit agreements specifying that all vendor guarantees be issued to the contractor, even if the contractor is placing the orders as purchasing agent on behalf of his client. From the export credit agency point of view, this avoids disputes between their local vendors and the agency's debtor.

For the same reason (avoidance of disputes with their debtors) these credit agencies also often try to include a provision in their loan agreements stating that: if their debtor refuses to pay, citing as reasons faulty work or inherent defects, the agency has full automatic recourse to the contractor for the amounts owed to it.

Vendor progress payments. Suppose the contractor is purchasing materials and equipment in his own name. Here, care should be taken that the progress payment provisions—including documentation requirements—of the export credit agreements and the relevant Letters of Credit (L/Cs), are similarly included in his procurement contracts with vendors.

Letters of credit. Disbursement of the loan proceeds for a project is normally effected through the lead commercial bank for the financing package opening one or more L/Cs in favor of the contractor and/or vendors.

The methods-of-payment section of the commercial contract, the export credit agreements and the other loan agreements should provide for:

1. A regular automatic loan disbursement procedure to increase the unused amount of the L/Cs to match future expenditure estimates, including purchase order commitments, or an agreed-upon progress payment schedule in the case of lump sum contracts.

2. Issuance of L/Cs directly in favor of vendors if the contractor is ordering as purchasing agent on behalf of his client.

3. Documentation required to draw on the L/Cs. Can the contractors/vendors draw unilaterally or only against invoices and other documentation countersigned by the client?

Performance bonds. In particular, in Third World countries, the performance bonds often are issued by commercial banks. These may be in the form of Standby Letters of Credit rather than the bonds issued by insurance companies—standard procedure for U.S. domestic projects.

These performance standby L/Cs often contain provisions permitting the beneficiary to draw at first demand without presenting documentary justification. If drawn upon, the opening bank automatically debits the account of its client. As a result, such L/Cs are classified by banks as demand loans extended to their clients.

Unfortunately, the U.S. government, unlike other governments, does not offer U.S. companies insurance against the unjustified calling of performance bonds.

Clearly, negotiation of the text of performance Standby L/Cs is an important issue. They represent direct contingent demand charge against an opening party's assets.

As one supplier has found out to his dismay, it is a good idea to order performance Standby L/Cs with first demand provisions to be issued only after you have received and verified the text of the loan proceeds disbursement L/Cs.

Part 2: Managing People

SUBJECT-PROJECT PHASE MATRIX	PROJECT PHASE				
SUBJECTS	1 PREAWARD	2 INITIATION	3 ENGINEERING	4 PROCUREMENT	5 CONSTRUCTION
A FINANCIAL/CONTRACTUAL					
B ORGANIZATION/EXECUTION PLANNING					
C MANAGING PEOPLE/COMMUNICATION	●	●	●	●	●
D ESTIMATING/COST CONTROL					
E RISK ANALYSIS					
F SCHEDULING					
G TRACKING/TRENDING					
H PROGRESS/PRODUCTIVITY MEASUREMENT					
I MATERIAL MANAGEMENT					

Chapter 4
Lead Your People Effectively

C. H. Vervalin

The supervisory manager in the hydrocarbon processing industry (HPI), like supervisors everywhere, is the *person in the middle.* Sandwiched as he is, between management and non-managerial employees, he faces the dilemma of attempting to adequately represent the needs of both management *and* his subordinates. When differences emerge between management's "view" and the employees' "views," it is the supervisor who must reconcile, assuage, attempt to get consensus, and otherwise weld the work group into a cohesive, productive entity. It is a tough, demanding job to walk the endless, relentless tightrope between managers and subordinates.

Leadership. The supervisor must be a *leader* to function effectively as management's emissary, and the employees' representative. But what is *leadership?* It has been conceptualized as a function of three things: (1) The *leader* himself (personality, needs and behavior), (2) The *situation* (external environment, personalities and behavior of the members; and the *group* itself—its structure, size, history, goals, outside pressures, etc.) and (3) *interaction* of leader and the situation variables.

In other words, leadership is *situational.* It has more to do with the dynamics of the supervisor's environment and its demands upon him, and less to do with *traits.* Traits involve such factors as self-confidence, sociability, willpower, dominance and many other characteristics that people commonly associate with leadership. But the behavioral sciences have, in recent years, dispelled the "trait" rationale for selecting supervisors. There is no "leader personality." The empirical approach stresses what a leader *does* rather than what he *is.*

Theory X, Theory Y. The late eminent management authority, Douglas McGregor, characterized supervisory practices as being broadly divided into Theory X and Theory Y assumptions about people, and how they behave in an organizational setting. (See Table 1.) Supervisors whose dominant managerial style follows the assumptions of Theory Y are performing largely in accordance with the prescription of today's behavioral-science-oriented authorities on the practice of management.

Operation of a supervisory strategy based on Theory Y includes four phases:[1]

1. The clarification of the broad requirements of the job
2. The establishment of specific targets for a limited time period
3. The management process during the target period
4. Appraisal of the results

Management by integration and self-control is *strategy*—a way of managing people.

Motivation's role. Good supervisors are often characterized as persons who have the ability to "motivate people." Again, behavioral science has shown that people cannot be "motivated" by others—at least not directly. Rather, people motivate themselves—positively or negatively—in response to their environment, and internal *drives* accumulated over their lifetime.

The classic studies on motivation done by Frederick Herzberg a decade ago have stood the test of time.[2] As shown in Table 2, Herzberg identified two categories that impact motivation. Job "dissatisfiers" were found to de-motivate people if they were not up to the individual's expectations. And yet, if these factors were up to "expectations" they could not *motivate*. The motivators, on the other hand, are the "satisfiers" shown in the table. In other words, *the job itself* is the motivating force that drives people to produce, and to feel good about it in the process.

First things first. Under Herzberg's rationale, the supervisor—in performing his job—cannot take advantage of the group productivity that flows from *satisfiers* until the *dissatisfiers* have first been met and resolved.

The *job* motivates, not the manipulative ability of the supervisor to get people to *do things*. The effective supervisor, then, is one who can best broaden factors that lead to "job satisfaction" of his subordinates.

The effective supervisor, using Herzberg's guidance, focuses on "job enrichment" of his subordinates. This simply means designing jobs to include more of the "satisfiers."

TABLE 1—Distinctive types of managerial rationale

Theory X

1. The average person has an *inherent dislike for work* and will avoid it if he can.
2. Because of this dislike for work, most people must be *coerced, controlled, directed, threatened or punished* to get them to put forth adequate effort toward the achievement of organizational objectives—even promise of reward is not enough. People will accept and demand more. *Only threat will do the trick.*
3. Average person prefers to be directed, wishes to avoid responsibility, has little ambition, and wants security above all—*mediocrity of the masses.*

Theory Y

1. Expenditure of physical and mental effort in *work is as natural as play or rest*—depending on controllable conditions, work may be either a source of satisfaction of dissatisfaction.
2. External control and the threat of punishment are not the only means for bringing about effort toward objectives. *Man will exercise self direction and self control in the service of objectives to which he is committed.*
3. *Commitment* is a function of the rewards associated with their achievement.
4. Under proper conditions *people will not only accept but seek responsibility*—avoidance of responsibility, lack of ambition, emphasis on security are consequences of experience, not human characteristics.
5. *Capacity to exercise imagination, ingenuity, creativity is widely, not narrowly, distributed.*
6. *Intellectual potential* of the average person is being only *partially utilized.*

Implications

Theory X

1. Central principles of organization derived from Theory X is that of *direction and control through exercise of authority.*
2. *Organizational requirements take precedent over needs of members.* In return for rewards offered, the individual will accept external direction and control.
3. *We do not recognize the existence of potential in people and* therefore there is no reason to devote time, effort, and money to discovering how to realize full potential.

Theory Y

1. *Central principle derived from Theory Y is integration:* The creation of conditions such that members of the organization can achieve their goals best by directing their efforts toward the success of the enterprise.
2. The organization will be more effective in achieving its objectives *if adjustments are made to the needs and goals of its members.*
3. *We are challenged to innovate,* to discover new ways of organizing and directing human effort.

(From *The Human Side of Enterprise*, Douglas, McGregor, McGraw Hill Publishing Co., New York.)

TABLE 2—Herzberg's list of motivational factors

JOB DISSATISFACTION ENVIRONMENT	JOB SATISFACTION WHAT THEY DO
Company policies and administration	Achievement
Supervision	Recognition
Working conditions	Work itself
Interpersonal relations	Responsibility
Money, status, security	Professional growth

(From *The Motivation to Work*, Frederick Herzberg, Wiley Interscience Publishing Co., New York.)

SUPERVISOR'S 'GAME PLAN'

Exxon's F. D. McMurray identified questions most often asked by new supervisors and by supervisors enrolled in a company supervisory training program.[3]

- **Question 1.** As the leader, should my emphasis be on the people or on the job? *Answer: Productivity and morale are higher under employee-centered supervision than under production-centered supervision.*
- **Question 2.** How tight a rein should I keep? *Answer: Loose supervision of a group's activities results in higher productivity and morale than does close supervision, especially when the face-to-face interaction among the subordinates is high.*
- **Question 3.** How much does the group influence the individual? *Answer: The behavior of a subordinate is influenced by the degree to which he identifies with a cohesive group (a group with "team spirit").*
- **Question 4.** Does team spirit work for me or against me? *Answer: Group cohesiveness results in greater productivity when the organization is seen as supportive, rather than threatening, to the member's sense of personal worth and status.*
- **Question 5.** What will happen when I put pressure on the group to get the job done? *Answer: Pressure for productivity usually results in higher productivity; morale is highest under moderate pressure.*
- **Question 6.** How can I make them accept my goals? *Answer: Group members are more likely to accept goals as their own, and to work toward those goals, when they have participated in setting them.*

- **Question 7.** How much should I expect from my people? *Answer: Productivity of a group depends to some extent on the level of the leader's expectations.*
- **Question 8.** How can I get cooperation rather than obedience? *Answer: Power which is maintained by punishment or fear of punishment results in obedience and acquiescence rather than in voluntary acceptance, cooperation and positive effort.*
- **Question 9.** How important are my technical skills? *Answer: For promotion to a supervisory position technical skills seem more important than human relation skills during periods of rapid organizational change.*
- **Question 10.** All things considered, what style of leadership works best? *Answer: Democratic leadership has certain advantages over autocratic leadership.*

A coach. The behavioral scientists conclude that there is a close corollary between supervision and coaching. The coach leads in formulating plans and goals, properly identifies and uses talents of various players, administers training (preparation), and serves as a *fair* arbiter/evaluator of performance. Ultimately, he encourages Herzberg's "satisfiers" to manifest themselves on a daily basis within his work group, using—as a working hypothesis—McGregor's Theory Y assumptions.

Use dynamic communication

If *leadership* is the vehicle for implementing dynamic supervision, then *communication* is the fuel that runs it.

It will help to understand the distinction between communication (singular) and communications (plural). Communication is the *process* of transmitting, receiving and interpreting information. It involves many elements—among them semantics, "body language," empathy, vocabulary usage, vocal tone and voice inflection, and listening-for-content ability (See Table 3).

TABLE 3—The common denominators of good communication

- It is more or less continuous.
- It deals with both big and little matters with equal care and thoroughness.
- It is concrete and specific. It shows as much as it tells.
- It explains why.
- It acknowledges risks and difficulties, if any, and reports steps to minimize them.
- It lists benefits that could result, but lists them realistically.
- It solicits questions or feedback, to help cut off the rumor mill.
- It invites participation.
- It avoids surprise to minimize upsetting people.
- It sets standards because people want to know what's expected of them.
- It contacts informal leaders—especially important among hourly employes.
- It praises, genuinely and sincerely.
- It repeats, using fresh examples, different approaches.

Communications (plural) are the product—a memorandum or report, an interview, a performance appraisal, a paper or speech, a recording, a staff meeting and so on.

The two—communication and communications—are inseparable if the supervisor is to be an efficient communicator. They must be meticulously blended together and orchestrated in much the same way that a symphony orchestra presents music. Think of your ability to understand the process of communication as the musician within you. Think of your skill in writing, listening, speaking and reading as the instruments you will use. When *process* skills are blended harmoniously with proper use of the "instruments," the message flows clearly and sweetly.

Communication guidelines. Excellent guidelines for the supervisor stem from work at the Communication Research Center, Purdue University, as reported by J. S. Morgan.[4]

1. Know your audience. This seems obvious. But many people don't see the obvious. For instance, some managers remain blind to what motivates employees. Thus, they don't communicate in terms of employee interests, and they don't get across completely.

2. Build on the past. Knowing your audience includes understanding on yet another level. Your employees have their prejudices, limits of knowledge and understanding. Judge the boundaries carefully. Then aim your communication toward what your people already accept and know.

3. Know your purpose. Keep your objectives always in mind. Try to do more than tell your people what to do or make announcements. Stick with the facts in dealing with employees, without partiality.

4. Think and organize. The old axiom "look before you leap" applies here. Plan your communication well in advance when possible, anticipating likely problem areas or objections, and have a plan to cope.

5. Accent the positive. Tell your people what they do *right*. Praise employees for their skills and good workmanship. Watch the negative-prone employees—the ones who become easily discouraged or who have a tendency toward low spirits and pessimism. Go a little out of your way to encourage them. When criticism becomes necessary, give it in as helpful a way as possible. Tell why a poor practice cannot be tolerated. Show the right way to do the job. Criticize impersonally, not pesonally.

6. But don't eliminate the negative. Bad news, however, does turn up. Never sugarcoat it. Never suppress it. "No news is good news" is a myth. Bad news always surfaces eventually. You gain when you give it in your own way and at your own time.

Employees want both the good and bad news about their employer and the business situation. Indeed, if they receive nothing but good news, they suspect managers of holding out on them.

7. Guard your credibility. It is difficult to acquire and easy to lose.

Do you consistently give deadlines that are shorter than necessary?

Do you exaggerate a reprimand that your boss has given you concerning your staff?

In making disagreeable assignments, do you attempt to dodge blame by claiming fictitious protests about them to your own superior?

Such subterfuges damage your credibility.

8. Act on what you say. This builds credibility more than any other factor. Inaction or slow action often are the more common problems. Make no commitments unless reasonably certain you can and will act on them. If you promise to do something and then circumstances rule that you cannot, report at once. Tell why you can't perform as promised. Tell what you plan to do as a result of the change.

9. Keep your emotional content up. Psychologists have concluded that facts alone will seldom persuade. Facts that go counter to emotional self-interests will almost never persuade. But facts will do the job when presented eloquently and in terms of listeners' emotional interests.

10. Give a rounded picture. This stems from the suggestions on credibility and emotions. In communicating on controversial subjects, don't load your side of the argument unfairly. This doesn't mean you give the opposition's arguments without rebuttal. This does not mean that you do not point out errors or fallacies in the opposing arguments. But you do round out the picture from your point of view.

Studies show that employees want managers to present the management interpretation of the situation, but in a fair-handed way.

11. Communicate a little at a time. When you have a complicated message, give it bit by bit. Even the most intelligent people have trouble grasping new or more complicated messages in one bite. When in doubt, break your bits into even smaller pieces.

Make your bit-by-bit approach persistent and consistent. Tell the same, continued story when you break things into their parts. And keep it up. Communication is a year-round job. Also, repeat—until you just begin to try your employees' memories or intelligence.

12. Tell the story in different ways. Use all appropriate media available to you: word of mouth, memo, announcement in the company house organ or whatever. And always leave the way open for "feedback" or questions.

13. Build in feedback. Know your score in communicating. The best indicator of your performance is the job your people do. If they aren't doing well, look to your communication for some of the trouble. Even when they do well, check regularly on how you're getting across. You can always improve.

14. Watch the nonverbal aspect. Listening is most important. You can't do it if you can't stop talking. Listen quietly, attentively, politely. A good communicator spends more time listening than talking. What's your ratio? Don't just guess at it. Keep a diary for a day or two and time yourself.

THE 'MECHANICS'

The supervisor's communication "tools" are reading, writing, listening, speaking and meeting leadership.

Reading. The keynotes are speed and retention. With proper training, it is possible to improve both. You may want to consult your organization's training director about training opportunities. Alternately, training advice is available from the American Society for Training and Development, Madison, Wis.

W. H. Perkins identifies four "levels" of reading: skimming, scanning, intensive reading and critical reading.[5] There are specific scenarios that call for each of the four. The supervisor who is an efficient reader will know how and when to read in a particular *way*.

Writing. Supervisors who write well have fewer problems with management or subordinates. Writing is a cornerstone of good communication. Mueller offers 10 "Principles of Clear Statement:"[6]

- **Keep the sentences short.** On the *average,* most sentences should be shorter than 25 words. But sentences should vary in length and structure.
- **Prefer the simple to the complex.** Avoid complex sentences and phrases. Write "try to find out," rather than "endeavor to ascertain."
- **Prefer the familiar word,** but build your vocabulary. If a reader doesn't understand your words, he can miss your meaning. But you may want to use long words in some cases—to clarify your point.
- **Avoid words you don't need.** Extra words weaken writing. Make every word carry its own weight.
- **Put action into your verbs.** Passive verbs tire the reader. Write "We intend to write clearly," not "Clarity in composition is our intention."
- **Use terms your reader can picture.** Choose short, concrete words your reader can visualize, not abstract terms. Don't say "industrial community" when you're describing a "factory town."
- **Tie in with your reader's experience.** The reader probably won't get your *new* idea unless you link it with an old idea he already understands. If you're describing how a new pump works, compare its operation with that of an old, standard pump.
- **Write the way you talk.** Or at least try for a conversational tone. People rarely use business jargon when they talk.
- **Make full use of variety.** Vary the length of words and sentences, and arrange them in different ways. Avoid monotonous patterns of writing.
- **Write to EXpress, not to IMpress.** Don't show off your vocabulary by using needlessly complex words.

Listening. There is a great deal more to listening than merely absorbing words. The effective supervisor listens with what author Leroy Wilkie terms the "inner ear."[7] The sensitive listener knows the importance of *semantics* in translating and enunciating thoughts. He also knows how to "read" the speaker's "body language," vocal tones and inflections, and other "signals" that enhance understanding of the message. He learns techniques for *concentration,* to avoid "dropping out" of the listening mode (rehearsing what you're going to say in rebuttal, for example).

TABLE 4—Types of questions that get response

Information

"What do you remember about _____?"
"Can you explain what happened in _____?"
"Tell me how it looked to you."
"How did it happen that _____?"

Suggestions

"How do you think we should handle this?"
"You know what this equipment is supposed to do; how do you think we should operate it?"
"I have a problem—the facts are these _____.
What would you do if you were in my shoes?"
"I have been thinking about this new idea: _____.
How do you evaluate it?"

Opinion

"Why did this happen, in your opinion?"
"What do they mean by _____?"
"Would you say that _____?"
"Now that you have had a chance to work on _____, what do you think of it?"
"_____looks like _____that happened a couple of months ago. How do you compare them?" This kind of questioning is designed, first, to open up a work-connected conversation. Problems can be solved. New problems can be uncovered early. But they also provide the employe with recognition, and the feeling that his ideas count for something.

Speaking. Speaking skills can range from articulate conversational ability to making a complex technical speech easy for a layman to understand. Author Joe Powell points out that society meeting papers don't have to be read in a dull monotone.[8] He offers a number of means to enliven a presentation and keep the listener's interest alive in the process.

Moreover, there is an aspect of speaking to which many persons give little thought: *questioning*. The carefully thought-out question is a major vehicle for sensitive, emphatic communication. Table 4 alludes to some of the ways that well-posed questions can get a desired response.

Meeting leadership. Tables 5 and 6 list points that the supervisor should keep in mind when in his meeting-leadership role. In addition to being aware of those factors, the supervisor needs a grasp of visual aids alternatives. Mobil Oil's D. G. Treichler published a handy checklist for this.[9]

Meetings can also be an excellent vehicle for "team building." (See Table 7.)

TABLE 5—Steps to more productive meetings

1. Don't call a meeting to decide something you could and should decide yourself.

2. Never get people together if a series of phone calls to individuals would serve your purpose.

3. Never invite anyone who is not essential, but make sure that all in this category are included.

4. Insist on punctuality. If you're 2 minutes late for a 20-man meeting, you waste 40 man-minutes.

5. Keep the purpose of your meeting firmly in mind, and be sure it can be achieved.

6. Draft an agenda that breaks all subjects down into their simplest constituents. A lengthy agenda, if well constructed, often means a short meeting.

7. Before sending out your agenda, read it all through from start to finish and examine all the points that can be misunderstood. In most meetings, most disagreements occur because people are not talking about the same thing. If the issues are crystal-clear, the muddlers will have less chance of confusing them.

8. See that the agenda is circulated in sufficient time for people to read it before they come, but not so far ahead that they will have forgotten all about it by the time they arrive.

9. Set time limits for each section of the discussion. Make sure there is a clock everyone can see. Discussion, like work, expands to fill the time available.

10. See that whoever is in the chair acts as chairman; i.e., that he states the issues, keeps to the agenda, lets everyone have a fair crack at the subject, cuts them short if they wander, and sums up succinctly as soon as all have had their say.

TABLE 6—Behaviors that increase or block a meeting's success

Increase success	Block success
Acceptance	Disagree
Credit and thank	Impatient
Praise others	Argue
Recognized ideas	Defend
Openness	Turn off
Willingness	Nit-pick
Well informed	Don't listen
Awareness	Complain
Usefulness	Disapprove
Trust	Questions
Esteem	Tell "war stories"
Approval	Be hurt
Adequacy	Sulk
Comprehension	Take offense
Honesty	Don't think
Empathy	Become bored

TABLE 7—Building team-enhancing factors

- Try to create a climate which is relaxed, informal and comfortable
- Encourage and provide the time for group discussion and communications.
- Make sure that objectives and goals are well defined, pinpointed and understood by all team members.
- Coach team members on good listening techniques.
- Make allowances for the airing of disagreements and differing points of view.
- Encourage "levelling" and frank and open criticism.
- Provide an atmosphere where subordinates are free to express their feelings.
- Make sure no one team member assumes a dominating role.

Appraise employees fairly

The argument for and against *formal* employee appraisals still rages—especially relating to "professional" employees such as engineers. Engineers—it is said—are supposed to be "self starters" on the *motivation* side of the appraisal ledger, and that they have "too many variables in their jobs and methods for feasible measurement and analysis" on the *production* side of the appraisal ledger. This may or may not be true—depending on the person and the nature of his duties.

Everyone appraises. One point seems clear. *All* companies have employee appraisals. Every supervisor—in one way or another—appraises his subordinates. Every subordinate—in one way or another—appraises his supervisor. Both of them appraise top management and vice versa. So—with or without the now-common conventional appraisal forms and interviews, appraisals are going on all the time. And they dramatically affect production and interpersonal and intergroup relationships up and down the line.

It is in the area of *superficiality* that appraisal critics have their most convincing argument. The supervisor's paramount fear is that unresolvable or embarrassing issues will be raised by the subordinate. The subordinate fears that he will not get a fair and objective hearing or that he is "on trial." Yet, considerable evidence suggests that people *do* welcome fair and even unflattering comments if made in a total context of honesty, empathy, and trust. Thus, the right climate for the interview calls an attempt by the parties to get at the truth. Technique is important, but secondary.

Benefits. There are a number of benefits to the appraisal, identified by behavioral scientists:

1. It makes as a matter of record the job performance history of each employee.

2. It points out gradual changes that may have occurred in an employee's job performance over a long period of time. When such a change occurs, either for the better or for the worse, it may happen so gradually that it is not noticed by the supervisor until he compares the present appraisal with one made previously.

3. The supervisor can use the appraisal to help him clarify the kind of training his employees need. Employees can also use it to help them in their self-development efforts.

4. It can help the supervisor in his own self-development efforts through the practice he gets in appraising employees and conducting interviews with them.

5. It can help the supervisor and employee establish a better working relationship through providing the opportunity for an exchange of viewpoints during the interview.

6. It provides an over-all evaluation that is based on deliberate and careful consideration by the supervisor rather than on spontaneous judgments resulting from casual day-to-day observation of an employee's behavior and work. Consequently, it should be more accurate because it should be less susceptible to the many pitfalls inherent in making judgments about people.

7. It provides the employee with assurance that he is being evaluated on the same aspects of job performance and as far as possible, against the same standards as are other employees.

A work-centered approach. Further insight into formal-appraisal benefits is offered in a work-centered approach:

1. Personality changes and alterations in basic behavioral patterns are not likely to be accomplished, and activities based on such expectations are to be avoided.

2. Personnel are employed primarily to implement corporate objectives and to contribute to the attainment of corporate goals.

3. The true measure of an individual's performance is the degree to which his activity contributes to or detracts from goal attainment.

Under the above three-part rationale, then, appraisals are work centered and are designed to do the following:

1. Measure the subject's performance against objectives, determining why and how he contributed to "success" or "frustration"

2. Determine how his efforts might better be directed

3. Estimate his potential capabilities and those areas in which his future activities would be most appropriate.

With respect to the technique to be used in the appraisal process, there are six points:

1. A statement of objectives for the period under review

2. A description of the individual's functions designed to contribute to goal achievement

3. Statements of accomplishment and limitations

4. A description of the subject's performance as it related to Item 3

5. A discussion with the subject to elicit his views, observations and suggestions

6. Descriptions of performance areas to be strengthened, those to be avoided, and an outline of the means to be taken for such purposes.

An extension of management by objectives. Perhaps the most popular approach to appraisals is the "results-oriented" method, which is an extension of the "management by objectives" concept.[10] (See Fig. 1.)

In his book, *The Human Side of Enterprise,* McGregor recommends that appraiser and subordinate begin by jointly arriving at a clear statement of the subordinate's major responsibilities. Working from this statement, the subordinate then establishes short-range targets (say, three months ahead) and a plan of action for meeting them. He goes over the plan with his superior and together they modify it until they are both satisfied. When the target period is up, the subordinate evaluates what he has done, discusses it with his boss, and the process repeats itself. Thus, the appraisal interview becomes a joint examination by the superior and the subordinate of the latter's self-appraisal that culminates in resetting targets for the next three-month period. This, then, becomes a self-generating process, shifting the focus of appraisal from the person to his accomplishments, and changing his role from passive to active in the process.

Commonalities. There are other approaches to appraisals. But most have a number of elements in common. Most significant of these are:

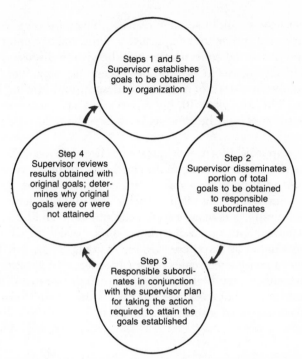

Figure 1—The forced-planning nature of management by objectives features a continuous-flow way to get work done.

- Superior and subordinate jointly reach agreement on critical elements of the subordinate's job.
- Superior and subordinate jointly decide on ways performance will be measured.
- Superior and subordinate jointly develop short-term targets.
- Main emphasis is placed on superior-subordinate counseling, using objective data wherever possible.
- Appraisal focuses on the results achieved by the subordinate rather than on his personal characteristics.

Job description. The question of employee appraisals naturally raises the issue of job descriptions. Before any formal appraisal can be effective, an employee must enter the interview situation with a clear concept of his job. He must have a view of:

1. What he is supposed to do
2. The limits of his authority and responsibility
3. How well he is expected to perform his job
4. How well he is actually performing.

The supervisor should also have conceptualized his own idea of how these four elements relate to the appraisee. Thus, the two enter the interview with preconceived concepts that will be ideally discussed in depth, and amendments made in a mutually acceptable way. The employee should write the first draft of his own job description. Having done this, and compared his analysis with his supervisor's assessment in the interview, his position should be clear as related to the following points:

Forms. The appraisal form—or questionnaire—has been the subject of keen debate. One almost unanimous conclusion from the controversy is that questions relating to personality "traits" or other broad generalities should be avoided unless handled in such a way that they have minimum bias. Many investigators of appraisal techniques also challenge weighing employee characteristics or performance on a "scale" in which the appraisee is evaluated as Excellent, Good, Average, Poor, etc. Investigators experienced with such scales report a tendency of appraisers to rate subordinates either very high or very low or to lean toward the "average." Industrial psychologists refer to this as the "halo" effect—and it can render an appraisal almost meaningless.

Manage your time better

The supervisor who is making optimum use of his time (1) employs a program of "management by objectives" (2) plans his workday systematically and (3) knows how and when to delegate work to others.

Management by objectives (MBO). This cyclic approach to planning and scheduling tasks and goals is illustrated in Fig. 1. Under MBO, each subordinate periodically (usually quarterly) sits with the supervisor to *jointly* plan the subordinate's goals and objectives for a specific period of time. At the end of the quarter, or at intermediate checkpoints along the way (for complex goals), these two get together again to "check signals" and amend the plan if necessary. At this time, they also establish goals for the next quarter.

The description of MBO is somewhat of an oversimplification. A fully integrated system involves documentation, integration with long range planning, etc. However, even the above communication setup can do wonders to help the supervisor make the best use of time. Lawrence Steinmetz offers a good, brief description of how to establish an MBO system.[10]

Time management. MBO preserves the supervisor's time and creative energies by helping him to "track" the activities of his group, as they meet organizational goals. But the supervisor also needs a "handle" on his own activities, day-to-day and week-to-week. In evaluating how you currently make use of your time, you may find that you have taken on tasks that are or should be someone else's responsibility. You may also find that, by becoming immersed in too much detail, you have overlooked time-saving approaches.

You may find you have been concentrating heavily on only the areas that interest you—then must scramble to dig out from under routine, low-interest functions that could save time if attacked headon.

A five-phase reevaluation will help in your time-saving program: (1) redefine your real objectives, (2) confine your attention solely to these objectives, (3) define the subsidiary objectives that affect your overall objectives, (4) establish or reorient programs for attaining subsidiary objectives, and (5) determine which duties to delegate or seek help on.

After this analysis, set up a *daily timetable* of activities.

How to organize a timetable. The management consulting firm, Henry Schindall Associates, New York, suggests an 11-step time-scheduling approach:

1. Set up a long-range worksheet. This is done a month or week ahead, depending on how much time you allot various objectives and subsidiary objectives. The style of this table should be designed to suit your individual needs.

2. Set up a daily worksheet. This should complement the long-range worksheet and be specific enough to assure that you are devoting some time to all of your objectives.

3. Take a day's end inventory. Each afternoon, jot down all tasks you want to accomplish the next day. At this point, don't worry about their relative importance or the order or means in which you want to handle them.

4. Transfer these tasks to daily worksheet. Write in tasks that must be handled at a certain time of day, such as conferences, accommodation of job peers who will be out of the office, etc.

5. Take other tasks in order of importance. Write these into your work schedule, taking them in order of how critical they are. At this point, consider the time of day in which you work most efficiently.

6. Take a time estimate. Beside each task, note how long you think it will take. Indicate specific deadlines.

7. Add up the hours for each task. If the time allotted totals more hours than you plan to work, remove the least important tasks, to be fitted in on more flexible days.

8. Transfer next day's tasks to a memo pad. A desk calendar may be suitable. You can now leave the office or plant with a clearly defined workday format in mind for tomorrow.

9. Check off completions. As each task is completed, check it off of the memo sheet and daily worksheet, and make comments on performance criteria. Is more followup needed? Do you need consultation? If so, these go to a specific time slot on future work sheets.

10. Indicate time taken. As you complete each task, note how long it took, on your daily worksheet. Compare how long it took with your estimate of how long you *thought* it would take. As you gain experience in this kind of estimating, you will eventually be able to come within minutes of calculating a time scale for similar functions in the future.

11. Follow the Procedure Daily. Disciplined use of this technique will enable you to "roadmap" your timetable. Consistent, steady use of work scheduling will free many hours.

Other approaches. Some authors have proposed time-control programs that have even more depth and sophistication than the stepwise approach outlined above.[11-13] Which approach to use will depend on individual need.

Delegation. Failure to delegate properly has been identified as one of supervisors' major shortcomings. Non-delegators are often found among persons labeled "workaholics." (See Table 8.) They are also found among those who try to delegate *everything*, and thus produce cynical, embittered subordinates.

Author Eugene Raudsepp, writing on delegation, quotes the guidelines of management consultant C. C. Gibbons,[14] who offers the following eight-part system.

1. Be sure you and *your* boss agree on what your job is. In defining your job, take all the initiative you can without encroaching on the rights of others. A narrow definition of your job restricts you and will serve neither your interests nor the goals of the company.

TABLE 8—Is this managing or doing?

1. Explaining to one of your company's managers a possible solution to a problem which he and his people face in your functional area of responsibility.

2. Explaining how to solve a work problem which one of your people has just brought to you.

3. Filling out a form to recommend a salary increase for one of your people.

4. Interviewing a prospective employe who was referred to you by an employment agency.

5. Giving a telephone report of progress to your superior.

6. Reviewing monthly reports to determine progress toward achieving specific objectives for your area of responsibility.

7. Drafting an improved layout of facilities.

8. Attending a professional or trade organization in order to improve functional knowledge and skills.

9. Making a talk about your company's progress and plans to the local Chamber of Commerce.

10. Transferring responsibility from Employe A to Employe B because Employe A did not devote the necessary effort.

11. Phoning a department to request help in solving a problem which one of your people is trying to solve.

12. Planning the extent to which your people should use staff services during the next year in accomplishing your department's objectives.

See answers next page

---

2. Be sure your subordinates understand what you expect them to do. The simplest way to delegate is to tell your subordinates what authority you reserve for yourself and what is theirs.

And don't forget to let each subordinate know exactly what results will add up to a job well done.

3. Prepare written policies your subordinates can use to guide their decisions. A soundly conceived and clearly understood set of policies permits subordinates to make decisions and take action with confidence.

4. Be humble enough to admit that someone else might be able to do the job as well as you can. The manager of a baseball team might be an excellent pitcher, catcher and first baseman, but he cannot play all these positions simultaneously.

5. Make subordinates responsible to you, in organizing your work group. Such a flat organization will help you communicate, make decisions, take action and exercise control. It is possible only if you have capable, well-trained subordinates, and if you delegate real authority to them.

Answers—Delegation quiz that appears on preceding page

1. Doing. This is technical problem-solving within the function of engineering, marketing, production, or the like.
2. Managing. This is supervising—assuming the manager doesn't require his people to come to him for answers to routine problems.
3. Doing. This is clerical work. Instructing your secretary to fill out the form would be delegating, an element of managing.
4. Doing. Although it may be essential work, it is a personnel function. Deciding to hire someone after the recruiting and selecting had been done would be staffing, an element of managing.
5. Managing. This is communicating for purposes of control if the manager is seeking guidance and direction. Otherwise, it is plain communicating which anyone does.
6. Managing. This is measuring and evaluating for purposes of control.
7. Doing. This is a methods engineering function. Deciding to obtain an improved layout would be improving, an element of managing.
8. Doing—if one's intent is primarily to improve his own effectiveness at technical problem-solving.
   Managing—if one's intent is primarily to improve the results he gets through his people.
9. Doing. This is a public relations function.
10. Managing. This is correcting for purposes of control. This might also be disciplining as a part of supervising.
11. Doing. This may be necessary but it is getting results *for* the subordinate, not getting results *through* him.
12. Managing. This is developing a program to achieve group results.

---

6. Make subordinates responsible for accomplishing results rather than activities. Once the expected results are spelled out, the subordinate should be able to choose the methods he will use in accomplishing them. He can make his fullest contribution only if he is free to exercise some initiative and ingenuity in carrying out the work. If you delegate effectively, subordinates will understand that the real boss is the task to be performed.

7. Reward the persons who get things done. You cannot delegate unless your subordinates will accept responsibility. They will accept responsibility and actively participate in accomplishing objectives only if they feel that rewards go to the persons who get things done. The rewards for being right must always be greater than the penalties for being wrong.

8. Distinguish between rush jobs and the less immediate but more important things you have to do; try to spend more time on the important tasks. Delegate operating details that periodically become urgent and free yourself for the management functions for which you are responsible.

Improve your decisions

Decision-making can be methodical. You can improve your ability to make decisions in all managerial activities if you feel there is a need to do so. You can get an indication of this need by determining what you would decide in this situation: John Stanton, one of your key people, has just turned in a letter of resignation. He says he has accepted a better job with another organization. Assuming that John has had responsibilities vital to your operation, which of the following choices is the best statement of the problem(s) you face?

A. How can I get John to change his mind about quitting the job he has held?

B. How shall I fill the position that John held?

C. How can I reassign the duties and responsibilities that John had?

D. How can I get John to stay with our organization even if he doesn't go back to the position he held?

E. _____

_____

_____

The answer. What you decide in a situation depends on problem definition. The trap many managers fall into is stating a solution in defining the problem. On this basis, the choices A, B and C are poor statements of the above problem. Choice D defines a problem—assuming John would be a valuable employee in some other capacity. But it overlooks your need for finding his replacement.

You face a two-part problem:

(1) How shall I see that the duties John had are carried out?

(2) How can I convince John to stay with our organization?

Once you have your problem defined, you may still be in deep water unless you know the real cause. Otherwise, you may decide on wrong solutions. In checking with John, for example, you may find that the real cause is his wife's attitude toward his job.

Methods. Tables 9 and 10 show simplified, stepwise approaches to processing a decision effectively. A slightly different approach is suggested by Kepner and Tregoe in their "landmark" book, *The Rational Manager* (McGraw Hill Publishing, New York). Making the best decision, they say, involves a sequence of procedures based on seven concepts:

1. The objective of a decision must be established first.

2. The objectives are classified as to importance.

3. Alternative actions are developed.

4. The alternatives are evaluated against the established objectives.

5. The choice of the alternative best able to achieve all the objectives represents the tentative decision.

6. The tentative decision is explored for future possible adverse consequences.

7. The effects of the final decision are controlled by taking other actions to prevent possible adverse consequences from becoming problems, and by making sure the actions decided on are carried out.

So important has a rational approach to decision-making/problem-solving become in today's complex industrial society, that a host of methods and training programs have appeared. There are parallels between each of them—yet they are different, too, in significant ways. Among

---

TABLE 9—Steps to making better decisions

1. Classify the problem. Is it generic? Is it exceptional or unique? Or is it the first manifestation of a new class of problems for which a rule has yet to be developed?

2. Define the problem. What are we dealing with?

3. Specify what the answer to the problem must satisfy. What are the "boundary conditions"?

4. Decide on what is "right," rather than what is acceptable, in order to meet the boundary conditions. What will fully satisfy the specifications before attention is given to the compromises, adaptations and concessions needed to make the decision acceptable?

5. Include in the decision the action needed to carry it out. What does the action commitment have to be? Who has to know about it?

6. Seek feedback that tests the validity and effectiveness of the decision against the actual course of events. How is the decision being carried out? Are the assumptions on which it is based appropriate or obsolete?

TABLE 10—A problem-solving method

1. State the problem

- What has happened where and when that can have a negative effect on what you are trying to accomplish through your people?
  - Who is affected?
  - What is likely to happen if problem is not solved?
  - How soon is solution required?
  - What are possible causes?

2. Get facts and opinions

- Are there policies, procedures or precedents which apply?
- Are there reports, records or manuals that you should review?
- Who has solved a similar problem in the past?
- What are possible causes and solutions as suggested by those affected?
- Does problem need to be redefined into one or more problems?

3. Select the best solution

- What is the simplest solution?
- What are likely reactions to solution?
- What could go wrong?
- Should there be both short and long-range solutions?
- Can solution be tested?

4. Sell the solution

- What acceptance do you need within and outside of your department?
- Is management approval required?
- Should you sell key people individually?
- What should be put in writing?
- When will timing be best for selling your solution?

5. Implement solution and follow up

- What are immediate reactions and results?
- Are there unforeseen problems?
- Does solution need revision?
- What reporting of results is required?
- Did solution solve the problem?

the approaches are: (1) KTA problem-solving system, (2) creative problem-solving, (3) synectics and (4) value analysis. There are others, as well, discussed along with these four by author Raymond Loen.[15]

Alternatives. The four approaches above are useful tools for building a systematic program for making decisions and solving problems.

- **KTA method.** Kepner-Tregoe training emphasizes the importance of drawing tight boundaries around a problem to find its true cause. Once the cause has been determined, the elimination process begins. This leads to a detailed "action sequence" system that is used for all problems. Once in place, the KTA system becomes the organization's model for attacking all problems and decisions—but particularly those with many variables and complexities.
- **Creative problem-solving,** as a planned system, got its first big push more than 25 years ago with publication of Alex Osborn's celebrated book, *Applied Imagination* (Scribners, New York). Since then, creative problem-solving programs have become ever more sophisticated. Osborn emphasized "brainstorming." A newer, and widely accepted method is synectics.
- **Synectics.** In this unique approach, the individual uses analogies to bring his preconscious mind to the surface. Problems are defined by making the "strange" familiar, then the "familiar" strange. Analogies are used. The best metaphor is usually the one that is the most peculiar or "farthest out."

An atmosphere of creativity is attained by removing psychological blocks. Synectics' practicioners indulge in fantasies in arriving at solutions to problems.

One of synectics' better known analogies resulted in a thermostatic roofing compound that is black in cold weather and white in warm. The analogy: that a flounder changes its color to match its environment.

- **Value analysis.** Although there are many versions of the value analysis (VA), this description should suffice:

Phase 1—Information gathering. Selection of appropriate objects, collection of information about projects, definition of basic and secondary functions of each project

Phase 2—Speculation. Generation of as many ideas as possible for performing the necessary functions identified in Phase 1

Phase 3—Planning. Condensation and analysis of data concerning ideas generated in Phase 2

Phase 4—Execution. Selection of one or more feasible ideas offering the best value

Phase 5—Reporting. Development of a plan for presenting the ideas and gaining commitment.

LITERATURE CITED

[1] Moody, G., "Manage better with Theory Y," HYDROCARBON PROCESSING, August 1970, page 91.

[2] Gellerman, S., "Motivation through job enrichment," *Hydrocarbon Processing*, November 1968, page 252.

[3] McMurry, F., "The art and science of leadership," *Hydrocarbon Processing*, June 1962, page 191.

[4] Morgan, J., "Apply communication wisdom," *Hydrocarbon Processing*, August 1970, page 95.

[5] Perkins, W., "Improve your reading skills," *Hydrocarbon Processing*, April 1971, page 173.

[6] Mueller, D., "Put clarity in your writing," *Hydrocarbon Processing*, June 1980, page 76.

[7] Wilkie, L., et al, "Listen your way to supervisory success," *Hydrocarbon Processing*, August 1962, page 146.

[8] Powell, J., "Technical speeches can be fun," *Hydrocarbon Processing*, February 1972, page 121.

[9] Treichler, D., "Use visual aids to make your point," *Hydrocarbon Processing*, December 1966, page 158.

[10] Steinmetz, L., "Management by objectives: How it works," *Hydrocarbon Processing*, September 1967, page 193.

[11] Loveless, W., "Chart your way to task analysis," *Hydrocarbon Processing*, February 1969, page 109.

[12] Lakein, A., "Get control of your time," *Hydrocarbon Processing*, February 1977, page 145.

[13] Bilinsky, S., "How to increase your job output," *Hydrocarbon Processing*, October 1970, page 141.

[14] Raudsepp, E., "Why managers don't delgate," *Hydrocarbon Processing*, October 1976, page 187.

[15] Loen, R., "How to make better decisions," *Hydrocarbon Processing*, August 1970, page 81.

(**NOTE:** Articles in the literature citations also have been republished in the book *Management and the Technical Professional,* and the book *Communication and the Technical Professional,* Gulf Publishing Co., P.O. Box 2608, Houston, Texas 77001.)

Chapter 5

Form Better Teams for International Projects

	PROJECT PHASE				
SUBJECTS	1 PREAWARD	2 INITIATION	3 ENGINEERING	4 PROCUREMENT	5 CONSTRUCTION
A FINANCIAL/CONTRACTUAL					
B ORGANIZATION/EXECUTION PLANNING					
C MANAGING PEOPLE/COMMUNICATION	●	●	●	●	●
D ESTIMATING/COST CONTROL					
E RISK ANALYSIS					
F SCHEDULING					
G TRACKING/TRENDING					
H PROGRESS/PRODUCTIVITY MEASUREMENT					
I MATERIAL MANAGEMENT					

SUBJECT-PROJECT PHASE MATRIX

H. M. McCamish

It is not possible to form a project team in which each member is highly capable in all elements. Nor is it even necessary for successful project execution. On the other hand, the project team as a whole must be capable in all elements to be successful. Where weakness exists in one aspect in one team member, it must be offet by strength in this same aspect in other team members. Certain elements are more important than others in various project positions. And, there is a limit to the amount of weakness that can be tolerated in any given position, as well as in the team as a whole.

EVALUATION OF INDIVIDUALS

Eight elements of capability are required for a comprehensive evaluation, with a minimum amount of overlap between them: 1. General capability, 2. experience in function, 3. experience with facility, 4. experience with location, 5. adaptability and stability, 6. people consciousness, 7. cooperativeness, and 8. language ability.

Note the inter-relationship between elements. But with proper definition they can be evaluated as separate items.

"General capability" is probably easily understood although it is not an easy element to evaluate. "Experience in function" means the experience which relates to the function of the particular position—for example, experience as a project engineer. Previous experience as an engineer, but not as a project engineer, would be considered related experience. Another example would be for the technical services manager position where previous experience as a technical services manager would be "experience in function" whereas experience, say as a cost control engineer, would be considered as related experience Similar principles apply to the elements of "experience with facility" and "experience with location." The remaining four elements of capability are probably self-evident. The somewhat abstract elements, 5, 6 and 7, are seldom easy to evaluate.

A grading scale for capabilities based on grades from 1 to 10 is in Table 1. The scale provides definitions for the various grade levels which serve as guides to the person doing the grading. When an individual has been graded, an individual rating profile can be prepared as shown in Fig. 1.

TABLE 1—Grading scale for capabilities

1. General capability (overall for this type of work)
	1.	
Low	2.	Marginal
	3.	
	4.	Lower average
Medium	5.	
	6.	
	7.	Upper average
	8.	
High	9.	Outstanding
	10.	

2. Experience in function (for particular position)
	1.	Related experience—less than 10 years
Low	2.	Related experience—more than 10 years
	3.	Less than 2 years in function
	4.	Lower—less than 4 years in function
Medium	5.	
	6.	
	7.	Upper—10 years in function
	8.	11 to 15 years in function
High	9.	16 to 20 years in function
	10.	Over 20 years in function

3. Experience with facility (for specific type of plant)
	1.	None
Low	2.	One similar project
	3.	Several similar projects
	4.	One identical facility
Medium	5.	One identical facility plus one similar project
	6.	Two identical facilities
	7.	More than two identical facilities
	8.	More than two identical facilities plus one similar project
High	9.	More than two identical facilities plus several similar projects
	10.	Numerous identical facilities/top level understanding

4. Experience with location (specific country)
	1.	Never overseas
Low	2.	Visited overseas
	3.	Short overseas assignment at different location
	4.	Long assignment overseas
Medium	5.	Multiple assignments overseas
	6.	Numerous assignments overseas
	7.	Multiple assignments overseas, one in a similar location
	8.	Multiple assignments at similar location
High	9.	Single assignment at same location
	10.	Multiple assignments at same location

5. Adaptability & stability
	1.	Very inflexible/unreliable
Low	2.	
	3.	
	4.	Lower normal flexibility/reliability
Medium	5.	
	6.	
	7.	Upper normal flexibility/reliability
	8.	
High	9.	
	10.	Looks for change/highly reliable

6. People consciousness
	1.	Totally self-centered
Low	2.	
	3.	
	4.	Lower reasonable awareness
Medium	5.	
	6.	
	7.	Upper reasonable awareness
	8.	
High	9.	
	10.	Constantly, fully aware of human aspects

7. Cooperativeness
	1.	Hostile/insecure
Low	2.	
	3.	
	4.	Lower social acceptance
	5.	
	6.	
	7.	Upper social acceptance
	8.	
High	9.	
	10.	Very amenable/skillful mediator

8. Language ability (for location in question)
	1.	
Low	2.	Limited
	3.	
	4.	Lower conversational
Medium	5.	
	6.	
	7.	Upper conversational
	8.	
High	9.	Fluent (speaks, reads and writes)
	10.	

The rating profile for project manager Jim Jones on Fig. 1 is typical of the type of profile one can expect for a person of medium capability overall. A proper rating for almost any individual will show different strengths for the various elements of capability. When subsequently these individual profiles are used to evaluate the composite team the rating for each element of capability becomes particularly important rather than just the overall rating for the individuals.

Weighting factors. For the purpose of comparing individual candidates for a given position, weighting factors are used which take into account the fact that certain elements of capability are more important for one position in the project team than for another. Table 2 shows such weighting factors and a weighting table developed from these for the various senior project positions. These weighting factors can be applied to the individual ratings to derive weighted ratings for comparative purposes.

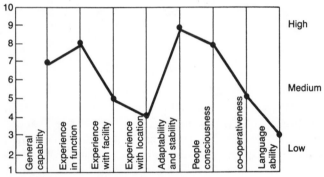

Figure 1—Individual rating profile of Jim Jones, project manager.

TABLE 2—Weighting factors

Very important aspect*	X	2.5
Important aspect*	X	2.0
Useful aspect*	X	1.5
Unimportant aspect*	X	1.0

* For the particular position and the particular project

Weighting table

	Project mgr.	Project eng.	Procurem. mrg.	Constr. mgr.	Tech. serv. mgr.	Admin. mgr.
General capability	2.5	2.5	2.5	2.5	2.5	2.5
Experience in function	2.5	2.5	2.5	2.5	2.5	2.5
Experience with facility	1.5	2.5	1.0	2.0	1.5	1.0
Experience with location	1.5	1.5	2.0	2.5	1.5	2.5
Adaptability/stability	2.0	2.0	2.5	2.5	2.0	2.0
People consciousness	2.5	2.0	2.0	2.5	2.0	2.5
Cooperativeness	1.5	2.0	2.5	2.0	2.0	2.5
Language ability	2.0	1.5	2.5	2.0	1.5	2.5

TABLE 3—Individual weighted ratings

Project managers (maximum rating = 160)			
John Smith	Weighting factor	Rating	Weighted Rating
General capability	2.5	8	20
Experience in function	2.5	5	12^1/$_2$
Experience with facility	1.5	6	9
Experience with location	1.5	2	3
Adaptability/stability	2.0	7	14
People consciousness	2.5	6	15
Cooperativeness	1.5	7	10^1/$_2$
Language ability	2.0	4	8
John Smith		**Total**	**92**
Jim Jones			
General capability	2.5	7	17^1/$_2$
Experience in function	2.5	8	20
Experience with facility	1.5	5	7^1/$_2$
Experience with location	1.5	4	6
Adaptability/stability	2.0	9	18
People consciousness	2.5	8	20
Cooperativeness	1.5	5	7^1/$_2$
Language ability	2.0	3	6
Jim Jones		**Total**	**102^1/$_2$**

In Table 3 there is a weighted ratings comparison between two candidates for project manager. Using the weighting factors developed for the particular project, Jim Jones appears to be a stronger candidate than John Smith. It is possible, however, that when considering the inclusion of Jim Jones or John Smith in the composite team, John Smith would produce a better balanced team because of the weaknesses and strengths of the other available team members.

TEAM EVALUATION

When the number of candidates for the positions have been narrowed down to two or three for each one, it is possible to proceed with a team evaluation. For team evaluations the composite of senior team members only is developed. For a medium sized engineering/construction (E/C) project the team members to be evaluated might be 1. project manager, 2. project engineer, 3. procurement manager, 4. construction manager, 5. technical services manager and 6. administrative manager. For a smaller project fewer members might be evaluated. For a larger project additional members should be evaluated such as assistant project manager, assistant project engineers, accounting manager, and personnel manager, etc.

Subjective. Even with the best of refinements the grading or rating of employee capabilities is more subjective than objective. So, it is reasonable to reduce the scale of 10 ratings to categories of High, Medium and Low for the team evaluation. For this purpose, Low is taken as 1 to 3, Medium as 4 to 7 and High as 8 to 10.

A typical team evaluation is shown in Fig. 2 for a medium sized project. The team shown is one of medium capability (e.g., the composite result of the strengths and the weaknesses of the individual team members results in a composite team of medium capability). In completing the evaluation for this team compared to an alternative team, the importance of particular elements of capability for the particular project should be taken into account. For example, the weakest element for this team is "experience with location" and this might not be considered a major aspect for the particular project. In any case, alternate candidates for project engineer and personnel manager should be reviewed to see if candidates for these positions can be located with stronger "experience with location." "Language ability" might or might not be of particular significance. One aspect particularly important for projects in areas lacking the usual amenities is that of "people consciousness." In such areas a good deal of attention must be paid to living conditions.

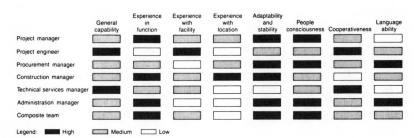

Figure 2—Team evaluation.

EVALUATION PROCESS

The development and evaluation of a project team is normally the responsibility of an area manager. The evaluation takes place when real candidates have been designated. Obviously, the same procedure could be applied by senior team members to candidates for positions within their organizations.

No one grading scale or series of weighting factors is necessarily the best. The same process could be carried out with gradings from 1 to 5 and with weighting factors of different values. But whatever factors are used, the person responsible for the team selection should be comfortable with them. While the suggested procedure cannot be considered a concise method, its use will greatly improve the process for selection of project teams as compared to selection of *individual* team members only.

ACKNOWLEDGEMENTS

Adapted from a paper presented at Internet 82, Danish Project Management Society, as presented in *Project Management—Tools and Visions*.

SUBJECT-PROJECT PHASE MATRIX		1 PREAWARD	2 INITIATION	3 ENGINEERING	4 PROCUREMENT	5 CONSTRUCTION
SUBJECTS		1	2	3	4	5
A	FINANCIAL/CONTRACTUAL	●	●			
B	ORGANIZATION/EXECUTION PLANNING					
C	MANAGING PEOPLE/COMMUNICATION	●	●			
D	ESTIMATING/COST CONTROL					
E	RISK ANALYSIS					
F	SCHEDULING					
G	TRACKING/TRENDING					
H	PROGRESS/PRODUCTIVITY MEASUREMENT					
I	MATERIAL MANAGEMENT					

Chapter 6

Strengthen Client-E/C Relations

Kenneth G. Wolfe

An effective, cooperative relationship between an engineer-constructor (E/C) and its client is essential to completing a project on time and within cost parameters. To understand how client-E/C relations are strengthened, we really must look at the *whole* project environment. We must consider the project's definitions, its restrictions and limitations, its goals and rewards, its risks and its people.

Key factors. Three major aspects contribute to and make up this environment. The first and the key item is the contract between owner and E/C. This document provides the framework by which the entire project is governed. It addresses itself, more or less, to each of the preceding environmental factors.

Second, the contract defines what is to be done through scope documents, specifications, drawings and the like and sets forth the time and money frame for accomplishing the project. But it must be augmented by procedures which provide guidelines as to *how* the contract is to be implemented.

Contracts normally contain a fair degree of standardization, at least on fundamental project requirements. On the other hand, the implementation guidelines range from little or nothing to fairly voluminous coordination procedures, plans of action or other defined working bases.

Many projects have been completed without a contract being executed. Likewise, many projects have been accomplished with few defined working procedures or coordination programs. Nonetheless, we are not looking for the exception. We are trying to define procedures and relationships to assure success over the long run.

Along with these two key elements—"what" is to be done and the "how" it is to be done—must go the "who" factor or, in simpler terms, the people aspect. The project with a good contract supported by complete and competent operating procedures can fall on hard times if the parties are not dedicated to accomplishing the project in accordance with them. An owner representative may feel he is entitled to more than is specified and take the upper hand by withholding acceptance and payment. Or an E/C may plan to bring the job to its knees by inflexible or unreasonable contract interpretation or by lack of diligence. Such tactics may eventually be brought into line, but the effective interface is destroyed. For success, the project should be conducted within the spirit and intent of the agreement.

Contract equity. While a contract is intended to be fair to both parties, there is a distinction in the relationship between owner and E/C. Fundamentally, the E/C has agreed to provide certain services under the terms and conditions defined in the contract. His role is to provide a service and to take the actions necessary to accomplish the defined tasks and scope of work. Obviously, his desire to provide a high level of performance and quality in the services for which he is responsible will have a direct, significant bearing on project success. Likewise, the owner has a specific role as a party to the contract: *performance assurance.* It is his right and responsibility to assure that the services, materials and equipment are provided in the amounts and to the quality and performance level stipulated in the contract.

Immediately, the specter of unfair or unreasonable contract or specification interpretation crops up. Just as quickly, we can only put it down by referring to the somewhat intangible people relationship. A good, concise, clear contract will do much to overcome the frailties of human nature. But I doubt if any contract can adequately preclude difficulties arising through interpretation, intentionally or unintentionally, in an unreasonable and unfair manner by either party.

Project team. A further item in the people-oriented realm relates to the so-called "project team." Contracts are hard-pressed to specify the degree of cooperation between the parties or the manner in which they should work together to best accomplish the contractual requirements. The exception is the specific rights and obligations referred to above. The contractual documents for any project are, in fact, nothing but a series of writings on paper. They are a very inanimate foundation from

which an extremely animate and vital relationship develops and ma-
tures.

The words in the contract and its supporting documents do not and
cannot define all activities and obligations of the parties. But neither do
they preclude activities and relationships which constitute a cooperative
team-approach to accomplishing the project. This in no way is intended
to allow the owner to assume the role of the construction expert and tell
the E/C how and when to make each move. In other words, a project
operating as a team of owner and E/C—with each having his principal
obligations and limitations clearly defined—will commonly emerge as a
success.

WHY A CONTRACTOR?

There are many ways for the design, procurement and construction of
a plant to be set up by an owner. At one extreme, the owner handles all
aspects of process design, detailed engineering, procurement and construction or construction management. At the other extreme, the owner
may provide only fundamental design criteria. It gets the rest of the
functions from an E/C on a turnkey basis. The variations between these
two limits are many. But this article will refer to the most *common* construction basis whereby the owner obtains his construction services from
an independent E/C.

The E/C is presumed to have the resources, expertise and experience
which allow him to construct a broad range of plants and facilities at a
high level of performance, quality and efficiency. Owners are not remiss
in not having such talent in their own houses. Many do! On the other
hand, this is not the primary business of the process facility owner. For
him to maintain such a staff and to develop such expertise could put unreasonable strain on facilities and resources which could otherwise be
better applied to his basic business.

The explanation of "why a constructor?," is basic to the owner-E/C
relationship. It establishes the role and purpose of the E/C, namely to
provide to the owner, under specific contractual conditions, the services
and expertise required to construct a given project.

This article examines how this is translated into requirements and
procedures for successful project implementation. No single set of conditions for client-E/C relationships will ensure a successful project. Nonetheless, there is a clearly identified relationship between effective client-
E/C interface and successful projects which justifies striving for a good
interface as a positive factor of project success.

The construction of a new plant should be a challenging and rewarding experience for both owner and E/C as they work toward their mutual goal.

THE CONTRACT

If the contract is a key to a successful owner-E/C interface, what factors contribute to a good contract and, correspondingly, to a high project-success ratio?

Project scope. Probably the most significant of these is the project scope and description of services to be performed. If we played the old game of naming the first word that comes to mind in response to a specific stimulus, surely "extras" would crop up frequently in response to "contract." Many owners would feel this reaction is a natural one, explaining their basic antagonism toward E/Cs.

Likewise, many E/Cs also recognize this as a natural reaction. They may have found over the years that the best or maybe the only way to work successfully with a contract is to press the extras and change orders. This reaction is an indictment of contracts rather than of contracting and E/Cs.

So I put definition of the work and services at the top of the list of items contributing to a good contract. Admittedly, it is difficult, particularly on a "fast track" type project, to define scope completely. In addition—especially on the more complex and innovative type of projects—the owner may desire to make changes. Or, his processes may require items that could not readily be foreseen and written into the initial project definition. It would seem to follow that a clearly defined procedure for handling changes, for whatever reason, should also be a high-priority item in any contract.

Further, this change procedure should consider the size and number of changes which might occur. For example, the relative cost to the E/C and the manner in which he is reimbursed by the owner are less significant for minor changes on a major fixed-price contract than they are on a project which was preliminarily defined and for which the changes may result in a major change in the over-all project.

Contract liabilities. The next big item in a good contract relates to liabilities of the parties and indemnification against errors, accidents, gross negligence, lack of proper project information and so forth. Entire books have been written on this subject. For now, it is sufficient to say that the liabilities of each party to the other and to third parties should be clearly stated. They should be understood at the outset of the project. Liability terms are basically a protection, not a punitive weapon. This concept should be readily discernible in the contract.

A further factor to consider is the terms of payment. It should be fundamental in any contract that the E/C is entitled to payment for services performed. Therefore, a yardstick is needed for determining the extent of services performed.

E/C-owner relationships are sorely strained when the E/C feels his payment is being withheld unreasonably for the services which he has performed in accordance with the contract. An amount retained by the owner against performance completion is common in contracting. This concept is not unreasonable. What is unreasonable is arbitrarily withholding payment, or the so-called slow pay operation. This puts the E/C in a cash-flow bind.

Disputes. What is the best way to settle disputes or areas of complete disagreement? Honest disagreements or questions of interpretation can arise during any project. These might not be within the limits of jobsite solution. Normally, an arbitration procedure is specified to cover such occurrences. Without such terms, either or both parties may be uncomfortable during the course of a job. Each may feel that in the final showdown he has little chance of coming out with an equitable decision.

Termination. For many reasons, either party may desire to terminate a contract. Most commonly, need for termination arises when the owner recognizes that he no longer requires the services as defined. A good contract will provide in clearly understandable terms the rights and obligations of each party when termination is involved.

STRENGTHEN CLIENT-E/C RELATIONS
Do's and Don'ts
For the owner:
- *Don't* assume the constructor plans to give you less than his best.
- *Don't* attempt to force the constructor to jump through an imaginary hoop, one that is not defined by contractual bases.
- *Don't* ignore his suggestions for alternative ways to accomplish the project. They may save both of you money.
- *Do* cooperate with your constructor; remember, the job he is doing is for you.

For the constructor:
- *Don't* assume the owner is an unreasonable ogre intent on shooting you down.

- *Do* recognize his intent to assure that the project will meet specifications.
- *Do* keep the owner informed of your plans, of changes, of problems.
- *Do* keep your paperwork and administrative requirements current. It will make it easier for the owner to approve progress payments and changes where appropriate.

For both:
- *Do* operate at all times within the spirit and intent of the contract.
- *Do* keep the contract and the coordination procedures close at hand as your guide for day-to-day implementation of the project.
- *Do* attempt to work the project as a team effort, not as an adversary exercise.

CONTRACT IMPLEMENTATION

Much as a transportation ticket, properly made out and paid for, won't get you to your destination without an appropriate vehicle, the contract cannot guarantee success without appropriate implementation procedures. The owner's representative and the E/C's representative should not have to live out a project facing each other like two strange cats in the alleyway. Generally these two key "cats," assuming they survive the life of the project, will have developed working relationships and procedures, written or unwritten, to do the job.

Lack of prior planning is doing it the hard way. Far better, there should be developed for each project operating guidelines, coordination procedure, project plans or whatever names best suit the parties. There is no hard and fast rule as to what items should be included in the contract specifically, by reference only, or not at all. Project operations, especially where changes may be involved, are generally facilitated by minimizing such data in the contract.

Commonly, one group of implementation procedures consists of those items which the owner requires to monitor the project. In this category are procedures for scheduling, controlling and forecasting progress and costs, for reporting expenditures and cash flow requirements and for similar types of information. Most of these items—especially schedule and cost data—are necessary. Only with them can the E/C conduct the project properly through the planning and execution stages. However, some items may be useful, primarily to the owner, to meet his internal requirements and obligations. Where this latter type of documentation is required by an owner, it should have been indicated in the bidding stage rather than during construction.

Operating day-to-day. A second category of implementation items usually is prepared jointly by the E/C and the owner for day-to-day operation. These procedures will identify the respective organizational structures, listing responsibilities and personnel. Also, they will include safety and security procedures, starting and quitting times, holidays, schedules of meetings, reporting guidelines, material receiving, handling and storage requirements, fire protection and all other items which make up the operations of a project.

Some of these items may not be significant in themselves. The important benefit is derived from the understanding by both owner and E/C of the rules by which the game is to be played. This minimizes misunderstandings and disputes. It is especially valuable to develop these procedures by mutual effort.

In summation, the ideal owner-E/C relationship has the highest likelihood of being reached when the rules of the game—the contract and its accompanying implementation procedures—are clearly stated, accepted and understood by both parties. Each can then feel confident in his role; namely, that of monitor for the owner and of performer for the E/C.

SUBJECT-PROJECT PHASE MATRIX	PROJECT PHASE				
SUBJECTS	PREAWARD 1	INITIATION 2	ENGINEERING 3	PROCUREMENT 4	CONSTRUCTION 5
A FINANCIAL/CONTRACTUAL					
B ORGANIZATION/EXECUTION PLANNING		●	●	●	●
C MANAGING PEOPLE/COMMUNICATION		●	●	●	●
D ESTIMATING/COST CONTROL					
E RISK ANALYSIS					
F SCHEDULING					
G TRACKING/TRENDING					
H PROGRESS/PRODUCTIVITY MEASUREMENT					
I MATERIAL MANAGEMENT					

Chapter 7

What is a Good Project Manager?

J. H. Hanna

Successful project management requires more than charts, procedures and methods. The appropriate authority, responsibility, style and training for the project manager are vital.

Project management will not reach its full potential unless hard thought is given to the position and how the person filling it relates to the project team.

Creative endeavor. A "project" as we now use the term is a one-time unique endeavor by people to do something that has not been done the same way before. A *successful* project is finished within a time and for a cost that makes it economical or profitable, and serves its intended function.

Because of its uniqueness, a project can turn sour by being finished late or over budget, or by not performing the desired service. And unexpected problems will usually arise to jeopardize success, unless the management is structured and prepared to cope with these problems.

To successfully complete a project using the traditional vertical pyramidal organization is possible. But success is more likely by adopting the *project team and project management* concept. In this concept, a separate team is formed of personnel from the various functional groups. A project manager is the leader. However, success isn't assured unless there is also a good understanding of why a project manager is needed and what he is to accomplish.

73

Why a manager? The need for using project management arises from the difficulty the "boss" of the pyramidal organization has in expeditiously handling the *extra* problems of the project in addition to his other responsibilities. What is needed is an extension of this "boss"—the manager who has the responsibility for the project and the long-term traditional organization. By having a project manager fill this role, the objectives are:

- Centralize in one person, who has no other duties, all the responsibility for the project.
- Have realistic goals set for the project (for all participating groups), considering the resources that each can bring to bear.
- Have decisions made on the project quickly enough to meet its needs, and benefitting the project as a whole—not just a portion.
- Provide a means of anticipating the problems during the course of the project.
- Give one person the responsibility of quickly developing solutions to the problems, so that the project will stay on target for cost, schedule and serviceability.

Success in accomplishing these objectives will depend on the kind of person selected as the project manager and how his position is set up. Thus, we need to consider his authority, responsibility or accountability, reporting relationship, the style of project management, and the type of training required for him.

Authority and responsibility. Perhaps the hardest problem is to decide on what authority a project manager will have. Unless a separate organization is set up for a project, with no connection whatsoever to the original, the heads of the functional departments must retain authority over their departments. This means that managers of sales, engineering, procurement, construction, estimating, manufacturing and accounting will still report to the "boss" at the top of the pyramidal structure. So, the project manager will have no authority in the permanent organization structure.

A project manager should have the *same* authority as the "boss" for his project, and only his project. He and his boss should *share* the responsibility for the project. To do this, the project manager must report to the "boss." Any other solution makes the project manager a mere coordinator. As such, he can't achieve the objectives previously stated.

The right to lead. A project manager—to achieve a successful project—must have a "stick" to induce progress. This is true because the needs of the project can appear to threaten the security and prestige of the permanent functional organization. Unless the project manager has a lever to properly assign personnel, and motivate them to meet needs (give priority to the project work), an effective *team* may never be realized. The project will not be successful.

A project manager can create this lever by *his own personality*. Or it can be created by written directives from the "boss." In effect, this lever must be the same authority held by the man at the top of the pyramid. The project manager thus is an extension of management itself.

By the same token, the *responsibility* of the project manager must be a share of that held by the "boss." If a project goes sour, the "boss" is accountable. The project manager must share this.

Style of management. If the project manager reports to the "boss," sharing his authority and responsibility, then the style with which the project is managed must reflect the influence of both personalities involved. There is no single type of personal approach to managing a project, which is successful. On the contrary, considerable variation is tolerable.

Should the project manager take a very forceful lead, or simply observe and report results? He will probably aggressively manage in some areas, coordinate in others, and in some situations only observe.

Leadership factor. Think in terms of what the project manager contributes. If the project would proceed as well without him, he is contributing nothing. Merely observing and reporting events to his superior throws the job of managing the job back to his superior. Furthermore, he makes little contribution if he does not anticipate problems and take action to head them off. This is particularly true if the project manager only criticizes the group perceived to be at fault when things go wrong. The other groups in the project team will do this anyway. They need no help from a project manager.

A project manager should be an aggressive leader. He should really be a manager. He should set realistic objectives for the team—planning, scheduling, arranging for staffing, motivating, directing and measuring results.

Discreet use of power. He must control, but not in a way that stifles creativity of other team members. Innovation should be encouraged because of the project's uniqueness. But the project team members need a *leader* if a team effort is to result, and the project is to be on time, on budget and satisfactorily completed.

In thinking about style the project manager should review the project status and evaluate his own contribution. Is the project proceeding better because of his contributions? Or would it be going as well without him? Is his objective setting, planning, scheduling and motivating saving money? Is it saving time and improving the serviceability? Or is it the reverse?

If the project manager cannot say that he *is* making a meaningful contribution, he should change style.

Experience requirement. Suppose that the project manager does report to the officer or manager having overall responsibility for the project. He does share this authority and responsibility. He uses a style of aggressive leadership. Given these points, what then should be his background?

In projects that involve sales, engineering, estimating, procurement, construction and accounting, the project manager cannot be expert in all these. Perhaps by a rotation of assignments he can have some experience in all of these. But this does not necessarily create expertise.

Selecting a project manager is like selecting managers in general. But there is a difference. A project manager deals with a task that has a specific start and end. It has a scope that is or will be well defined.

Planning and scheduling. The decisions to be made by a project manager generally relate to "what" and "when" tasks are to be done. The decisions on "how" tasks are done is usually made by the project team group heads. These decisions are probably based on policies and procedures established by their permanent functional department heads. Thus, the problem of deciding what background a project manager needs is simpler than for a functional manager.

On the other hand, a good project manager must possess a multitude of diverse skills and good judgment in many areas. He must be able to set goals, plan, schedule, organize, motivate and measure results.

More than this, he must be people-oriented. He must be dedicated to helping others to do their work in a manner that contributes to the satisfactory completion of the project. In addition, there is one more necessary characteristic. It isn't as widely recognized or understood. This has to do with exercising control over the decisions made by the groups in the project team so that these decisions aid and do not detract from achieving over-all project objectives.

Decision making. Successful project management requires an understanding of the decision making processes used by functional groups working on a project. Particularly decisions which can be made by one group that significantly affect what other groups must do.

A good project manager minimizes decisions made unilaterally by one group of the team without careful consideration of the effects on over-all project costs, schedules and quality.

Examples of these types of unilateral decisions are many. For instance, engineering may specify a material which is only marginally better than another for the service conditions, but which will require longer delivery and will upset the sequence of planned construction operations. The same results can be caused by procurement selecting a vendor's price that is lower, but for which a longer delivery time will probably result.

On the other hand, construction could decide to try to finish the job sooner, to save on overhead type costs, without considering the extra costs that will be required for overtime in engineering or premium freight costs for expedited deliveries.

In the final analysis, the important objectives are the over-all cost and time requirement of the project. Savings in one sector are only meaningful if larger expenditures are not required in other sectors.

Knowing the people. The best equipped person for the position of project manager is one who knows and understands the working of the project-team group that will make the most decisions affecting other groups and over-all project objectives. Usually, most of such decisions are made by engineering. Once the work of engineering is finished, the problems of other groups on the project are "cast in concrete." They cannot be changed.

The easiest way to gain this knowledge and understanding is by doing engineering design work. This isn't the only way. A person experienced in other fields, who is perceptive, objective and thoughtful can by observation and inquiry develop a good, and perhaps better understanding of the impact of engineering decisions on the work done by other groups.

In any case, the good project manager cannot have a distorted view of the importance of the work done by one particular group. Like a sports team, each group on the project team needs understanding and guidance. Only then can the efforts of all members contribute to satisfactory completion of the project.

Part 3: Initiating the Project

SUBJECT-PROJECT PHASE MATRIX

SUBJECTS	1 PREAWARD	2 INITIATION	3 ENGINEERING	4 PROCUREMENT	5 CONSTRUCTION
A FINANCIAL/CONTRACTUAL					
B ORGANIZATION/EXECUTION PLANNING		●			
C MANAGING PEOPLE/COMMUNICATION		●			
D ESTIMATING/COST CONTROL		●			
E RISK ANALYSIS					
F SCHEDULING		●			
G TRACKING/TRENDING					
H PROGRESS/PRODUCTIVITY MEASUREMENT					
I MATERIAL MANAGEMENT					

Chapter 8

When You Initiate a Project . . .

A. E. Kerridge

A new project is "initiated" when owner and contractor enter into a contract or agree to start work with a "letter of intent" while the contract is being finalized. From the contractor's viewpoint, the owner has now become the client.

MANPOWER BUILD-UP

To build a plant, an engineering construction contractor (E/C) must spend money at the proper rate to meet the required completion schedule. Money translates to manhours whether it is home office engineering hours, manufacturing hours, or field construction hours. To achieve progress, manhours must be spent. On a project where a short schedule is the prime consideration, calendar time can be saved by selecting designs already completed, standard equipment already fabricated, or material in stock. Even when these methods are used, there are still large numbers of hours in engineering, manufacturing, and construction which must be expended during the project execution.

The E/C must achieve a rapid mobilization and a smooth application of manpower, without flat periods, fluctuations, or excessive peaks, which will match the project budget and schedule. This is where the skill of the E/C plays an important part. Fig. 1 shows the relationship between home office, manufacturing and construction manhours. The solid curves show the desired rate of mobilization and build-up with rapid spread of work through manufacturing and construction giving

81

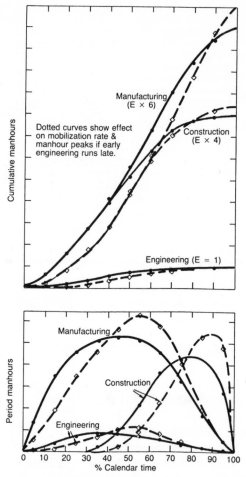

Figure 1—Manhour curves for engineering, manufacturing, and construction.

optimum peak manpower application consistent with the needs of the project schedule. The dotted curves show the impact if early engineering is delayed. This results in steeper mobilization curves in manufacturing and construction with higher manpower peaks which in turn, lead to inefficiency and greater costs.

Fig. 1 illustrates the importance of a fast effective start in engineering. Every manhour below the optimum curve during the early engineering phase may add four to five times these hours to the peak during the manufacturing and construction phases if the scheduled end date is to be

TABLE 1 — Project initiation steps

Review precontract documents
Establish client communication channels
Hold client kick-off meeting
Establish project code of accounts
Prepare project plan
Determine project organization
Hold project kick-off meeting
Issue project design data
Initiate process design
Prepare project coordination procedure
Analyze preliminary project estimate
Issue preliminary project schedule
Review engineering plan
Review procurement plan
Review construction plan

met. Conversely, overstaffing in the early phases ahead of data development will also lead to inefficient manhour expenditure.

MAJOR INITIATION STEPS

As soon as a project has been awarded, a project manager (PM) begins a race against time as the leader of a team, when the team, the rules, and the course may yet have to be defined. The initiation of a project puts great pressure on him to get the project moving. Steps in the initiation are in Table 1. The list is not comprehensive but shows the more important of the PM's activities.

These steps do not necessarily occur sequentially. Several may occur in parallel. The Table 1 list can be assembled into an activity network as shown in Fig. 2. All of these activities should be undertaken within the first few weeks of project award. Each of the above steps is described in more detail in the paragraphs which follow.

REVIEW PRECONTRACT DOCUMENTS

Prior to the project award, the E/C will probably have submitted technical and commercial proposals. The PM's job of initiating a project may be easier if the proposal period has been fairly extensive and the E/C has spent a considerable amount of time and effort preparing detailed technical and commercial proposals.

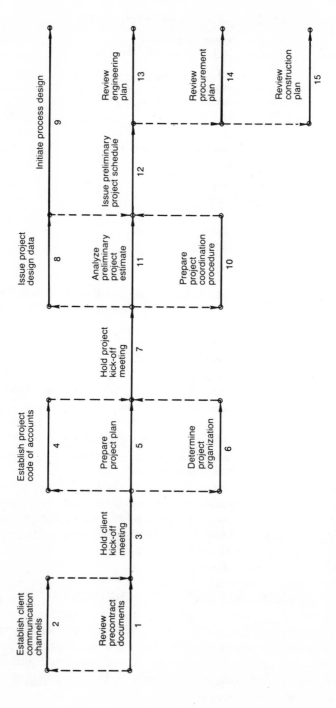

Figure 2—Project initiation network.

At the time of award, the scope of the project may have changed from the inquiry document. The proposal may have been modified, added to or adjusted by a series of letters or clarification meetings held prior to the award. It is essential that the PM carefully check through all of the proposal documentation and assemble a complete file of all the proposal documents, letters, telexes, telephone and meeting notes. He thus has a complete record of what was requested, what was offered, and what was accepted in the award.

Following this, the PM will hold a meeting with the sales manager to review the proposal documents and to discuss any additional points mentioned during the meetings with the client. The PM will particularly want to be informed of any client concerns, preferences or priorities.

To ensure continuity and a smooth job start, the E/C will attempt to involve the nominated PM and the key members of the proposed project team in the proposal activities and pre-award contract discussions.

ESTABLISH CLIENT COMMUNICATION CHANNELS

If a PM is to maintain control over the project, he must establish with the client that he is the official communication channel between the E/C and the client for all major aspects of the project. During the proposal stage, contacts with the client may have been many and varied from sales, project and process engineering, legal, financial, and others. A client may have become used to dealing with a number of people and expect to continue to do so.

The PM has to take over the scene delicately but firmly both with the client and within his own organization. This ensures that all future communications are channeled through him so that he can maintain control. He will recommend to the client that a similar arrangement is followed in the client's organization. A client PM should be appointed through whom all major communications are channeled. This does not mean that there is no communication or direct contact between other members of the client and the contractor's organization. It does mean that any such communications and contacts are held either in the presence of the PM or with his prior knowledge and that the subject matter is properly recorded and approved by the PM.

CLIENT KICK-OFF MEETING

As soon as possible, after project award, the PM will hold a kick-off meeting with the client and go through a checklist to make sure that there is total agreement between the contractor and the client with regard to the project requirements. If there has been a detailed proposal, then it may be a simple matter of confirming that the data in the proposal stand unchanged for the project. It is rare, however, that the proposal is totally definitive in all areas. Normally, the meeting agenda and checklist cover:

- Scope of work and services
- Basis for process design
- Project design data
- Engineering
- Procurement
- Construction
- Administration procedures (approvals, controls, reports, documentation, distribution, financial)

ESTABLISH PROJECT CODE OF ACCOUNTS

A comprehensive project code of accounts is necessary for effective project management. A code of accounts makes it possible to organize and control a project in a systematic manner using the codes to identify and reference technical, planning, reporting, accounting, and administrative documents produced throughout engineering, procurement and construction.

An E/C normally has a standard code of accounts covering equipment, materials, and services which must then be adapted to suit the needs of a specific project. The basic areas to which a project numbering system and code of accounts are applied are:

- Tagging and identification of equipment and material.
- Numbering of technical documents, specifications, data sheets, drawings, requisitions and purchase orders.
- Procurement commodity codes.
- Scheduling activities in engineering, procurement, and construction.
- Estimating equipment, materials and services.
- Recording manhours on timesheets in the home office and in the field.
- Recording project scope changes.
- Project accounting and invoicing.
- Project cost and progress reporting.
- Project document filing.

In addition, a large project must be subdivided into its various units, areas and plant elements to facilitate control and reporting. Too great a degree of subdivision merely adds to work and confusion. The best solution is to have the minimum number of sub-project numbers which will give reasonable control. On a major multi-unit project, the following breakdown is recommended:

- Overall project number for summary cost reports and common/bulk requirements
- Individual sub-project numbers for each major identifiable process unit within the complex
- One or more sub-project numbers for offsite systems, depending upon size and scale
- Separate sub-project numbers for geographically distinct locations such as marine terminals, remote road or rail loading or dispatching stations, etc.

PREPARE PROJECT PLAN

On completion of the above steps, the PM should prepare the Project Plan. This plan defines the project objectives, priorities and philosophies. Its preparation fulfills a number of functions:

- It requires that the PM, as leader of the project, takes the time to assess the project needs at an early date and present his intended plan of execution. Individual communications or meetings are no substitute for the written plan.
- It provides a basic reference and briefing document for those who will ultimately be involved in the project execution.
- It allows the E/C management to review the plan, provide guidance and assistance and, thereafter, support the plan throughout project execution.

The project plan will normally include background data; scope of work and services by E/C and client; split of work with others (process licensors, other contractors); basis of contract (liabilities, guarantees); regulatory and other approvals; project identification and code of accounts; dimensions, units, language; client participation, reviews and approvals; specific project needs and highlights; project design philosophies; and project schedule criticalities, project control procedures and reports.

In addition, the project plan will contain separate sections dealing with engineering, procurement, construction, operating and financial as appropriate. A financial plan for a major project may include such things as financing arrangements, money management, cash flow control, accounting and auditing procedures. The project plan contains the outlines and major features of the individual plans which are produced separately under each of these headings.

DETERMINE PROJECT ORGANIZATION

Most contractors are organized administratively into functional departments covering the basic engineering, procurement and construction functions. Fig. 3 shows a typical functional organization.

Once a project has been awarded, the project management function takes the lead role in the execution of the project, liaising directly with the client and drawing upon the resources in the functional departments. Fig. 4 shows the resources available to the PM. His first action is to form a project team organization. The project team will vary to suit the needs of a specific project, but in general will follow Fig. 5. The first members assigned to the project team for the project initiation are:

- The project manager
- The project engineering manager
- The project process manager

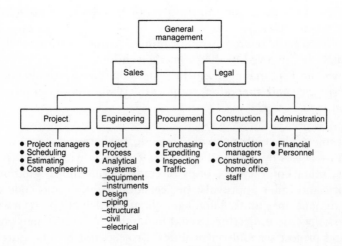

Figure 3—A typical contractor's functional organization.

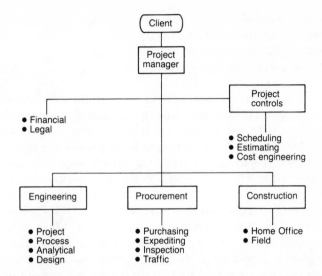

Figure 4—The functional departments provide resources for the project manager.

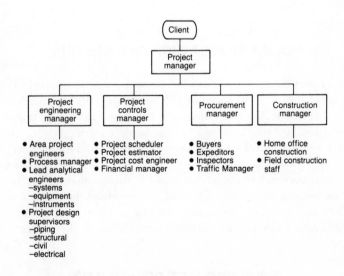

Figure 5—A typical project team organization.

- The project scheduler
- The project estimator/cost engineer
- The project procurement manager
- The project construction manager

These key members participate and assist in the development of the detailed project execution plans. Additional members are assigned to the project team as the work progresses. It is desirable that the lead members to be assigned to the project team from each of the disciplines are named from the project outset. They can thus be kept informed of project developments and become briefed before they are called upon to participate.

Fig. 6 shows the organization matrix which is set up when the project team is formed within a functional organization. Once project team members are assigned from their functional departments, they become project oriented, reporting to the PM for their project execution functions. They continue to report to their functional department heads with regard to quality, standards and methods. This ensures that there is a two-way control or a system of checks and balances during the project execution. The PM is totally concerned with and dedicated to the execution of the project. The departmental managers are responsible to ensure that quality and method are compatible with the schedule and cost objectives established in the project plan.

HOLD PROJECT KICK-OFF MEETING

At an appropriate time, when the project scope is properly defined, the PM will call a kick-off meeting. This meeting will be attended by the E/C's management, the sales manager, the functional department managers, and the key staff selected for the project team.

The sales manager reviews the events leading up to the project award. He highlights the key points which were raised during the pre-award discussions and contract negotiations and identifies outstanding items requiring immediate attention. The PM then reviews the project plan, recapitulates the objectives, priorities and philosophies, and establishes the team spirit necessary for the successful execution of the project.

ISSUE PROJECT DESIGN DATA

The PM arranges for the completion of the project design data. The form covers the subjects listed below and is developed by the project,

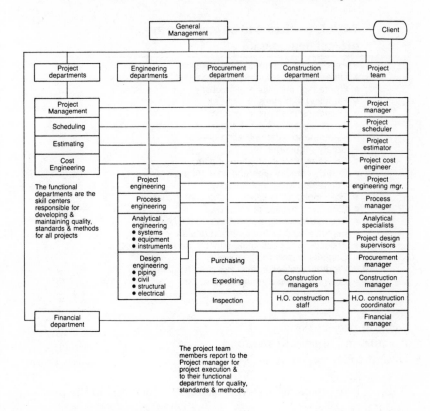

Figure 6—The organization matrix.

process and design engineers. The form, when completed, is approved by the client and becomes the basis for engineering specifications and engineering design work.

- Feedstock and other data
- Product data and specifications
- Utility, auxiliary, and chemical systems
- Electrical systems
- Waste disposal and environmental requirements
- Climatic conditions
- Soil data
- Site access
- Water supply data

TABLE 2 — Items to be included in project design data

- Feedstocks, intermediates, products
- Utilities, catalysts, chemicals, consumables
- Operating reliability and flexibility
- Handling and storage facilities
- Delivery and shipping logistics
- Spare equipment and parts
- Maintenance and operating needs
- Safety requirements
- Economics for evaluation of alternates
- Energy conservation and cost criteria
- Equipment design philosophy
- Philosophy for isolation and decontamination
- Block and bypass philosophy
- Environmental considerations
- Electrical and instrumentation design
- Philosophy for buildings, shelters and enclosures
- Communication requirements
- Property protection and industrial hygiene
- Equipment spacing and plant layout

- General project design data
- Permits and approvals required
- Design codes and standards applicable

Table 2 lists typical items which should be included in the project design data.

INITIATE PROCESS DESIGN

Before engineering, procurement and construction commences, it is essential that process design is complete. The overall schedule is very dependent upon the speed, accuracy and completeness of the process design. Hence, this activity must be started as soon as possible. Process design is normally initiated at the time of project award and proceeds in parallel with the other project initiating activities. The process design package consists of the following:

- Process flow diagrams
- Process material balances
- Process specifications and load sheets for equipment items
- Utility systems concept and balance diagrams
- Environmental systems concept and balance diagrams

The above will take from two to five months for completion depending upon the size and complexity of the project. Normally, preliminary process flow diagrams are produced as a first step and reviewed with the client. Following on from this, critical process equipment specifications and data sheets are issued for early procurement. The utility and environmental concepts and balance diagrams follow.

PREPARE PROJECT COORDINATION PROCEDURE

The project coordination procedure is prepared by the PM as early as possible in the project and is submitted to and approved by the client. The following typical subjects are covered. Additional paragraphs may be added to suit the specific project.

- Job titles and numbers
- Contract data
- Scope of work
- Duties of client
- Correspondence, contacts and addresses
- Approvals
- Engineering
- Procurement
- Construction
- Operating and startup
- Accounting
- Project controls, changes and reports
- Job closeout

The following additional documents are prepared as exhibits or attachments to the project coordination procedure: Project code of accounts; Distribution of documents; Standard drawing title blocks; Organization charts and Project document control and filing system.

ANALYZE PRELIMINARY PROJECT ESTIMATE

When initiating a project, the PM requests a project estimate, no matter how preliminary. The detail and potential accuracy of an early estimate prepared for job scoping can vary to a great degree depending upon the extent of the work put into the proposal prior to contract award. It may vary from an order-of-magnitude dollar value for the total installed cost to a fully defined estimate.

A preliminary estimate can be subdivided into values for home office services, equipment materials, bulk materials, construction labor, construction supervision and indirects. Having established the dollar values of these components, the home office manhours, the field labor manhours, and the construction supervision manhours can also be determined. Even though these methods may only give approximate values, they do establish the general magnitude and complexity of the work to be performed and provide a basis for preliminary planning.

When the process design is approved, the project estimator prepares the first control estimate. This estimate provides a firm budget for equipment and home office costs with factored estimates for bulk materials, construction labor and field indirects. A defined estimate is prepared on completion of the analytical engineering phase, at which time bulk materials are taken off and priced. The defined estimate provides the firm basis for cost control for the ongoing project execution.

Each estimate on completion should be formally reviewed, a contingency, sensitivity and risk analysis performed and an appropriate contingency included as an integral part of the estimate. Items to be considered are escalation, import duties, taxes, freight, insurance, changes in foreign currency exchange rates and other miscellaneous costs.

ISSUE PRELIMINARY PROJECT SCHEDULE

An important project initiation step is to issue a project schedule. If the project definition has not been developed to the point where firm equipment and material deliveries can be determined, a preliminary project master schedule should be issued (1) to establish desired milestone and target dates; (2) to perform preliminary planning and budgeting; (3) to identify and establish schedule dates for critical project activities and (4) to identify critical equipment and material items.

To evaluate whether or not the preliminary schedule is achievable, a preliminary estimate is also essential. This quantifies the work to be performed within the project schedule time frame. The PM should review the preliminary project master schedule to ensure that any milestones or time delays which are specific to the project (such as funding approvals, regulatory approvals, site access limitations, manpower availability problems, weather problems, etc.) have been taken into account. Manpower loading curves should also be prepared to check that the proposed schedule does not create unrealistic manpower peaks.

To ensure that the project proceeds without delay, a starter schedule is issued along with the preliminary project master schedule. The starter schedule lists the important activities to be performed during the first 30 to 90 days of the project while the project master schedule is being developed. The project master schedule is issued together with detailed engineering and procurement schedules, on completion of process design, when delivery times for critical equipment and materials can be established. Detailed construction schedules are developed during the engineering phase prior to start of work in the field.

REVIEW ENGINEERING PLAN

The engineering plan prepared by the project engineering manager expands the project plan in the areas relating to engineering, providing more specific information on the following topics:

- Engineering work scope
- Design basis for process units and offsites
- Engineering and design evaluations
- Maintenance, reliability and flexibility needs
- Material selection criteria
- Engineering economics and design philosophy
- Design specifications and standards
- Applicable codes and regulations
- Equipment layout and plant arrangement
- Use of models
- Engineering problems specific to the project

The PM reviews the engineering plan prior to its release by the project engineering manager.

REVIEW PROCUREMENT PLAN

During the project initiation phase, the first task of the project procurement manager is to prepare the procurement plan amplifying the procurement aspects of the project plan. The procurement plan establishes the procurement philosophy for the project. It identifies the critical items of equipment and material; lists those items which will be provided "sole source," that is, from a specified supplier; notes materials which are "free issue," provided by subcontractors or from other sources; establishes quality and cost philosophies; the number of competitive bids required; whether or not the policy is to purchase locally, nationally, or worldwide. The procurement plan is reviewed by the PM and may be subject to approval by the client before issue. Following on from the procurement plan, detailed procurement procedures are drawn up which specify the purchasing forms to be used, the approval levels, the routing and distribution of purchase documents and any special referencing and numbering codes to be used.

Along with the above, an approved bidders list is prepared reflecting the policies established in the procurement plan. The approved bidders list is set up by project code of accounts for each category of equipment, material, and service. All bidders on the approved list will be suppliers who have performed satisfactorily in the past and have proved themselves by their quality and reliability. The project procurement manager also participates in the preparation of subcontract, expediting and inspection plans. Traffic surveys are initiated early for difficult site locations since transport requirements may impact upon the engineering/procurement effort and could require special marshaling yards, handling facilities or customs arrangements.

REVIEW CONSTRUCTION PLAN

The project construction coordinator prepares the construction plan during the project initiation phase. The following points are considered:

- Site and local area survey
- Site preparation, site access and weather restrictions
- Temporary construction facilities
- Heavy rigging studies
- Construction equipment requirements
- Construction priorities and erection sequence
- Construction methods and procedures
- Material receiving requirements
- Prefabricated modular sections
- Site fabrication shop vs. field fabrication
- Site fabricated vessels and tanks
- Construction staffing and organization
- Field inspection and quality control
- Field safety procedures
- Union/non-union requirements
- Labor availability and hiring plans
- Labor relations
- Labor housing camp
- Construction subcontract arrangements
- Local codes and permits
- Construction planning, scheduling and cost control

The PM satisfies himself that the construction plan fulfills the project needs. Early planning of all these aspects is essential for smooth and effective construction mobilization at the appropriate time.

At this stage, the project has been initiated. If the PM has directed his efforts to ensure that the basic project initiation steps have been properly completed, he will no longer be the leader of an unfamiliar team in a race against time on an unknown course with undefined rules. He will now have an organized integrated team, all working to a common plan. The overall success of the project can depend to a great extent upon how thoroughly the project initiation steps have been carried out.

SUBJECT-PROJECT PHASE MATRIX

SUBJECTS	1. PREAWARD	2. INITIATION	3. ENGINEERING	4. PROCUREMENT	5. CONSTRUCTION
A FINANCIAL/CONTRACTUAL					
B ORGANIZATION/EXECUTION PLANNING		●			
C MANAGING PEOPLE/COMMUNICATION					
D ESTIMATING/COST CONTROL			●		
E RISK ANALYSIS					
F SCHEDULING			●		
G TRACKING/TRENDING			●		
H PROGRESS/PRODUCTIVITY MEASUREMENT			●		
I MATERIAL MANAGEMENT					

Chapter 9

Control Your Costs with Earned Value Concept

J. J. S. Wynton

The earned value concept (EVC) implies the measurement of accomplished work at any time in the course of the project in terms of budgets planned for that work. Furthermore, it implies the use of these data to quantify contract cost and schedule performance. The earned value concept of project cost/schedule performance measurement is being applied to engineering/construction (E/C) of HPI facilities. Although its introduction to HPI has been promulgated by the U.S. Department of Energy (DOE) in connection with awards of coal conversion projects, several internationally prominent U.S. E/C companies have experienced the earned value concept implementation in the nuclear power and nuclear fuels reprocessing industries.

Precision. The design and construction of today's complex plants demands exacting approaches for controlling cost and schedule performance. Half-baked means to half-baked management include (1) the old fashioned bar charting, (2) estimating spending variance as the difference between what was budgeted and what was spent, (3) meticulous tracking of the productivity ratio expressed as percent physical complete over percent manhours spent.

Increasing societal involvement of E/C companies through the DOE-sponsored work predicates use of a project control system assuring the highest possible return on evey taxpayer's dollar. Improved visibility and provision of early warning on project status and problems is what is required. Only with this can one keep the project moving toward the technical, schedule and cost goals despite changes, economic factors and unforeseen problems.

EVC's origins. EVC as a management technique was first established in 1967 by the U.S. Department of Defense (DOD). DOD Instruction 7000.2, "Performance Measurement of Selected Acquisitions" expressed this concept in terms of 35 Cost/Schedule Control System Criteria (C/SCSC) constituting the standards of acceptability for contractor management control systems. The 35 criteria can be grouped into five general categories: Organization; Planning and Budgeting; Accounting; Analysis; and Revisions.

In late 1974, the Energy Research and Development Administration (ERDA), one of DOE's predecessor agencies, initiated a program to improve its project management capability. The ERDA Reactor Development and Demonstration (RDD) Division took the lead role in implementing the earned value concept. They called it the Performance Measurement System (PMS) although it was based on the DOD C/SCSC.

The first full PMS implementation by DOE took place on the Clinch River Breeder Reactor Project. Partial implementation experience has been gained to date from over 20 other projects. Some of these, such as the Gas Centrifuge Enrichment Plant in Portsmouth, Ohio, are very large. The present DOE policy on major system acquisition projects was established on September 25, 1979 by a DOE Order 2250.1 titled "Department of Energy Cost and Schedule Control Systems Criteria for Contractor Performance Measurement." By this order, full earned value concept implementation is a fact of life on all DOE projects in excess of $50 million.

EVC quantification. The EVC is quantified by means of three basic indicators. They are: the Actual Cost for Work Performed (ACWP), the Budgeted Cost for Work Performed (BCWP), and the Budgeted Cost for Work Scheduled (BCWS). All other PMS indices are derived from these three.

- **ACWP represents the costs actually incurred** and applied or distributed in accomplishing the work performed within a given time period. It is a familiar indicator to all, the one which makes or breaks all projects. ACWP, when interacted with other PMS parameters, serves as a reference point for the earned value data elements relationships.

- **BCWP is the earned value.** BCWP signifies the value of completed work. As such, it reflects the progress made along the contract plan. BCWP is derived by determining the budget for all completed work, including the completed portions of in-progress work. In contrast to the traditional measurement of actual costs against the budget, the earned value is the performance indicator of both cost and schedule. The reason for this dual characteristic is that the budget plan is firmly tied to specific increments of work, called elements of the project work breakdown structure (WBS), rather than to expenditure of funds.

Instead of merely stating whether or not money is being spent as fast as it was planned to be spent, BCWP, when compared with ACWP, indicates whether the progress achieved is worth the money spent. Since in effect BCWP relies on the work scope WBS elements and dollarized schedules in taking credit for work accomplished, it provides integration of physical progress, cost and schedule. It eliminates "guesstimating" of the project status based on the funds to be expended versus the work to be done.

• **BCWS represents where the project manager planned to be** by a certain date; it is the sum of the budgets for the scheduled work packages. BCWS is similar to a timephased budget plan or spend plan. However, it is directly related to the manner in which the work is to be performed rather than how the money is to be spent. BCWS is the indicator of planned progress. BCWS becomes meaningful when the budgets are relatable to the work scope WBS elements. Furthermore, the budgets for the individual work elements must "add up." That is, the sum of distributed budgets, undistributed budgets, and management reserve should equal the negotiated contract cost plus the estimated cost for authorized, undefinitized work.

Use of EVC as a management technique demands rigorous organization of the project work for the purposes of proper budgeting and scheduling.

Project work organization. A major consequence of EVC implementation is development of an end product-oriented, family-tree-type diagram for subdivision of the overall work effort into identifiable smaller activity packages. This diagram, the *Work Breakdown Structure*, establishes the framework for contract execution, cost reporting, schedule and technical performance.

The WBS illustrates a structure of products and services comprising the entire work effort. It facilitates uniform planning, assignment of responsibilities, and measurement of project status. Only one WBS is developed and used for each project.

A project WBS. Fig. 1 shows a typical project WBS. Level 1 represents the quantified project objective, i.e., the total facility. Level 2 contains

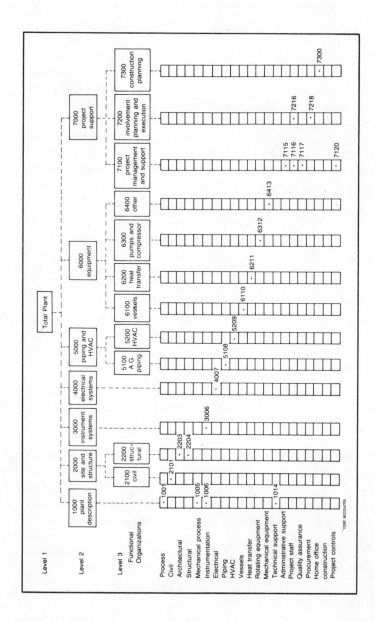

Figure 1—Contractor work breakdown structure.

the major work segments grouped as subprojects. These work segments may be several process units comprising a process area or aggregations of services, e.g., coordination of subprojects or instrumentation and control systems integration management.

Level 3 is subordinate to Level 2 and further defines the project in terms of individual plant units as in a process area. Each descending level provides increasing detailed definitions of the individual tasks. The individual work tasks specified at each level in the WBS are defined as WBS elements. Each WBS element is described separately in a document called the *WBS Dictionary.*

A breakdown of the lowest WBS level leads to formation of a matrix. This matrix features the lowest WBS elements at the top and the contractor's functional organization at the side. The project functional organization consists of disciplines, subcontracts, and other specialties. Participation of each performing organization is indicated at the intersection of the functional organization elements with the WBS elements by a unique cost center number. The matrix so formed becomes the project responsibility assignment matrix (RAM).

Each block identified as a cost center is in effect a management control point and may be referred to as Discipline Contract (DC). The DC is the lowest project WBS level at which organizational responsibility exists. This is the level for authorizing budgets, collecting costs, and measuring performance.

An identified manager, Cost Account Manager (CAM), is responsible for the DC. Virtually all aspects of the project control system intersect at the DC including budgets, estimates, schedules, work assignments, cost collection, problem identification, and corrective actions. The CAM develops a plan listing the work packages, milestones, and time-phased resources required to perform the work identified in the DC. This plan, when baselined, constitutes the BCWS.

Categories defined. The work breakdown structure defines and establishes reporting categories. These reporting categories are used for the project management control. However, the WBS is just one of several reporting categories that may be used to define contract objectives. The others include cost element, organization/function, and contract line item. Typically, the DOE or its prime contractor requires vertical summation of costs. This means that cost information is provided along all ascending levels of the project WBS, starting with the individual cost centers. Traditionally, cost reporting and budgeting have been produced along the organization functional divisions. This, too, can be provided at the lowest WBS level by horizontal summation of costs.

Earned value data. For performance measurement purposes, a unique set of earned value data elements is generated from the three basic indicators described under the previous heading "EVC quantification." Fig. 2 schematically illustrates the relationships between the ACWP, BCWS, and BCWP.

Cost variance is determined by comparing BCWP and ACWP. The difference of the labor and/or materials taken as credit for work done and the labor/materials budgeted for the work is termed the cost variance (CV).

A negative CV indicates an unfavorable situation.

The difference between the BCWS line and BCWP line is the schedule variance.

Schedule variance is expressed in dollars. It represents the value of over or under accomplishment at the given point in time.

In a real project environment, it is often difficult to determine if the cost and schedule variances are remaining constant, increasing or decreasing. Expressing the variances in percentages tends to alleviate the problem. Use of cumulative data helps additionally. The cost index (CI) is determined by dividing the cumulative cost variance to date by the cumulative BCWP to date.

The schedule index (SI) is computed similarly.

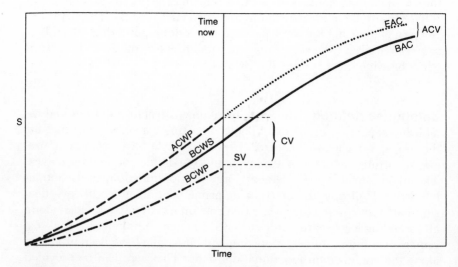

Figure 2—Earned value data elements relationships.

Cost estimates. During the course of the project, the contractor makes estimates of cost at completion (EAC) for the actual cost-to-date, plus the latest estimate for the remaining, authorized work. The EAC is based on the knowledge of performance to date and the actual costs to date applied to the future. Because the budget at completion (BAC) can be readily obtained by summing all the budgets allocated to the contract, the difference between EAC and BAC signifies at completion variance (ACV).

Again, a negative value indicates an unfavorable situation.

Several other cost/schedule indices have been defined. However, as in the case of the primary indices presented above, they too are based on the ACWP, BCWS, and BCWP.

EVC benefits. From DOE's point of view, the major benefit is that the contract performance is being measured against a formal, contract-related baseline rather than against a contractor's internal operating plan. The latter may represent something other than the contractual commitment.

From the contractor's point of view, the most significant benefit is the overall management control system discipline that the implementation of the concept imposes. It leads to

- identification of problems not previously recognized
- ability to trace problems to their source
- determining the cost impact of problems
- objective rather than subjective assessment of project status.

Finally, although from the viewpoints of certain employees primarily, the EVC implementation extends an opportunity to engineers to obtain *managerial* training.

SUBJECT-PROJECT PHASE MATRIX

SUBJECTS	1 PREAWARD	2 INITIATION	3 ENGINEERING	4 PROCUREMENT	5 CONSTRUCTION
A FINANCIAL/CONTRACTUAL					
B ORGANIZATION/EXECUTION PLANNING		●	●	●	●
C MANAGING PEOPLE/COMMUNICATION					
D ESTIMATING/COST CONTROL		●	●	●	●
E RISK ANALYSIS					
F SCHEDULING		●	●	●	●
G TRACKING/TRENDING		●	●	●	●
H PROGRESS/PRODUCTIVITY MEASUREMENT	●	●	●	●	
I MATERIAL MANAGEMENT					

Chapter 10

Integrate Project Control with C/SCSC

A. E. Kerridge

Engineering/construction (E/C) companies performing work under U.S. Department of Energy (DOE) or Department of Defense (DOD) contracts are being evaluated largely in terms of how well they follow cost/schedule control systems criteria (C/SCSC). C/SCSC demands an integrated approach to project controls that interrelates the work scope definition, the schedule, the estimate or budget, the physical performance and the actual expenditure. A change to any one of the input elements of work scope, schedule or budget must be examined to determine its impact upon the other two.

DOD/DOE criteria. There are five subdivisions of the DOD/DOE criteria: organization, planning and budgeting, accounting, analysis, and revisions and access to data.

ORGANIZATION

Step 1—define the work. The first step in project control is to define the project scope by dividing the project into its elements and account codes, using a Work Breakdown Structure (WBS). The WBS is a hierarchial family tree which subdivides a project from top to bottom, into successively greater levels of detail. All the elements of engineering, procurement, construction and subcontract services are displayed relative to each other, and to the overall project, within the WBS. Each vertical subdivision into greater detail represents a level in the WBS.

The WBS has two discrete sections. The higher levels of the WBS, known as the Project Summary Work Breakdown Structure (PSWBS), are specific to the project. They define the subdivisions into which the project will be divided, for control. The number of levels in the PSWBS is governed by project size and complexity. The objective is to divide down to a "manageable" unit. For a hydrocarbon processing (HPI) complex, the first subdivision might be the processing facilities and the offsite facilities.

The second subdivision would be the individual process units and the individual offsite units. The third subdivision might be an area or geographical subdivision within each of the units.

The lower levels and more detailed elements of the WBS, known as the Contractor's Standard Work Breakdown Structure (CSWBS), define the project scope in terms of account codes and work packages. Each E/C company has its own standard account codes which cover home office and construction direct and indirect services, and the procurement of equipment and material. The home office and construction account codes are then further subdivided into activities or work packages, against which hours can be estimated and performance can be measured.

The CSWBS remains the same for each project, and is appended to the lower levels of the PSWBS. For a specific project, not all of the standard account codes will be required. A WBS dictionary is prepared. It lists the specific account codes that apply for the project. Fig. 1 illustrates a typical WBS that might be developed for an HPI complex.

Step 2—coding and numbering. For effective project control, logical, interrelated coding and numbering systems are required. An individual code is used to define a piece of data so that it can be stored, accessed, updated and retrieved in a computer data base. Individual codes are the building blocks for a project control system. Codes are used to define levels in the WBS, organizational elements, types of activities, work packages, estimate, budget and cost information, and types of documents. Individual codes may then be combined into numbers which tie together the data related to the codes for a specific purpose.

At the detail level, correspondence and documents such as drawings, requisitions, purchase orders, inventory lists, commodity descriptions, etc., carry a code. This code may be a part of or be linked to the overall project coding system. A major project code number is the WBS code, which links together the levels in a WBS. In the organizational phase of the project, it is important that the coding and numbering systems are established in conjunction with the WBS, and that a WBS dictionary is

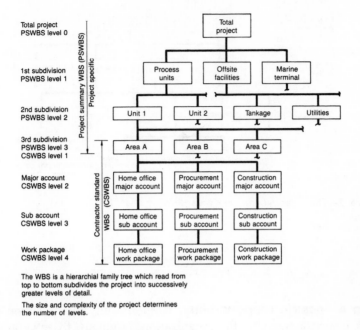

<table>
<tr><td>Total project
PSWBS level 0</td></tr>
<tr><td>1st subdivision
PSWBS level 1</td></tr>
<tr><td>2nd subdivision
PSWBS level 2</td></tr>
<tr><td>3rd subdivision
PSWBS level 3
CSWBS level 1</td></tr>
<tr><td>Major account
CSWBS level 2</td></tr>
<tr><td>Sub account
CSWBS level 3</td></tr>
<tr><td>Work package
CSWBS level 4</td></tr>
</table>

The WBS is a hierarchial family tree which read from top to bottom subdivides the project into successively greater levels of detail.

The size and complexity of the project determines the number of levels.

Figure 1—The work breakdown structure (WBS).

set up to define each element in the WBS, together with its corresponding code.

Step 3—define the organization. The next step in the organizational phase is to define the organizational elements responsible for performing the work, by means of an organizational breakdown structure (OBS). An OBS is similar in concept to the WBS, being an hierarchial family tree defining the organizational elements in successively greater levels of detail. Most traditional organization charts are set up in the form of an OBS.

Whether a project is being handled by a project task force or by functional departments in the company, a specific OBS for the project depicts those organizational elements responsible for performing the work. Fig. 2 illustrates a typical OBS required to perform the work defined in Fig. 1.

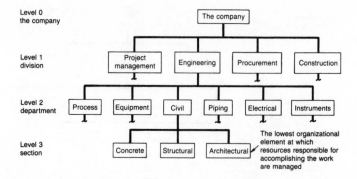

Figure 2—The organizational work breakdown structure (OBS).

Step 4—assign responsibility. Responsibility for execution of the work is next assigned to the organizational elements by integrating the WBS and the OBS to form the responsibility assignment matrix. This ensures that every element of work scope is assigned to a single organization, and that there are no omissions or duplications in the work assignments. The intersection of the WBS and the OBS creates a management control point. The manager of the responsible organizational element becomes the control point manager. The integration of the OBS and the WBS is illustrated in Fig. 3.

The C/SCSC requires that this integration be performed in a manner that allows for cost and schedule performance measurement by WBS and OBS elements. This means that the organizational elements must be subdivided to the level at which the individual organizational resource is managed. Similarly, the WBS must be subdivided down to an account code level where all of the work is handled by a single organizational element. An example of this might be a WBS account code for civil design activities which would then be linked to the civil-design organizational element responsible for accomplishing this work.

PLANNING AND BUDGETING

Step 5—schedule the work. The first step in the planning and budgeting phase is to schedule the work defined in the WBS elements in a manner which describes the sequence and identifies inter-dependen-

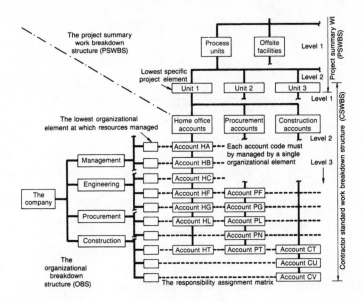

Figure 3—The integration of the OBS and the WBS.

cies. This generally means using networking techniques and the critical path method of scheduling.

A series of hierarchical schedules are prepared of successively increasing detail, starting with a project master schedule down to the detailed task schedules. Strict traceability is maintained between all the tiers of the schedules, between performing organization interfaces, and between the WBS levels. The scheduling system therefore is able to provide parallel schedule reports by WBS elements and by responsible organizational elements. This requirement highlights the need for a logical, interrelated coding system between the account and work package codes in the WBS, and the organizational elements in the OBS. Fig. 4 illustrates hierarchial, traceable schedules by WBS and OBS.

Step 6—estimating/budgeting. The next step is to prepare estimates or budgets for the work scope in accordance with the WBS account code and work package subdivisions. Every resource to be applied to the project must be estimated separately. This includes home office

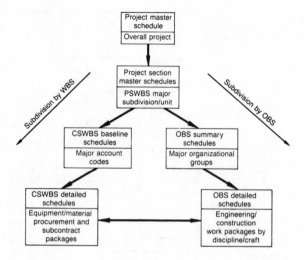

Figure 4—Hierarchical, traceable schedules by WBS and OBS.

man-hours and indirects (reprographics, computer expenses, etc.), direct purchased equipment and material, subcontracts, field supervision, labor and construction indirects. Estimating units used within an account code must be compatible (manhours, lineal feet, cubic yards, quantities, etc.), and all must be capable of being translated into dollars. Although performance for individual cost elements may be measured in man-hours or quantity units, overall performance measurement for combined cost accounts can only be measured in terms of cost (dollars).

Step 7—establish performance baselines. The next and perhaps the most important step in the C/SCSC is to integrate the schedule and the cost elements to create performance measurement baselines for each account code in the WBS.

Resource loading curves and performance measurement baselines are created by spreading (time-phasing) the estimate/budget values of a work package over the scheduled duration, in accordance with a selected distribution profile. The sum of the estimate/budget values in each reporting period for all the work packages in that account code gives the total resource loading value for the reporting period.

These values may be in manhours, dollar costs or quantities (if common quantity units are used for all work packages). The cumulative values for the reporting periods for the total schedule duration of the account code provide the scheduled progress curve or performance measurement baseline. Resource loading and baseline curves are summated from each account code through the WBS to provide performance baselines for the major project subsections and the overall project. Resource loading in terms of dollars yields cash flow requirements.

The performance baselines use the original budget and schedule data and provide the background against which all subsequent project performance is measured. Fig. 5 illustrates the integration of the budget values of the work package elements in the WBS with their schedule durations in the activity networks to create performance measurement baselines.

In parallel with the development of the performance measurement baselines, it is necessary to identify the physical achievements, milestones, technical performance goals or other indicators that will be used to measure performance for each individual account code and work package. Performance measurement for all directly applied engineering, procurement, subcontract and construction activities must be by means of measureable, physical yardsticks such as quantities installed or preset milestones achieved. Performance may not be measured in terms of calendar time or man-hours/costs expended. An exception to this is allowed for supervisory and indirect costs known as "level of effort." For this, performance may be claimed on a prorated or calendar basis.

Step 8—review and authorize. Steps 5 to 7 complete the planning and budgeting function. The final step in this phase is to review the WBS, the organization, the assignment of responsibilities, the interfaces, the schedules, the estimates, the budgets and the baselines in light of the overall project objectives. If necessary, plans may require revision to optimize results. The review process must check that all the internal accounts and work package budgets sum up through the WBS to equal the total overall cost of the project. Also in the budgeting process, it is desirable to set aside a management reserve or contingency.

When the completeness and quality of the project definition and plans are satisfactory, then it should be approved and signed by the project manager. At this time, the commencement of work may be formally authorized by means of contracts, directives and other work authorization documents.

ACCOUNTING

Step 9—record actual costs. At each reporting period, the actual manhour and cost expenditures by WBS account code and work pack-

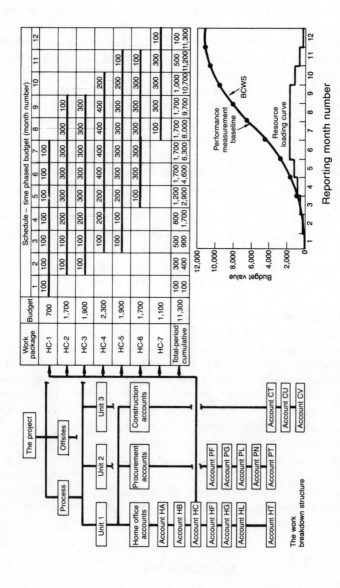

Figure 5—Integrating cost and schedule to create performance measurement baselines.

age and by organizational element are recorded, corresponding to the work performed. Contract costs should be charged directly to a single cost account in the WBS without allocation to two or more WBS elements. Costs should be accumulated and summarized from the bottom of the WBS upwards. Costs should be recorded in a manner which matches and is consistent with estimates/budgets.

The project accounting system must record all costs associated with a project, and ensure that they are entered into their proper place in the WBS such as:

- Home office man-hours and payroll costs
- Home office non-payroll costs and expenses
- Purchased equipment and material costs
- Subcontract material and services costs
- Construction direct labor man-hour and payroll costs
- Construction supervisory man-hour and labor costs
- Construction non-payroll costs for equipment, materials, facilities and services
- Overheads and other distributed costs.

Fig. 6 illustrates the various mechanisms for tracking and recording project costs.

Step 10—measure performance. At each reporting period, in parallel with the recording of costs, physical progress is measured in terms of achievement milestones by WBS account code and work package, and by responsible organization, corresponding to the work performed. It is measured independently of manhour and actual cost expenditure or calendar time.

Physical progress is determined as earned value by measuring work accomplished in terms of manhours, costs, quantities or other measureable units relative to the estimate or budget. Preselected progress milestones are established for each type of work package. When progress reaches a milestone, a preset percentage completion value is earned. The percentage completion times the budget provides the earned value for the work package. The sum of the earned values for the work packages divided by the total budget for the account gives the percentage completion for the account code. Earned values may be in terms of manhours, quantities or costs, depending upon the units used to establish the budgets for the work packages.

In engineering, progress measurement is performed at the work package level. Each discipline prepares a list of the work items to be performed (specifications, drawings, equipment required for the project).

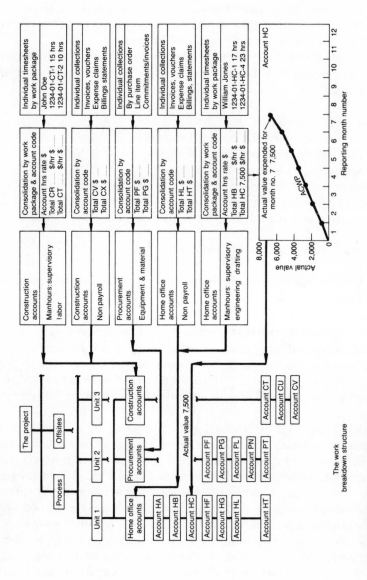

Figure 6—Tracking and recording project costs.

Each work item has a budget and has predetermined milestones that correspond to specific percentage progress achievement points. Progress percent completion is credited to each work item as milestones are reached. Earned value is determined by multiplying the percent complete by the budget for each work item. The sum of the earned hours for all the work items over the total budget hours gives the percent complete for the discipline. Physical progress for total engineering is determined by summating the weighted percent complete for each of the disciplines. This, in turn, rolls up to give the overall project completion by combining weighted engineering, procurement and construction physical percent completion.

Equipment and material physical percent completions are measured in a similar way, using quantity or cost values. Milestones are agreed for performance achievement points such as inquiry issued, material purchased, material delivered and material installed. The earned value is the physical percent completion times the budgeted cost or budgeted quantity.

Construction progress is measured in a similar manner. Earned value is calculated in terms of physical quantities installed against the budgeted quantities, or earned manhours against the budgeted manhours.

Fig. 7 illustrates the earned value method of performance measurement.

ANALYSIS

Step 11—compare planned progress, earned value and actual cost. At each reporting period, the data generated from the accounting, budgeting and progress measurement systems are prepared and tabulated for each account code.

- The planned progress is determined from the performance measurement baseline prepared under Step 7. This is known as the budgeted cost of the work scheduled (BCWS).

- The actual physical progress achieved is obtained from the performance measurement systems described in Step 10. The earned value or physical progress derived from the progress measurement system is known as the budgeted cost of the work performed (BCWP).

- The actual costs and expenditures corresponding to the work performed are obtained from the accounting system as described under Step 9. This is known as the actual cost of the work performed (ACWP).

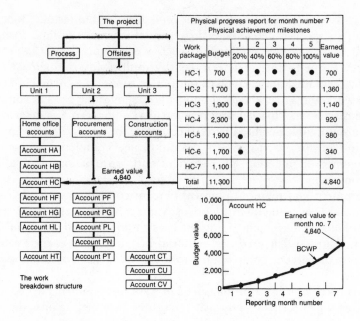

Figure 7—The earned value method of performance measurement.

These three values, determined at each reporting period and plotted cumulatively, provide a very precise picture of the performance of the account code against the budget and schedule. Fig. 8, taken directly from C/SCSC, shows the relationship between the three curves. The difference between the budgeted cost of the work performed and the budgeted cost of the work scheduled is known as the schedule variance (BCWP-BCWS). The difference between the budgeted cost of the work performed and the actual cost of the work performed is known as the cost variance (BCWP-ACWP). The graphical representation of these three curves provides an excellent tool for monitoring project performance on a monthly basis. Increasing divergence between these curves will be a matter for concern.

Based on the performance to date and on estimates of future requirements, a revised estimate or forecast of cost at completion is generated. This is known as the estimated cost at completion (EAC). The difference between the original budgeted cost at completion (BAC) and the estimated cost at completion (EAC) equals the at-completion variance

E/C contractor terminology	DOD/DOE criteria term	Acronym
Cost equivalent to planned/scheduled progress	Budgeted of cost work scheduled	BCWS
Cost equivalent to earned value/physical progress	Budgeted cost of work performed	BCWP
Actual cost of expenditures	Actual cost of work performed	ACWP
Current approved total cost budget	Budgeted cost at completion	BAC
Current forecast of total cost	Estimated cost at completion	EAC
Budget overrun/underrun to date	Cost variance (BCWP - ACWP)	CV
Schedule overrun/underrun to date	Schedule variance (BCWP - BCWS)	SV
Forecast of total cost overrun/underrun	At completion variance (BAC - EAC)	ACV
Ratio of budget to actual cost	Cost performance index	CPI
Ratio of earned value to planned value	Schedule performance index	SPI
Ratio of total budget to forecast cost	At completion CPI	ACPI

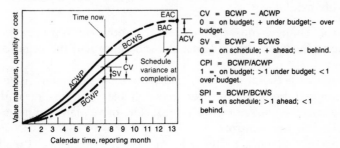

CV = BCWP − ACWP
0 = on budget; + under budget;− over budget.

SV = BCWP − BCWS
0 = on schedule; + ahead; − behind.

CPI = BCWP/ACWP
1 = on budget; >1 under budget; <1 over budget.

SPI = BCWP/BCWS
1 = on schedule; >1 ahead; <1 behind.

Figure 8—Performance reporting.

(ACV). Analysis charts of this type may be produced for each major account code. Budgeted costs, actual costs and earned costs may be summated through the WBS to give the same three curves at any required level or subdivision of the project, and finally at the total project level.

Step 12—reporting and monitoring. The comparisons described above provide a good mechanism for determining the specific problem account areas in a project. The next step is to determine the reasons for the deviations from the plan, and to assess what corrective actions are needed to get back on course. Corrective action should only be directed at significant or important variances. It is not productive to attempt corrective action for all variances that may be temporary trends. One approach is to set thresholds or tolerance lines. These are, in effect, parallel curves on each side of the baseline plan. As long as the cost and schedule deviations are within the thresholds or tolerance lines, then no specific corrective action is warranted. However, if a deviation crosses the threshold or tolerance line, then there is a full examination of the reasons for the deviation. A corrective plan of action is developed to limit further deviation and restore the account back to the original plan.

REVISIONS AND ACCESS TO DATA

The C/SCSC sets specific rules for the control of project changes, and requires that supporting data and documentation for report generation be readily available.

• Contract changes must be handled promptly with a proper recording of their effects on the budgets, the schedules and the organizational elements.
• Differences between current performance measurement budgets and the original budgets must be reconcilable in terms of authorized changes to the work, or internal transfers or re-planning necessary to achieve effective control.
• Retroactive changes to records and reports for work already performed are prohibited.
• Unauthorized revisions to the contract budget are not permitted.
• Performance measurement baselines may not be changed unless authorized. Scope, schedule or budget may not be changed independently of one another.
• The client (DOD or DOE) is allowed access to contractor support data and documentation for systems evaluation, monitoring and surveillance.

C/SCSC BENEFITS

C/SCSC was introduced to overcome undesirable practices in the project control systems of E/Cs. Typical of the major problems perceived were:

• Inadequate procedures and improper planning
• Failure to identify and define the total project scope
• Lack of systems to measure performance effectively
• No integration between schedule and budget to determine interdependency
• Inconsistencies between estimate/budget data and cost records
• Uncontrolled revisions to estimates/budgets and schedules
• No control of authorized changes
• Ineffective forecasting of results at completion.

All of these are eliminated with the proper application of C/SCSC.

Common sense. In the final analysis, C/SCSC is a practical, common sense approach to project control. It does not impose any specific systems on a contractor. It defines the required results and allows the contractor latitude in achieving these results. The following is quoted directly from the criteria:

"Implementation must be based on common sense, which means being practical, and keeping the overall need for contract performance measurement in its proper perspective. . . . The contractor should guard against requiring Work Breakdown Structures, operating procedures, reporting requirements and thresholds for variance analysis which go beyond the minimum necessary for effective management."

BIBLIOGRAPHY

There are many DOD and DOE instructions and procedures on this subject. The major two are:
1. DODI 7000.2, June 10, 1977, *Performance Measurement for Selected Acquisitions.*
2. DOE/CR-0014, August 1979, *Cost and Schedule Control Systems Criteria for Performance Measurement, Summary Description.*

Chapter 11

Use a Matrix for Project Plans

SUBJECT-PROJECT PHASE MATRIX	PROJECT PHASE				
SUBJECTS	1 PREAWARD	2 INITIATION	3 ENGINEERING	4 PROCUREMENT	5 CONSTRUCTION
A FINANCIAL/CONTRACTUAL					
B ORGANIZATION/EXECUTION PLANNING		●			
C MANAGING PEOPLE/COMMUNICATION					
D ESTIMATING/COST CONTROL					
E RISK ANALYSIS					
F SCHEDULING					
G TRACKING/TRENDING					
H PROGRESS/PRODUCTIVITY MEASUREMENT					
I MATERIAL MANAGEMENT					

Robert L. Kimmons

Two significant factors which determine the success of any project are the extent of *planning* the project execution and the *communication* of that plan to all personnel involved in the work.

Any effort whose success depends on work contributions by a large number of people should preferably be made in accordance with a written plan. This plan should be developed under the direction of the responsible manager.

Actual detailed plans should be developed by the supervisors in charge of the work. They have a comprehensive understanding of the necessary work content and work flow patterns at the level for which the plan is made. They may be assisted by other personnel who may be more proficient in planning techniques and who may be designated to reduce the resulting plan to writing.

The written plan. Unfortunately, a written plan is required very early in a project when many other high priority items compete for the project manager's time and attention.

Development of a written plan for a project with a multi-component spectrum may be a monumental task. But it can be simplified by using both a logical breakdown into discrete work areas and an organized attack on preparation of the plan.

In an organization where project execution represents a substantial portion of the corporate effort, standard procedures will have been highly developed. Written plans should not be used to reiterate these procedures. Rather, written plans should supplement them or point out exceptions in their application for the project.

123

Seek clarity. To be usable, written plans should be *specific, concise* and *clear.* Long documents, full of legalistic jargon, will generally not be read, let alone be understood or used.

In starting a plan, six words form the essence of knowledge needed by those employed in project execution. These words are *what, why, when, how, who* and *where.* Using these words, we will develop a framework for a plan.

USE OF MATRIX

As is so often the case in analyzing a complex problem, a matrix can be conveniently employed (see Fig. 1). In multi-component program matrix, the "actions" required can be arranged vertically. These will consist of elements suggested by the six key words applied specifically to project planning.

Horizontally, the various components of the multi-component project can be listed. These may be units, systems, geographic areas or any other convenient division applicable to the project. By numbering the matrix, both vertically and horizontally, the framework for preparing a written plan is established.

Draft of plan. The plan is then developed in draft form on index cards. These cards can be placed within the corresponding matrix areas as out-lined on a tack board. If this board is located centrally in the project area, it becomes immediately available for use by project personnel at a very early date. The project manager at this stage must carefully monitor the posted information and immediately correct any misconceptions of his plans.

Eight steps. Using the concepts covered above, we can then outline an eight-point action program for developing a written plan of project execution.

　　1. Develop the matrix and identify "action elements" of the plan and the components. In a multi-component plan, reserve the first column for plans covering the entire project or for plans common to all components. The matrix should be numbered vertically and horizontally to facilitate Step Two.

　　2. Index cards should be prepared and numbered. The project manager can then jot down briefly on these cards his initial ideas in each area. He can also designate specific responsibility for developing the de-

Actions		0 Over-all Program	1 First Unit	2 Second Unit	3 Third Unit	4 Fourth Unit
	Project definition	Brief definition of Over-all program	Definition of first unit	Definition of second unit	Definition of third unit	Definition of fourth unit
What	Definition of scope	For over-all program	For first unit	For second unit	For third unit	For fourth unit
	Identify unique problems	For over-all program	For first unit	For second unit	For third unit	For fourth unit
Why	Identify objectives	State objectives for over-all program	Specific objectives for first unit	Specific objectives for second unit	Specific objectives for third unit	Specific objectives for fourth unit
When	Assign work item priorities	Over-all priorities for program	Specific priorities for first unit	Specific priorities for second unit	Specific priorities for third unit	Specific priorities for fourth unit
	Identify major problems	For over-all program	For first unit	For second unit	For third unit	For fourth unit
	Develop detailed plans					
How	Definition of work elements	For over-all program	For first unit	For second unit	For third unit	For fourth unit
	Sequence of work	For over-all program	For first unit	For second unit	For third unit	For fourth unit
	Budget		Normally the same for all elements of project			
	Detailed execution	For over-all program	For first unit	For second unit	For third unit	For fourth unit
	Monitoring		Normally the same for all elements of project			
	Corrective action strategy		Normally the same for all elements of project			
	Feedback cycle		Normally the same for all elements of project			
	Reports		Normally the same for all elements of project			
	Changes		Normally the same for all elements of project			
Who	Organization and work assignments	For over-all program	For first unit	For second unit	For third unit	For fourth unit
Where	Geographic assignment of work	For over-all program	For first unit	For second unit	For third unit	For fourth unit

Figure 1—This matrix facilitates planning for a multi-component program.

tailed plan. Certain areas not yet fully defined may be designated "later" to permit an early first issue of the plan.

3. The Master Plan should then be developed for each matrix area by the individual/organization designated by the project manager, taking into account preliminary notes entered by the project manager. Where no specific deviations from standard procedures are necessary, the particular matrix area should be so marked or left blank.

4. Once the individual mini-plans have been completed on the cards, they should be tacked onto the board. Checklists can be very helpful in developing comprehensive plans.

5. The over-all plan is screened on the board by key members of the project team. At this time, optimization and finalization of the plan occurs. This is a very important step.

6. The plan is then assembled in edited written form from the numbered cards and issued to functional departments and to the owner's project manager for comments. A nominal time period is allowed for receiving comments. During the intervening period, the "for approval" issue of the plan governs execution.

7. A follow-up screening meeting should be scheduled with key project personnel at which time a definitive plan should emerge. This should be issued in written form as the "approved" plan of execution.

8. A revision should be made to the execution plan at any time during the project when it is necessary to substantially change the execution strategy.

ACTION STEPS

For a typical process plant project, the following list outlines "actions" which should be included in the project plan of execution. In all cases, these should be reviewed to determine their applicability in a specific project. Supplemental items should also be considered for inclusion.

WHAT

1. Define the project briefly so that the resulting document can be "self-standing" for the purpose of understanding the plan.

2. Define the scope of work briefly. Where this varies from component to component, this should be clearly indicated.

3. Identify problems unique to this project. The written plan should recognize these problems and provide solutions and safeguards.

WHY

4. State the objectives of the Owner and the project team. A clear understanding of the objectives is vital to preparing the execution plan strategy.

WHEN

5. Analyze major work items and assign priorities.

HOW

6. Identify major decisions which must be made, who will be responsible for making them and when the decisions must be made.

7. Develop execution plans stressing deviations from established practices and procedures unique to this project. The following areas should be covered:

- Detailed definition of work elements
- Schedule and sequencing of work
- Budget
- Detailed execution
- Monitoring
- Corrective action strategy
- Feedback cycle
- Reports
- Changes

Again, checklists can be of great help in making sure that all items have been considered.

WHO

8. The specific organizational format expanded by actual assignments of major work elements should be included. On a large, complex

project—where personnel from many functional organizations and usually more than two corporate structures are involved—a clear understanding as to responsibility is essential. The plan should provide this information.

WHERE

9. Location becomes important where a multi-pronged effort possibly involving multi-office execution is concerned or where a portion of the work may be done in the field to facilitate existing/new plant interfaces.

Fig. 1—a typical matrix—illustrates the planning elements. These should be considered in generating a written plan of execution for a typical four-component project.

'Cascade.' For very large, complex projects, this approach may be used in a cascading fashion. That is, the strategy may first be developed for the over-all program; and then individual disciplines may develop their own plan in much more detail using the same procedures. In this case, the matrix becomes three dimensional.

Efficiency in project execution depends upon a highly organized and well-directed project organization. The matrix approach described—with its corollary thrusts to develop a written execution strategy and to communicate it to all those involved in a timely fashion—can do much to facilitate productivity.

SUBJECT-PROJECT PHASE MATRIX	1 PREAWARD	2 INITIATION	3 ENGINEERING	4 PROCUREMENT	5 CONSTRUCTION
SUBJECTS					
A FINANCIAL/CONTRACTUAL					
B ORGANIZATION/EXECUTION PLANNING		●●			
C MANAGING PEOPLE/COMMUNICATION					
D ESTIMATING/COST CONTROL					
E RISK ANALYSIS					
F SCHEDULING					
G TRACKING/TRENDING		●●			
H PROGRESS/PRODUCTIVITY MEASUREMENT		●●			
I MATERIAL MANAGEMENT					

Chapter 12

Improve
Project Control

R. H. Dinger

Accurate project status and control information can be produced rapidly by applying a practical design engineering approach to project control. The solution is the Generalized Engineering Management System (GEMS). GEMS provides realistic project management services for the client on a dynamic design project. Moreover, the concepts as described here can be adapted to your company's own needs.

Combined system. The GEMS system combines schedule control, document control, budget control, labor forecasting, and progress reporting into a single easy to use system. The consolidation of several control systems into a single integrated project management data base improves turnaround, eliminates redundancies, and reduces costs. Data input requirements are minimized by using an integrated systems approach. Continuous employee feedback keeps the project manager accurately informed of project progress in a dynamic environment. GEMS combines these features into a compute-intensive project management data base with maximum flexibility for scope and schedule changes, while minimizing data storage requirements.

WHY ANOTHER SYSTEM?

The single most important factor in any project management system is information availability. The usual approach in a computerized system is to implement a system of interrelated information systems (data base). These data bases are highly save-intensive. That is, every conceivable piece of information is stored on the data base. Access to the information is, in theory, provided through a complex system of access codes known as search keys. When additional information is required the data base is revised and completely new access codes are developed. The result is that the user, the project manager, needs an advanced degree in computer science just to find out if a certain drawing has been issued.

The dynamic nature of a hydrocarbon processing plant design project forces the project manager to keep close tabs on design progress. Most engineering control systems are a montage of independently developed systems that overlap in many areas. The sheer bulk of such existing systems makes timely response to change difficult at best. The results can be disastrous. Project managers are presented with reports that are of historical value, but do not provide the vital real-time information needed to make decisions today.

The GEMS approach solves the problem of complexity and bulk by using a compute-intensive data base. The compute-intensive approach is simple—if the information can be computed or inferred from other information don't save it. The resultant simplification of the data structure eliminates the complexity of the data base. Information becomes accessible on a real-time basis. Project managers have vital information available when they need it, not after the fact.

The cost benefits of the compute-intensive approach are an important consideration. The cost savings due to reduced data storage are obvious, but there are other less obvious cost benefits. Searching through an enormous data base costs money. The processor is tied up reading data and making comparisons. The more searching required the more money it costs. The hidden costs associated with not having critical information for decision making also need to be considered. The more critical the decision the more significant the cost or value of the information.

PROJECT CONTROL BY THE NUMBERS

The GEMS system is more an approach to project management than a specific management tool. GEMS, therefore, can be adapted to nearly any control technique popularly being used for the control of design engineering projects. Work breakdown structures, critical path methods, precedence diagrams, and bar charts are all adaptable to GEMS.

A common feature of all project control methods is the division of a project into a group of manageable tasks. Each of these tasks is then assigned a unique identification code. These codes are systematically assigned in accordance with a strict set of rules. Task codes are designed to provide a maximum amount of information about the task in a minimum amount of space. This key point is used to advantage in the GEMS system. This task code is generally a group of subcodes, each subcode defining an attribute of the task.

Task attributes. An examination of the various project control methods popularly in use in the construction of hydrocarbon processing plants reveals that these task attributes generally fall into seven major categories:

    1. Discipline code—in a broad sense a code that specifies the work discipline such as piping, vessels, structures.

    2. Function code—a code that specifies the actual function performed such as drafting, calculation, checking.

    3. Area code—a code that specifies a particular area of the processing plant such as hydrotreater, off-site tankage, utility area.

    4. Document code—a code that specifies a particular type of document such as drawing, specification, data sheet.

    5. Sequence code—a code that specifies position in a sequential list, usually required to maintain uniqueness.

    6. Revision code—a code that specifies the current revision status of a document.

    7. Cost type—a code that specifies a particular type of cost such as labor, bulk material, subcontract.

Some typical methods of applying these attributes are shown in Fig. 1. Some variations will occur from system to system, but the essential approach is the same.

In addition to a set of attributes a task will also have a title, scheduled start, scheduled finish, and budget. Actual time is accumulated against the task. Reports are prepared that show engineering progress and assorted variances from the original schedule and budget.

GEMS—AN OVERVIEW

GEMS, like most project control systems, begins by dividing a project into manageable tasks. A close inspection of the attributes used in a work breakdown structure and in a document numbering system, reveals important similarities. Both use the discipline and area attributes to define the qualitative nature of the subject. A project document list is, therefore, a detailed work breakdown for the project. The GEMS approach establishes project documentation as the key element in the control sys-

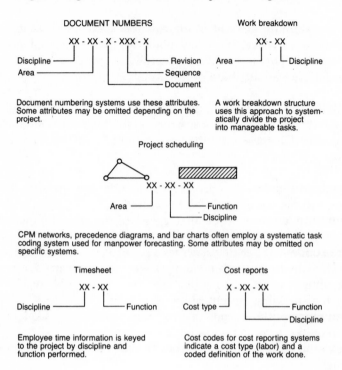

Figure 1—Typical use of task attributes in project control systems.

tem. Correspondence, such as memos, letters, and the like, are excluded.

Each project document is defined as a project task and the document number is the work breakdown structure. This approach requires that all project tasks be documented.

The discipline attributes in the document number must have enough breadth to cover the concept of a work breakdown structure. Hence, the normal concept of discipline is expanded to include areas of specialization such as pumps. For this discussion a two digit discipline code is used. In a systematic approach the first digit indicates a major discipline group and the second digit indicates an area of specialization. For example, if a first digit of 3 specified mechanical then 31 could indicate pumps, 32 compressors, etc.

The document sequence number is assigned within a given document code only and may be three or four digits depending on the size of the project. A separate document log is required for each document code. Each major discipline is assigned a block of sequence numbers to maintain their documents in sequence. With this system the document can be uniquely identified by the document code, sequence code and revision code. The user is now ready to begin constructing the project data base.

A data base is a structured organization of related information. The structure of the data base closely conforms to the actual interrelationships of the information. The project document lists forms the skeleton of the GEMS data base. Fig. 2 depicts a single data base record and how that record interacts in the project control environment.

The sample task D301A is also shown in Fig. 2. The task is subdivided into a series of subtasks depending on the document code and discipline. GEMS uses the concept of standard times for the control and reporting of engineering progress. Since the amount of time can vary widely from document to document this concept is modified to be a standard percentage of the total task budget. The percentages shown in Fig. 2 are representative of piping design drawings. Although any single task can be at variance with the standard, a definite productivity goal is established and variance from that goal indicates a potential problem.

Employee time reporting is accomplished by charging directly to the task. Since employees generally will have the document in their possession errors caused by using wrong costs codes on timesheets are reduced. The system interaction of a typical timesheet record is shown in Fig. 2. The function performed is indicated by a two digit code. In addition to the usual charge codes and time information specified by employees, a column labeled "Forecast" is provided. Each employee indicates here the time that employee estimates it will take to complete the task for the particular function being performed. This forecast provides continuous feedback on project progress at all levels of the project. Using a forecast is more straight-forward for employees to use and more reliable than a percent complete figure.

The employee time information is input directly to the project data base each period, updating the tasks with actuals. The data base is then ready for access by the various progress reporting application programs.

PUTTING THE SYSTEM TO WORK

Fig. 3 shows how the updating and reporting functions are performed on the project data base. Input information passes through the data base

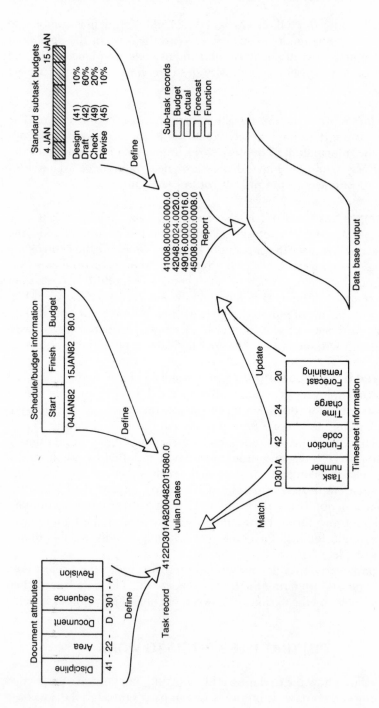

Figure 2—Sample record and system interaction.

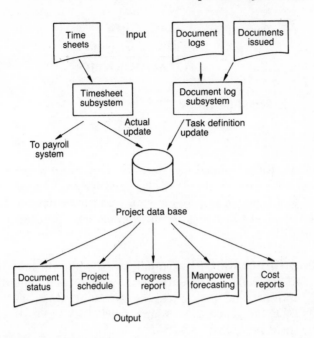

Figure 3—GEMS information flow.

and is captured for use by other systems. Repeated input to multiple systems is not required, reducing operating costs and potential errors. Actual data are captured in the time reporting subsystem. Task and schedule definition is controlled via the document control log subsystem.

Progress reporting and manpower forecasting are two features that provide the project manager with vital control information. The following control indices can be calculated for each task from the data base information:

1. Budget Index (BI)
$$BI = \frac{ACTUAL + FORECAST}{ORIGINAL\ BUDGET}$$

2. Percent WORK completed (%W)
$$\%\ W = \frac{ACTUAL}{ACTUAL + FORECAST} \times 100$$

3. Percent Schedule Used (%S)

$$\% \, S = \frac{DURATION \ USED}{TOTAL \ DURATION} \times 100$$

4. Schedule Index (SI)

$$SI = \frac{\% \, S}{\% \, W}$$

The indices are calculated function by function for a given task and for the total task. These indices are also summarized by area, discipline, document, and function to provide vital trend information. The use of continuous employee feedback, ensures maximum accuracy on current index trends.

Short term forecasting is accomplished by the evaluation of task forecasts and schedule constraints. At any point the remaining work equals the forecast and the remaining duration equals FINISH = CURRENT DATE. Then the resource level (LEV) that should be applied in the next period is:

$$LEV = \frac{FORECAST}{REM \ DURATION} \times DAYS \ IN \ PERIOD$$

This resource level forecast can be improved by adjustment according to the budget and schedule indices. This improved estimate of the resource loading for the next period (NEXT) is based on meeting the original schedule:

$$NEXT = BI \times SI \times LEV$$

This index scaling technique is a direct and effective method for adjusting task activity levels. Index values greater than unity accelerate activity and index values less than unity decelerate activity. The result is a rapid return to the original project plan.

The short term forecasts are summarized upward by area, document, discipline, and function to provide an accurate picture of the resource requirements for the next period. Summaries are sorted and arranged according to any desired task attribute or group of attributes.

Long range forecasting is performed by applying the budget and schedule trends to the remainder of the project. Thus if the piping discipline is trending to 10 percent over budget in the checking function, this figure can be forecast for the remaining piping tasks. The project manpower loading is adjusted accordingly and the project manager can implement proper control measures. Trend information keeps the project manager aware of the direction that the project is headed.

Long and short range manpower forecasting is a key feature of GEMS. The ability to produce reliable labor requirements forecasts for the project manager keeps the project on track. A practical and straightforward approach to the forecasting problem keeps the GEMS system simple and manageable. The net result—information is readily available to the project manager when that information is needed.

The 'zero' stage. When all forecasts for a given task go to zero, the document is ready for issue. The document status report indicates when this event should occur through an analysis of the data base variables. A complete-next-period flag is set in the data base record when the task should be finished in the next period. When the task is completed the issue date is entered via the document log subsystem. After issue the flag is changed to an issued flag and the document status report reflects this issued status.

Project cost accounting reports are generated by sorting the data base variables and totaling according to discipline. Cost codes are formed by prefixing the discipline attribute with a cost type attribute. The data base therefore contains all the information required for complete labor cost accounting. This information is also passed directly to a client billing application.

Estimating tool. Finally, a properly designed project data base system can utimately become a useful estimating tool. Once reliable standard percentages are developed for each document/discipline code, a project manpower estimate can be assembled more rapidly than through conventional means. If the standards are reliable the resultant estimate has better accuracy. In addition the system produces estimates segregated out by function code giving better insight into project staffing requirements.

Simplicity. The keys to success of GEMS are simplicity and multiple use of information. Simplicity is achieved through minimizing the amount of data stored on the data base and using simple methods to expand that data. Multiple usage of data is a natural result of implementing a single project data base. The result is an overall reduction in computer resources with an attendant reduction in costs. The compute-intensive approach to data base design reduces both the storage and processing requirements for the system. The use of simple relationships among data items leads to a straightforward data base design. Information is then more readily available. The bottom line: the project manager is better informed from start to finish.

Part 4: Scheduling

Chapter 13

Improve CPM Milestone Networks

SUBJECT-PROJECT PHASE MATRIX	PROJECT PHASE				
SUBJECTS	1 PREAWARD	2 INITIATION	3 ENGINEERING	4 PROCUREMENT	5 CONSTRUCTION
A FINANCIAL/CONTRACTUAL					
B ORGANIZATION/EXECUTION PLANNING					
C MANAGING PEOPLE/COMMUNICATION					
D ESTIMATING/COST CONTROL					
E RISK ANALYSIS					
F SCHEDULING		●	●	●	●
G TRACKING/TRENDING					
H PROGRESS/PRODUCTIVITY MEASUREMENT					
I MATERIAL MANAGEMENT					

Arthur E. Kerridge

The Critical Path Method (CPM) of scheduling plays such an important role in engineering and constructing a hydrocarbon processing plant that one probably can't know **too much** about it, and how to make it more effective. For this reason, an occasional review of the major elements of CPM should be a **must** for project engineers and managers. This article was prepared with such a review in mind.

We can begin with CPM's two basic elements, planning and scheduling.

Planning:

- List work activities
- Establish sequence and dependence
- Create network and test logic.

Scheduling:

- Add activity durations and manhours
- Check for "criticality" and "float"
- Allocate manpower
- Level uneconomic manpower peaks
- Recheck for "criticality" and "float."

The number of work activities may vary from a few thousand for a small simple project to the tens or hundreds of thousands for a major

141

project. Networks of great detail and complexity require computerized processing systems which can do the calculations quickly, perform the analysis, store the data and provide a variety of report forms. The computerized systems show the critical path with early and late start and completion dates for all other activities. They also provide many other benefits, such as:

- Manpower requirements by skill types
- Physical progress from activity weightings and percent completions
- Schedule trending and forecasting
- Integration with cost systems.

These computerized systems accept modified or revised planning data, and update reports accordingly, or merely show the impact of planning alternatives to provide a basis for decision making. A variety of output reports may be selected by criticality, by department, skill type, by activity code or by time frame periods. These reports may be obtained in tabular, barchart, network, curve, histogram or other graphic form. Most engineering/construction companies use a computerized CPM processor. A number of these systems are commercially available and some companies have designed and programed their own systems.

Advantages and problems. CPM methods are more precise than the older barchart methods of scheduling, and can do a much more thorough job. As with any sophisticated tool, they can be misused and misapplied, and are not without certain problems.

1. The precision of CPM logic requires that preceding and succeeding activities are properly tied without loops or free ends. To show overlap and paralleling between related activities, a single activity may become a number of subactivities to allow for the ties and restraints which are part of the CPM logic. This tends to increase the number of activities and complexity of the network.

2. The end result is often a complex network with many activities and reports which may be too extensive, detailed and time-consuming for most people to follow easily. The system requires the attention of senior planning and scheduling specialists with skill in activity coding to provide selective summary reports for different levels of management.

3. A detailed CPM network cannot be developed until there is full project scope definition and a complete listing of work activities. It may take some weeks after project inception before the detailed networks can be developed, and even at this time, there may still be insufficient information to generate detailed networks for the later engineering, procurement and construction phases. During the early developmental phases of a project, a realistic overall schedule is most needed for economic and financial planning purposes.

4. A complex computerized CPM network requires considerable servicing to reflect the project status accurately. Maintaining a large network demands time and effort from the planning and scheduling specialists. At the time that the project is going through its developmental and evolutionary stages, it can be costly and cumbersome to modify and maintain a detailed network to keep up with changes.

5. If the project network is complex the project manager may be overwhelmed with scheduling reports and data at a detailed level which require excessive time and effort to comprehend. Uneasiness with the summary reports may necessitate a large amount of time reviewing the detail networks. Alternately the project manager may resort to arbitrary adjustment of dates by means of "gut feel."

In short, if CPM is not applied intelligently, it will not be a helpful tool to the project manager.

CPM NEEDS TO BE FLEXIBLE

A complex CPM network with many activities is probably most effective for a manufacturing operation where every activity is finite and must be performed in a fixed sequence. When the manufacturing operation is repetitious, the time and cost spent developing a detailed network, which will remain unchanged, may be recovered and increased productivity and reduced cost spread over a large number of products.

No universality. A rather different situation applies to the engineering, procurement and construction of refinery and chemical projects. Some activities are common to most projects and must be performed in much the same sequence. But in practice, each project is unique due to individual client requirements, particular product and feedstock specifications, and specific site location conditions. There is no universal logic to suit the style and priorities of individual project and construction managers. The management philosophy on one project may be in direct contradiction to that applying to another. For example:

• If early completion is the top priority without regard for cost, conservative engineering assumptions can be made so that many engineering activities can proceed ahead of normal development time. Equipment may be purchased early based on conservative safe designs on a negotiated basis without competitive bidding.

- If cost is the prime consideration, then more engineering time may be justified to reduce design margins. Also competitive bids will be required for all material and equipment.
- With a remote location, maximizing home office engineering together with equipment and component prefabrication to reduce site labor requirements may be desirable.

Change. In addition to these basic philosophies which should be set at the project inception, there are continuing changes and adjustments which inevitably occur during project execution. For example:

- All bids for certain equipment are much higher than allowed. Should there be redesign and reinquiry or should the cost overrun be accepted?
- Exchanger deliveries are predicted much later than expected. What effect will this have on construction activities and schedule?
- To ship a large tower to the jobsite will require special handling at excessive costs. What are the cost/schedule effects if the tower is field erected?
- An excess of journeyman pipefitters and welders are available in the jobsite area. What would be the schedule/cost effects of a field pipe fabrication shop and the purchase of piping materials for direct delivery to the field?

The project manager's responsibility is to make the right decision quickly when problems of this nature arise during project execution. The project manager needs to be able to refer directly to the network supporting the schedule, and be able to adjust the project plan and schedule accordingly. His decision must not be constrained because of the time, disruption and cost effect it would have upon a detailed CPM network. He should be able to make his own assessment of the effect on the schedule and make his decision with a full understanding of the implications.

CPM MILESTONE NETWORKS

Having noted some difficulties that can exist with CPM, particularly in the early stages of a project, what then is the solution? How does the project manager use CPM scheduling as his personal dynamic tool?

How does he stay on top of the situation so that he is able to direct the project and not become mired in details? How does he maintain a responsive and flexible scheduling system which can accommodate changes quickly and effectively?

Fewer activities. One solution is the use of CPM Milestone Networks. A typical milestone network has less than 100 activities for an overall project. A super project having many units or areas may require a milestone network for each major area. The simplicity of the network is such that it is readily understood while setting the key dates for all major project activities.

Because of the condensation of activities in the Milestone Network to approximately 100, and the resultant coarseness, there has to be some license in its use and interpretation. There are many additional linkages and dependencies which cannot be shown. Also, in many cases, subsequent activities may start before the final completion of the preceding activity. However, in all cases, the preceding activity must reach a certain percentage of completion before it is possible to move to the next activity shown.

Target dates. The Milestone CPM Network identifies all major activities which interface between the various disciplines in engineering, procurement and construction. When the Milestone Network has been established and approved each Milestone date becomes a target completion date. CPM Networks for engineering, procurement and construction are then prepared as full definition becomes available with the Milestones built in as fixed dates into the detailed schedules. This provides the detail planning and scheduling required at all specific working levels.

The philosophy of the detail level networks is to incorporate "float" where practical within the Milestones except for those few activities which are on the critical path. This means that during the progress of a job, there is detailed schedule control and reporting in relation to the Milestone dates which are tied together by the Milestone Network. The objective is to work to meet each Milestone in the overall schedule so as to achieve the final completion date. The milestones are built in as fixed dates into the detailed schedules.

Reevaluate. If the detailed schedules indicate that a milestone date cannot be maintained even with maximum effort and extra resources, then it will be necessary to reevaluate the Milestone Network, and, if necessary, adjust subsequent milestone dates. These are then used for the detailed schedules which are developed for that phase of the project.

With this method of operation, maintaining an overview of the project and getting a feel for the impact of schedule slippage at any time during the project execution is always possible.

The ideal situation is for the project manager to become personally involved and work closely with the project planning and scheduling staff in the development of the Milestone Network. The reason for this is that the project manager makes the key decisions regarding how the project is to be executed and where priorities lie. He has to decide whether schedule overrides cost or other considerations. By becoming personally involved in the development of the Milestone Network, he transmits his objectives and philosophies to the planning and scheduling staff so they jointly produce a network which is workable and mutually acceptable.

The milestone networks in Figs. 1 and 2 are for a typical refinery or chemical process unit. The first network, covering engineering and procurement, contains approximately 40 activities. The second network, covering construction, contains approximately 18 major activities. These milestone networks also show some intermediate ties and restraints between major activities to improve the logic. However, taking all of these into account, the overall number of activities is still in the region of 100.

HOW TO PREPARE CPM MILESTONE NETWORKS

Having encouraged the project manager to use CPM Milestone Networks as his personal dynamic tool, how does he go about it?

The following are the basic steps.

1. Take a typical standard milestone network for the type of project under consideration. (The networks in Figs. 1 and 2 apply for a typical refinery or chemical process unit.) Add any significant activities which are specific for the project under consideration such as:

• Unusual equipment
• Process buildings
• Major planning or regulatory approvals.

Repress any inclinations to add unnecessary activities.

2. Insert any known time constraints or targets such as:

• Date site available
• Date funds available for placement of purchase orders

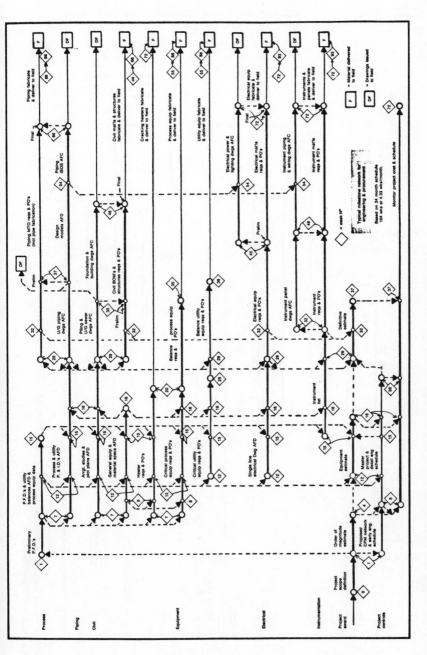

Figure 1—This typical milestone network for engineering and procurement assures timely, systematic preconstruction-phase activities.

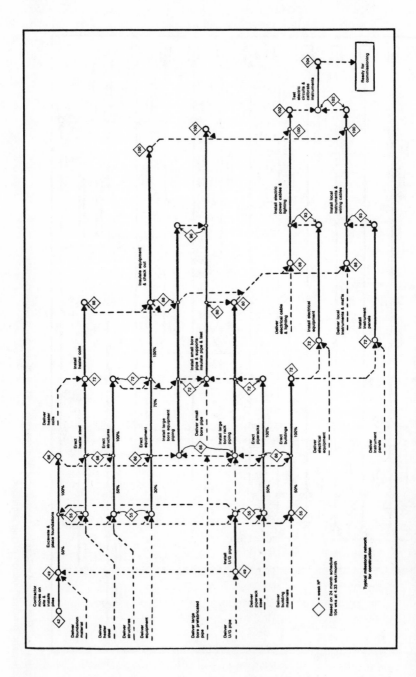

Figure 2—This typical milestone network for construction can be one of the project manager's most important aids.

- Target date for completion
- Date project is officially authorized.

3. Review equipment list and obtain current delivery periods for the major categories of equipment and materials.

4. Start at the beginning of the resultant network. Assign time durations in weeks for the activities shown which would normally apply for a project of the size under consideration. Add the time durations to give the week number by which the activity will be completed. Note the earliest dates when purchase orders for equipment can be placed. In setting these key dates, make proper allowance for the intermediate activities which must occur. For example, firm process data for critical process equipment items may be issued three weeks after project award. Before the purchase orders can be placed, the following typical activities must be completed.

- Mechanical data sheets and requisitions—2 weeks
- Issue inquiries and receive bids—5 weeks
- Evaluate bids and place purchase orders—2 weeks
- Total activity time—9 weeks
- Purchase order date—week 12 of the project.

Having established dates by which major groups of purchase orders will be placed, add the material delivery periods to arrive at the date when the equipment and material will be delivered to the field. Make sure that the delivery time allows for packing, transportation, shipment, customs handling, as may be applicable. Generally, "deliveries" are quoted ex manufacturing plants. From 2 to 8 weeks may be required for handling and shipping to the jobsite.

5. Next review the construction network and spot in equipment delivery times noting the dates when significant equipment deliveries commence and are 30/70/100 percent complete.

The equipment deliveries set the key dates for the construction schedule. Piping, electrical and instrumentation work which consumes the major portion of the construction labor manhours cannot commence until a significant portion of the equipment has been erected and cannot be completed until the final equipment items have been erected.

6. At this point in the development of the overall project schedule, a quick evaluation should be made to see whether the target completion date is reasonably achievable. Examine the time available between desired completion and the approximate dates for equipment delivery at 30, 70 and 100 percent complete. Obtain the estimated labor manhours required for piping, electrical and instrument installation. Divide the schedule time for these activities into the manhours to determine the average manpower loading. Allow for a peak loading of about 1.5 to 1.7 times the average.

Obtain from construction what is a reasonable manpower loading for a job of this size taking into account the number of equipment items and layout of the jobsite. If the peak appears to be excessive, then the target end date may be overly optimistic. Or alternatively it is necessary to obtain earlier deliveries of equipment to increase the time span for construction. If the target completion date is to be maintained, now is the time to look at possibly reducing the equipment delivery periods either by earlier placement of purchase orders or by reducing the delivery times quotes. The possibilities are:

- Conservative engineering assumptions to allow for earlier equipment inquiries.
- Negotiated purchases from selected suppliers eliminating the bidding period.
- Purchasing on the basis of minimum delivery schedules rather than on lowest cost.

7. Assuming that the equipment deliveries and target completion date fall within an acceptable time frame, then the next step is to look at activities which must be performed in readiness for equipment erection, such as site preparation, piling, foundations and erection of structures. Set suitable time periods for these activities which in turn will establish dates for start of work in the field and required dates for deliveries of drawings and materials for civil, structural and piping items.

8. Subtract the delivery times for civil materials, structural steel and piping materials to establish the latest purchase order dates allowable in engineering. Also note the dates drawings are required on site which set the latest allowable issue dates for "Approved for Construction" drawings. Check that the dates previously established in the engineering schedules are compatible with the dates required by the construction schedule. If not, the engineering dates may need to be moved forward or the construction start dates moved backwards or both dates adjusted to achieve a compromise.

9. Once the milestone networks for both engineering and construction have been completed with matching activity completion dates, then the final step is to recheck the manpower loading for each of the major disciplines in engineering and for the major crafts in construction. In engineering these are civil, piping, electrical and instrumentation. If the peaks are not excessive, then the schedule is reasonable. If a peak is excessive, then the activity time span may be too short and the schedule not achievable.

10. We now have a network schedule complete with activity durations and dates for the major activities.

This data is now input to the computer to check the logic and provide early/late start and completion dates for all activities.

HOW TO USE CPM MILESTONE NETWORKS

The project milestone networks are now complete and provide dates for completion of all the major activities required to achieve the overall target completion date. These milestone dates can now be used by the project team for developing detailed CPM networks for the imtermediate activities in engineering, procurement and construction. Equipment, material and drawings indices can be prepared on the basis of the milestone schedule dates established.

During the course of the project execution copies of the milestone networks are constantly referred to and marked to reflect current status.

If during the job there is a major change in the schedule due to change of scope or unforeseen delay, then it is a simple matter to reschedule and create a new set of milestone dates following the steps outlined above.

The example networks (Figs. 1 and 2) have been completed for an intermediate size project having an overall project schedule of 24 months. The size and scale of the networks are such that they can be followed personally by the project manager.

H.O. Cost as a function of project Cost

Let E = engineering (H.O.) cost
C = Project cost

$$E = 7.5 \, C^{0.78} \quad (1981)$$

eg for $C = 100 \times 10^6 \, \$$

$E = 13 \times 10^6 \, \$ = \underline{13\%}$

compare to 10%

Chapter 14

How to Develop a Project Schedule

	PROJECT PHASE					
	SUBJECTS	*1* PREAWARD	*2* INITIATION	*3* ENGINEERING	*4* PROCUREMENT	*5* CONSTRUCTION
A	FINANCIAL/CONTRACTUAL					
B	ORGANIZATION/EXECUTION PLANNING					
C	MANAGING PEOPLE/COMMUNICATION					
D	ESTIMATING/COST CONTROL					
E	RISK ANALYSIS					
F	SCHEDULING		●	●	●	●
G	TRACKING/TRENDING					
H	PROGRESS/PRODUCTIVITY MEASUREMENT					
I	MATERIAL MANAGEMENT					

A. E. Kerridge

Before developing a project schedule, some things must be known. Fig. 1 lists some key information which should be available. Additional information may be useful. But do not get into the trap of asking for too much information before starting a schedule. Too much information may merely confuse. It is possible to create a project schedule with even less information than listed, because much information can be developed statistically or by pro-rating.

A sample project. For illustration purposes, the following typical project is assumed.

- **Total installed cost** (engineering/procurement/construction—$100 million
- **Home office manhours** (at 10 percent at $35 per hour)—300,000 hours
- **Direct field labor hours** (at 20 percent at $15 per hour)—1,300,000 hours
- **Ratio of field labor to home office hours**—4.3 to 1
- **Type of project**—refinery hydro-desulfurizer for a major oil company
- **Operating conditions**—maximum temperature 1,200°F, maximum pressure 600 psig
- **Number of equipment items**—250 (approximate hours per piece—1,200)

153

- Approximate Total Installed Cost - Engineer/Procure/Construct
- Approximate Home Office Manhours
- Approximate Direct Field Labor Manhours
- General Description and Type of Project
- Source of Process Design and Engineering Design
- Maximum Temperature/Pressure Conditions
- Number and Type of Equipment Items
- Identification of Special Long Delivery Items
- Materials of Construction
- Maximum Size and Extent of Piping
- Major Structures Required
- Location Where Plant Will Be Built
- Site Conditions - Approximate Area of Plot
- Labor Availability (Union/Open Shop)
- Major Field Fabrication & Subcontract Items
- Procurement Policy and Material Sources - Local/Worldwide
- Approvals Required
- Schedule Constraints
    - date of award of work/start of engineering
    - date funds released for purchase
    - date site available
    - date of permits/approvals to build

Figure 1—The project specifics.

- **Equipment types**—exchangers, pressure vessels, compressors, furnace, towers
- **Long delivery items**—furnace tubes, compressors, and alloy exchangers
- **Materials of construction**—mainly carbon steel, but some alloy
- **Piping**—large bore pipe, and also alloy pipe
- **Structural steel**—major plant structures required
- **Plant location**—to be built on the U.S. Gulf Coast. Could be union or open shop labor
- **Site conditions**—level and clear/approximate plot area—400 ft × 400 ft
- **Field fabricated/erected items**—furnace and main tower
- **Procurement**—worldwide purchase based upon competitive price and delivery
- **Approvals**—client approves all major drawings
- **Schedule constraints**

  —Process design completed as a package to be released to engineering contractor three months after award
  —Start of engineering in three months
  —Release of funds to commit purchase in six months
  —Construction jobsite available in nine months

Major elements. The major elements or activities in any schedule are engineering, procurement, and construction. The first step is to develop independent subschedules for each of these major activities.

- **Engineering**—Process design, conceptual/analytical engineering, production design, specifications, requisitions and drawings
- **Procurement**—Inquiries, bid evaluations, purchase orders, expediting, inspection and delivery to jobsite
- **Construction**—Temporary facilities, material receipt and erection (civil, structures, equipment, piping, instruments, electrical, paint and insulation).

Schedule development can start with any of the above elements. A start should be made with either procurement or construction. Leave engineering until last. The reason is that engineering activities are the most flexible and adaptable. The engineering approach may well be modified or governed by schedule constraints arising in the procurement or construction areas. Construction logic is governed by the required building sequence. Procurement durations may be dictated by third parties.

PROCUREMENT

Procurement starts with an inquiry requisition and ends when material is received. The logic is simple. There are a large number of similar independent parallel activities. For each of these there are a fixed number of sequential subactivities.

The procurement schedule is influenced mainly by outside sources. Technical data and technical reviews are controlled by engineering. Approvals are governed by the client and/or management. Quotation durations, drawing and material deliveries are set by vendors. Inspection and transportation are also set by others. The durations directly controlled by the procurement group are a small part of the total time span.

Procurement cycle. The first step in the development of the procurement schedule is to establish a "procurement cycle." It lists the subactivities which must be performed from the inquiry requisition up to purchase order placement and receipt of vendor drawings. All subactivities should be included even though each one may only take a few days. Cumulatively, they can add substantially to the procurement schedule.

Fig. 2 illustrates a chart used to establish the procurement cycle. The left hand column lists the major sequential activities. The chart is completed by assessing the number of working days required for each of the subactivities. Working days are used in place of weeks to allow for the effect of weekends. Overall calendar weeks are determined by dividing the cumulative working days by five.

Since durations differ for major complex equipment items, standard equipment items, and bulk materials, three columns are included in the chart for three separate procurement cycles: 1. major complex equipment, 2. standard equipment and 3. bulk materials (such as piping, electrical, instruments, structural and civil).

When establishing activity durations, be realistic. Do not unreasonably shorten vendor bid times. Bids will merely be late or incomplete, which will require more rebid or follow-up time.

Having established the procurement cycle, which sets the time required up to the purchase order, add delivery and shipment times for each material category. This can be done with a chart as shown in Fig. 3.

Equipment/materials list. The first step is to list the major equipment and material categories required. Durations are then added from experience or by telephone contact with leading vendors. Vendors' telephone quoted deliveries are usually their best and most optimistic. Fre-

REF	ACTIVITIES		DURATIONS		
	NOTE Durations are working days ( ) are cumulative working days		COMPLEX EQUIPMENT ITEM A	STANDARD EQUIPMENT ITEM B	BULK MATERIAL ITEM C
1	Requisition Ready for Inquiry		0 (0)	0 (0)	0 (0)
2	Client Approval Received		8 (8)	5 (5)	5 (5)
3	Issue Inquiry to Vendors		7 (15)	5 (10)	3 (8)
4	Receive Quotations		30 (45)	20 (30)	15 (23)
5	Complete Bid Evaluation		20 (65)	15 (45)	7 (30)
6	Client Approval Received		10 (75)	10 (55)	5 (35)
7	Place Purchase Order		5 (80)	5 (60)	5 (40)
-	TOTAL EQUIVALENT WEEKS		16	12	8
8	Receive Preliminary Vendor Prints		20 (100)	15 (75)	10 (50)
9	Receive Final Vendor Prints		20	15 (90)	10 (60)
-	ADDED EQUIVALENT WEEKS		8	6	4

Figure 2—Procurement cycle chart.

ITEM NOTE: Delivery Promise Start Point P.O. = Purchase Order A.D. = Approved Drawing	Cycle Type From Fig. 2	Delivery Promise (Weeks)	Delivery Promise Start Point	Added Time From P.O.	Total Delivery (Weeks)	Shipment Time (Weeks)
EQUIPMENT						
Furnace - Structural Steel	A	14-18	A.D.	8	22-26	3
- Tubes	A	38-46	A.D.	8	46-54	3
Towers - Alloy	A	36-44	A.D.	8	44-52	4
- C.S. Heavy Wall	B	24-36	A.D.	6	30-42	4
Towers Field Erected - Materials	A	20-24	A.D.	8	28-32	3
- Erection	-	16-20	-	0	16-20	3
Exchangers S & T - Alloy	A	30-38	A.D.	8	38-46	4
S & T - C.S.	A	20-24	A.D.	8	28-32	4
Air Fin Exchangers	B	20-24	P.O.	6	26-30	3
Vessels - Alloy	A	36-42	A.D.	8	44-50	4
- C.S. Heavy Wall	A	24-36	A.D.	8	32-44	4
- C.S. Light Wall	B	16-32	A.D.	6	22-38	4
Tanks - Shop Fabricated	B	20-28	A.D	6	26-34	4
Tanks Field Erected - Materials	A	16-24	A.D.	8	24-32	3
- Erection	-	16-20	-	0	16-20	3
Pumps Process - Alloy	A	32-44	P.O.	0	32-44	3
- C.S.	A	24-32	P.O.	0	24-32	3
Compressors - Large Process	A	48-60	P.O.	0	48-60	4
- Light Utility	B	30-40	P.O.	0	30-40	3
Special Equipment - Packaged	A	32-52	P.O.	0	32-52	4
STRUCTURAL STEEL						
Major Plant Structures	C	12-20	A.D.	4	16-24	3
PIPING						
Large Bore - Alloy	C	24-40	P.O.	0	24-40	3
- C.S.	C	12-24	P.O.	0	12-24	3
Large Valves - Alloy	C	32-48	P.O.	0	32-48	3
- C.S.	C	16-24	P.O.	0	16-24	3
Pipe Fabrication - Alloy	C	16-24	A.D.	4	20-28	3
- C.S.	C	8-12	A.D.	4	12-16	3
INSTRUMENTS						
Control Valves	C	32-48	P.O.	0	32-48	3
Consoles/Panels	A	24-48	A.D.	8	32-56	4
ELECTRICAL						
Transformers	B	24-36	P.O.	0	24-36	3
Major Switchgear	B	24-36	P.O.	0	24-36	3
Motor Control Centers	B	16-24	P.O.	0	16-24	3
Power Cable	B	20-32	P.O.	0	20-32	3

Figure 3—Material delivery chart.

quently, a vendor's quoted delivery starts from receipt of approved drawings released for fabrication, not necessarily from receipt of purchase order. Also, promised delivery may be the day it is completed in the shop without allowance for inspection, witnessed performance test, or transportation arrangements.

Fig. 3 takes these factors into account by noting the procurement cycle type from Fig. 2, the delivery promise in weeks and the probable start point for the delivery promise which may be purchase order or approved drawings.

The chart also allows for transportation/shipment to the jobsite. Assessment of this duration may be difficult if the source is unknown, and could be overseas. However, it is best to be conservative. Shipment times can be the most unpredictable, varying from a few days to several weeks. If a conservative allowance is put in here, it can be a buffer to cover inspection delays, rejections or other transportation holdups.

CONSTRUCTION

Before construction can start, drawings and materials must arrive at the jobsite. Thereafter, construction proceeds in a sequence governed by the work's physical nature. Excavation precedes foundations which are followed by steel and equipment erection. Piping, electrical and instruments then commence in sequence, finishing with insulation and paint.

Sequences. In general, construction activities have a predetermined logic. They must follow one another in a set order like building blocks. The field has little opportunity to be flexible or adaptable. Drawings and materials must be delivered to the jobsite in the right sequence ahead of the time when they will be installed.

If it can be assumed that drawing and material deliveries will not present a problem, then how long should the construction work take? It becomes a matter of resource. How large a labor force is available and how many workers can be economically applied to the job? Too few and the job will take too long. Too many may mean lower productivity and inefficient working. There could also be problems of inefficient use of construction equipment and costly short term supervisory peaks.

Manhours. Fig. 4 shows a series of typical overall construction curves for one million labor manhours spread over construction durations of 6 to 36 months. Although the curve shapes are the same, the peak manpower requirements, as shown by the dotted line, increase exponentially as durations are shortened.

If manpower availability is not limiting, a method of determining the economic construction manpower peak is to evaluate the maximum density of labor per plot area. For a typical process plant, a construction worker requires an average working area between 150 and 250 square feet. For preliminary planning purposes, 200 square feet per man is a good number to use. This does not apply to offsite areas or to areas where pipe and equipment are more spread out. In these areas, the amount of work available may not support a labor density of one man per 200 square feet.

For the project under consideration, the plot area is 400 × 400 feet which equals 160,000 square feet. The economic peak manpower, therefore, is 160,000/200 = 800 men.

Field labor. Fig. 5 (top) shows a series of curves for a range of total field labor manhours in which the manpower peaks are plotted against construction durations. These curves are derived by the method shown in Fig. 4. For an economic construction peak of 800 men and field labor hours of 1.3 million the construction duration is approximately 18 months.

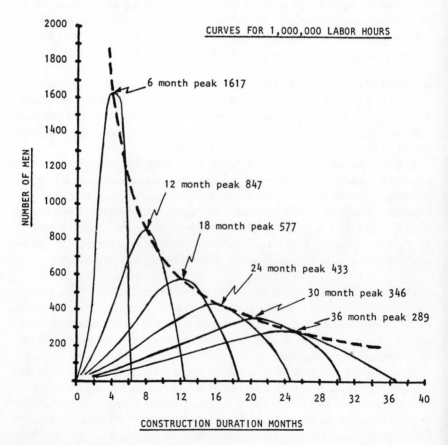

Figure 4—Effect of duration on manpower peak.

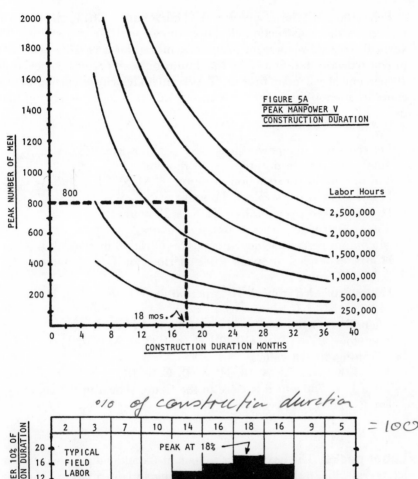

FIGURE 5A
PEAK MANPOWER V
CONSTRUCTION DURATION

Labor Hours
2,500,000
2,000,000
1,500,000
1,000,000
500,000
250,000

18 mos.

PEAK NUMBER OF MEN

CONSTRUCTION DURATION MONTHS

⁰⁄₀ of construction duration = 100 %

| 2 | 3 | 7 | 10 | 14 | 16 | 18 | 16 | 9 | 5 |

PROGRESS PER 10% OF CONSTRUCTION DURATION

TYPICAL
FIELD
LABOR
CURVE

PEAK AT 18%

PERCENT OF TOTAL CONSTRUCTION DURATION

T = Total Hours
P = Peak Number of Men
H = Hours Worked Per Week
M = Construction Duration Months
C = Peak % Progress Per 10% Duration
P = (T x C/100)/(H x 4.33 x M x 0.1)

COMPUTING THE MANPOWER PEAK

Figure 5—*Upper*: Peak manpower by construction duration. *Lower*: Percent of total construction duration.

Fig. 5 (bottom) shows a typical field labor curve. The horizontal scale represents the construction duration shown in 10% increments. The vertical scale shows percent progress achieved for each 10% increment in construction duration. The maximum or peak percent achieved per 10 percent of calendar time is 18 percent. This curve can be used to compute manpower peaks for a known duration in the following manner.

Let economic manpower peak = P (unknown)
Total construction duration = M months
Ten percent of construction duration = M × 0.1 months
Hours worked per week = H hours
Hours worked per month = H × 4.33 hours
Total construction labor hours = T hours
Maximum percent achieved per 10% duration increment = C%
Hours expended in peak 10% period for C% achievement = T × C/100 hours
Hours expended in peak 10% period for P men = P × H × 4.33 × M × 0.1 hours
Then T × C/100 = P × H × 4.33 × M × 0.1
Therefore, P = (T × C/100)/(H × 4.33 × M × 0.1)
Substituting known values
   T = 1,300,000, M = 18, H = 40, C = 18
   Then P = 750 which is close to the figure shown in the chart.
   For P = 800, M becomes 17 months.

Labor peaks. The next step is to look at the individual peaks for each labor craft. Fig. 6 shows typical craft timing and distribution. This chart shows the percentage of total hours for each craft, the start, finish, and duration time and the peak progress achieved for 10 percent of the craft duration. The previous formula can also be used to calculate the craft peak.

Taking the piping craft, Tp piping hours = T × 40% = 520,000 hours
Mp piping duration = M × 0.8 = 14.4 months
Cp peak piping progress for 10% duration = 16%
Therefore, Pp = (520,000 × 16/100)/(40 × 4.33 × 14.4 × 0.1)
= 334
This gives the peak piping labor force required for the project.

CRAFT	APPROX % OF TOTAL LABOR HOURS	% OF OVERALL CONSTRUCTION DURATION			PEAK PROGRESS PER 10% OF CRAFT DURATION	BAR CHART SCHEDULE
		START %	FINISH %	DURATION %		10 20 30 40 50 60 70 80 90
CIVIL	20	0	85	85	13	
STRUCTURAL	8	15	75	60	13	
EQUIPMENT	8	15	85	70	13	
PIPING	40	15	95	80	16	
ELECTRICAL	8	25	100	75	18	
INSTRUMENTS	7	35	100	65	18	
INSULATION & PAINT	9	50	100	50	16	
TOTAL CONSTRUCTION	100	0	100	100	18	

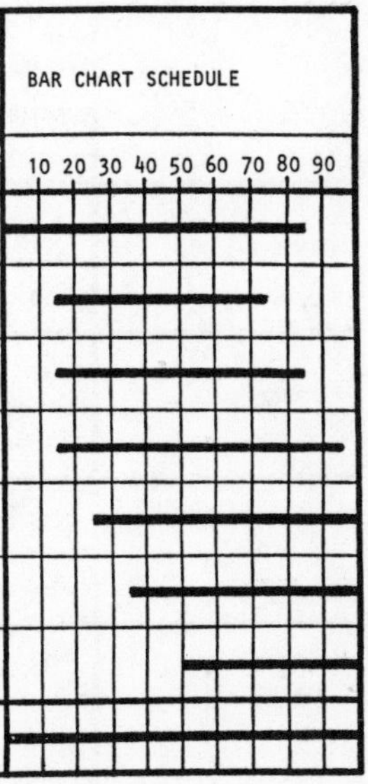

Figure 6—Craft timing and distribution.

Material deliveries. The final step is to determine the required material deliveries. All materials are required ahead of the craft schedule periods shown in Fig. 6. Fig. 7 plots the typical percentage progress completion curves for each craft over their duration. Material delivery requirements are added in ahead of these curves with adequate lead times as shown. For smooth construction work each craft requires a minimum backlog of material.

Across the top of the curves the actual construction duration for the project as determined previously is superimposed. This now positively identifies material delivery requirements in relation to the established construction duration.

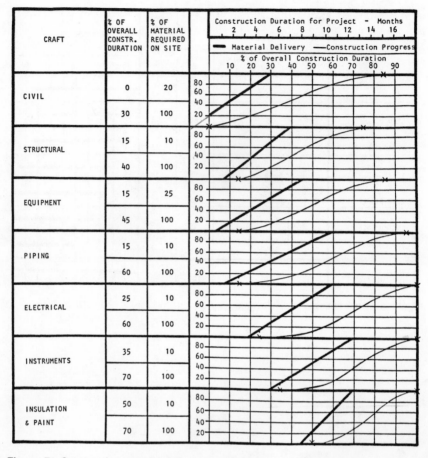

Figure 7—Construction material delivery requirements.

ENGINEERING

Engineering has been left until last because it is the most difficult to schedule. For many reasons, the sequence of engineering activities may not follow typical logic. It comes down to priorities, preferences, and discipline.

If minimum schedule is the priority, many engineering shortcuts can be taken based upon conservative, empirical assumptions. Equipment and material can be "sole sourced" to save time. The result may be a less than optimum design, with some added costs. If design optimization and/or minimum cost is the priority, then engineering may go through many recycles with consequent effect upon the schedule and manhours.

Orderliness. Even though engineering activity sequences and durations may be radically altered or rearranged by priority dictate, engineering development must proceed in an orderly progression. Secondary engineering or detail design must not be permitted to start until primary decisions have been made. Nothing is gained in the schedule by out of sequence working, resource is wasted and time is lost from recycle.

The fundamental steps in engineering are:

- **Process design**—process flow diagrams; heat and material balances; temperature, pressure, physical, chemical and flow conditions; process equipment specifications and data sheets; utility systems balance diagrams and environmental systems concepts and specifications
- **Basic engineering**—piping and instrument diagrams (process and utility); general engineering specifications; equipment mechanical specifications, data sheets and requisitions; plot/site plans (block model); plant arrangement studies (planning model) and single line electrical diagrams.
- **Production engineering**—final site and plot plans, production design model, civil and structural fabrication/erection drawings, final certified vendor drawings, piping key plans and isometrics, instrument and electrical field installation drawings and bulk material lists and requisitions.

In general, engineering development must proceed in the order of the above steps. A certain amount of overlap may be permitted, and on larger projects, specific areas or systems may be released ahead of others.

Spread charts. This fundamental staging of engineering work coupled with the fact that there is a typical inter-relationship between the manhours and timing of each engineering discipline makes it possible to develop prototype engineering discipline spread charts for typical project conditions. Fig. 8 is a typical chart for an EPC project initiated with a process design package which is a good starting point to develop an engineering schedule. This figure shows typically: the distribution of hours between disciplines, the start/finish point for each discipline relative to the overall project duration and the normal progress curve for each discipline.

A prototype chart of this type applies fairly consistently for the majority of process units. The unknowns are the realistic durations for each discipline's time span.

Quantify. The next step is to come up with some quantitative estimates of the work to be done by the key disciplines, by statistical methods.

Total home office manhours = 300,000

Total engineering manhours at 75% = 225,000

Individual discipline hours may be determined from Fig. 8.

Number of equipment items = 250

Number of P&ID lines = 250 × 6.5 = 1625

Number of P&ID's = 250/3 = 83

Number of model tables/planning areas = site area/10,000 = 160,000/10,000 = 16 (10,000 sq ft of site = a model table of 2½ × 4 ft @ ³⁄₈ in. = 1 ft)

Number of piping key plans = site area/4,000 = 40 (4,000 sq ft of site area = a drawing area of 19 in. × 29 in. @ ³⁄₈ in. = 1 ft)

Number of isometrics = number of lines = 1625

Having quantified the major categories of work, the next question is: How long should they take? The critical durations in basic engineering are: P&ID development time to production release, equipment design time to requisition issue, receipt of proprietary equipment vendor drawings and development of planning arrangement studies to production release.

An analysis of the work scope, the manpower availability in each discipline and matching these against the durations and progress curves shown in Fig. 8 suggest a realistic time span of six to seven months for basic engineering.

Critical durations. In production design these are piping and instrument production. A balancing of key piping manpower availability against the work scope of the 16 piping areas/40 key plans suggest an overall duration for piping production in the range of nine months.

CASE-EPC Project with Process Design Supplied Note Bar Charts show scheduled time to 90%					ENGINEERING DURATION TO 90% POINT FOR PROJECT (MONTHS) 2 4 6 8 10 12 14								
DISCIPLINE	% OF TOTAL HOURS	START %	90% POINT %	CURVE TYPE	% CALENDAR TIME TO MECHANICAL COMPLETION								
					10	20	30	40	50	60	70	80	90
PROJECT ENG. & ADMIN.	12	0	70	2	6	15	28	44	59	75	90		
P & I D ENGINEERING	16	0	35	2	15	44	75	90					
VESSELS	6	0	35	1	20	53	80	90					
EQUIPMENT	5	0	35	1	20	53	80	90					
PLANT LAYOUT & PIPING DESIGN	33	5	65	2	3	13	27	45	63	81	90		
CIVIL & STRUCTURAL	13	20	50	3			16	50	90				
INSTRUMENTS	10	15	70	3		3	12	26	46	64	90		
ELECTRICAL	5	20	70	3			7	22	42	67	90		
TOTAL ENGINEERING	100	0	65	-	6	19	37	46	71	84	90		

Basic Engineering 40%   Production Engineering 60%

Low 10%

Figure 8—Prototype engineering discipline spread chart.

Coupling the two together gives an overall engineering period in the region of 15 to 16 months.

This time scale can now be added to Fig. 8 above the total engineering duration, as shown. We now have the backbone of an overall engineering bar chart which shows start and finish points for each discipline and a typical progress curve. Dates for specific activities can now be determined from the individual discipline progress curves. Specific activity completion points can be related to specific progress completion percentages for that discipline which can now be related to a schedule date from Fig. 8.

THE TOTAL PROJECT

The last stage in the development of the project schedule is to integrate the three independent subschedules for engineering, procurement, construction to produce an overall master project schedule. This may require a series of iterations. Start with a standard master project schedule layout, and make a first assumption for a realistic (not optimistic) project schedule duration. There are two early indicators which can be used to make the first project duration assumption.

Engineering (to the 90% point) normally should not exceed 65 percent of the total project duration.

Therefore, if engineering = 15 to 16 months, then the total project duration = say 15.5 × 100/65 = 23.8 months.

Project construction (excluding pre-project early site development work) should normally never start earlier than 30 percent of the total project duration.

Therefore, if construction = 17 to 18 months, then the total project duration = say 17.5 × 100/70 = 25 months.

Master schedule. For a first pass, set up a master project schedule format assuming a project duration of 25 months from release of the process design package to mechanical completion. Starting from the front, lay in the engineering durations and requisition dates for equipment and bulk materials based upon the engineering schedule. Add onto these the material delivery times from the procurement schedule to give equipment and material field delivery dates.

Starting from the back end, lay in the construction craft durations and the construction material required dates from the construction schedule. Now look for "float" or "overlap." Float will show up if material deliveries are ahead of the construction material required dates. Overlap will show up if drawing or material deliveries are later than the construction required dates. The overall schedule may then be compressed or elongated to eliminate float or to accommodate overlap. Usually, the second pass will achieve a reasonable fit and produce a realistic balanced schedule.

Fig. 9 illustrates a typical master project schedule which integrates and balances the three separate project schedules of engineering (Fig. 8), procurement (Figs. 3 and 4), and construction (Fig. 7).

Comparative analysis. One final check is to look at the relationship between the progress curves generated from the master project schedule for engineering, material delivery, and construction. The relative positions and lead times between these curves must always fall within certain limits for all projects. If the progress curves for the project in ques-

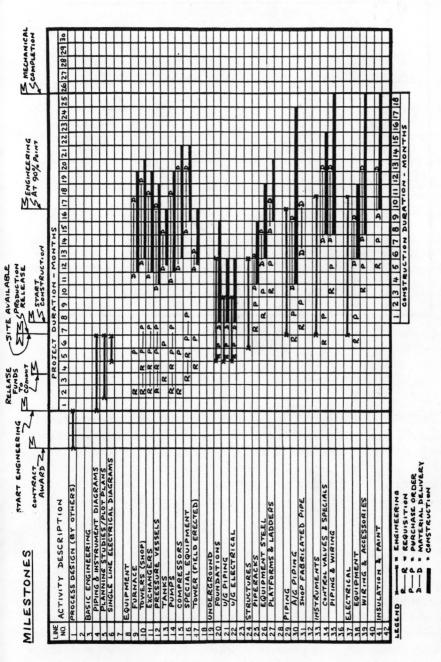

Figure 9—The master project schedule.

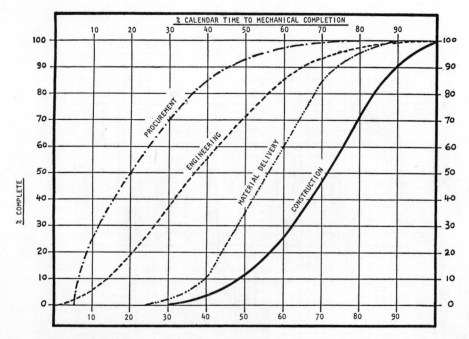

Figure 10—Typical project progress curves.

tion differ to a marked degree from the typical curves, then something is seriously wrong and we do not have a satisfactory preliminary master project schedule. It will be necessary to take another look at the points where the project progress curves deviate from the typical progress curves. Fig. 10 illustrates the shape and relationship between the engineering, material delivery, and construction curves for a typical project.

Make adjustments. Finally, the "realistic" schedule produced by this method (Fig. 9) is not necessarily the minimum schedule. If, after this exercise, the durations produced are unacceptable, then compress the overall duration to the desired point. Look at the overlaps to determine what positive steps must be taken to shorten what otherwise would be considered a normal duration. Extra priorities in engineering to make earlier decisions? More pressure in procurement for shorter cycle times and accelerated deliveries? More manpower peaking in the field? These are all options that can be considered.

The schedule format will show up "pinch" points at an early date so that schedule critical areas can be identified. This means that specific action plans and priorities can be directed to these areas from the project initiation if minimum schedule is an overriding priority.

Realistic milestones. A master project schedule developed by this "top-down" method provides realistic milestones. These can subsequently be used for the development of detailed schedules and networks within each of the engineering, procurement, and construction disciplines.

Chapter 15

Scheduling in the Engineering Phase

SUBJECTS	PREAWARD 1	INITIATION 2	ENGINEERING 3	PROCUREMENT 4	CONSTRUCTION 5
PROJECT PHASE					
A FINANCIAL/CONTRACTUAL					
B ORGANIZATION/EXECUTION PLANNING					
C MANAGING PEOPLE/COMMUNICATION					
D ESTIMATING/COST CONTROL					
E RISK ANALYSIS					
F SCHEDULING			●		
G TRACKING/TRENDING					
H PROGRESS/PRODUCTIVITY MEASUREMENT					
I MATERIAL MANAGEMENT					

William H. Holt and Joel L. Russell

Scheduling and manpower planning in the engineering phase of a project can be handled effectively, with a system based on the following assumptions:

- Historical project data can supply sufficiently accurate information to form the basis for manpower assignments and for project duration.
- The approximate cost of a project is based on the appropriation report or on the preliminary estimate. ("Cost" is the total installed cost of the project.)
- Engineering manhours for a project can be determined once the approximate project cost is known.
- The time required to engineer a project can be determined once the approximate project cost is known.
- Manpower staffing for a project follows an established pattern.

The system also allows management to apply judgment factors to all of the assumptions. Experienced personnel can adjust these factors based on their knowledge of the project.

Engineering manhours and calendar time. For a typical, medium-sized engineering company, one hour of engineering, design and drafting services will cost approximately $24.00. For purposes of this discussion, it is assumed that for projects valued up to $10 million, engineering will represent approximately 15 percent of the estimated cost. With these assumptions, one hour of engineering represents

TABLE 1—Engineering hours and
calendar time by project cost

Total estimated project cost	Engineering SVC. manhours	Average weeks to complete engr.
$ 100,000	625	8 - 16
200,000	1,250	12 - 22
500,000	3,125	20 - 30
1,000,000	6,250	30 - 40
5,000,000	31,250	50 - 70
10,000,000	62,500	60 - 90
20,000,000	116,000	80 - 115
40,000,000	172,000	100 - 140
60,000,000	215,000	110 - 150
80,000,000	225,000	120 - 165
100,000,000	250,000	125 - 170

$160.00 of constructed cost. Therefore, when the cost is known the man-hour requirement can be determined by dividing the cost by $160.00. (These figures can be modified to match historical data for each company and type of project.)

It is also assumed that the calendar time required to accomplish the engineering of the projects falls within the ranges shown in Table I. These ranges are determined by analyzing a company's historical track record.

For projects above $10 million, the engineering percentage will vary downward from 15 percent to approximately 6 percent. The curve in Fig. 1 shows the relationship between engineering hours and project cost. The curve in Fig. 2 shows the relationship between calendar time for engineering and project cost.

Engineering manpower distribution. Two manpower distribution schemes are considered. The first will be called a normal curve, the second will be called a bimodal curve.

The normal curve (Fig. 3) is approximately bell shaped. Having determined the total time for a project and the number of manhours to be used, the area under the curve represents the total number of manhours required to engineer the project. The curve's shape and crucial points were calculated from the company's historical performance. Formula 1 allows us to determine the value of point P. Once P is known, the value of the remaining points can be found.

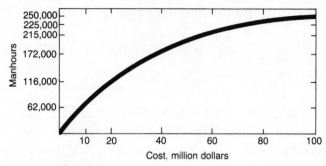

Figure 1—Engineering hours vs. total project cost.

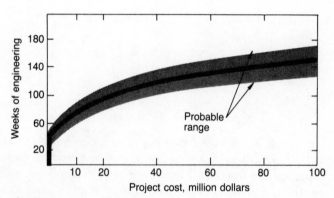

Figure 2—Calendar time vs. total project cost.

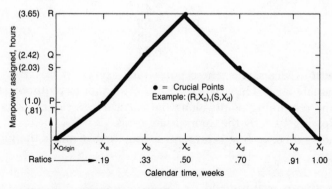

Note: $X_a = (X_f)(.19); X_b = (X_f)(.33) \ldots$
$T = (P)(.81); S = (P)(2.03) \ldots$

Figure 3—Normal project—manpower vs. calendar time.

Formula 1: Crucial Point Formula for Normal Curves

$$\frac{\text{Total}}{\text{Engineering}} = \frac{\overset{P}{(\text{MHrs at Xa})} \overset{\text{Constant}}{(3.5)} \overset{X_f}{(\text{Wks. to Comp. Engr.})}}{2}$$

$$P = \frac{(\text{Total Engineering Manhours}) \, (2)}{(3.5) \, (\text{Weeks to Complete Engineering})}$$

Crucial points. As shown on the conventional X-Y graph system (see Fig. 3), the normal curve is described by seven crucial points.

Time is measured along the horizontal, or X axis. The seven points along the horizontal axis are labeled X_{origin} through X_f. The relationships of these points to X_f are:

Point	Relationship
X_{origin}	0
X_a	.19
X_b	.33
X_c	.50
X_d	.70
X_e	.91
X_f	1.00

Therefore, when X_f, the total number of weeks required to engineer the project, is known, the remaining points can be found by multiplying X_f by the appropriate fraction. Manpower requirements are measured along the vertical, or Y, axis. The five points along the vertical axis are labeled X_{origin}, P, Q, R, S, and T. The relationships of these points to one "P" are:

P	1.0
Q	2.42
R	3.65
S	2.03
T	0.81

One point. Once again, these points are expressed in terms of one point, namely "P." Thus, when "P," the manhours required at X_a is shown, the remaining points along the vertical axis can be determined by multiplying "P" by the appropriate ratio.

The normal curve best represents a project that meets the following conditions:

- Information is well in-hand
- The scope is well defined
- Vendor data availability is not a problem.

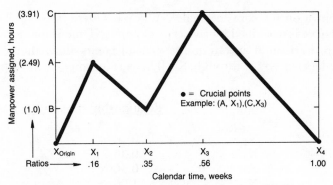

Notes: $X_1 = (Xy)(.16)$, $X_2 = (X_4)(.35)$, $X_3 = (X_4)(.56)$ $A = (B)(2.49)$, $C = (B)(3.91)$

Figure 4—Bimodal project—manpower vs. calendar time.

An example using the normal curve (Fig. 3) is shown in the example (see end of this article, and Fig. 8).

The second curve considered is called a "Bimodal" curve and is shown in Fig. 4.

Formula II: Crucial Point Formula for Bimodal Curves

$$\frac{\text{Total}}{\text{Engineering}} = \frac{\overset{B}{\text{(MHrs at X2)}}\ \overset{\text{Constant}}{(3.8)}\ \overset{X_4}{\text{(Wks. to Comp. Engr.)}}}{2}$$

$$B = \frac{(\text{Total Engineering Manhours})\ (2)}{(3.8)\ (\text{Weeks to Complete Engineering})}$$

When conditions differ from those which are represented by a normal curve, a new curve is required. The bimodal curve was developed to account for these differences. A bimodal curve characterizes a project having the following conditions:

- An ill-defined scope
- Limited access to vendor data
- Low degree of priority for the project
- Long "turnaround time" for client approval

The bimodal curve has five crucial points, the two peaks, a valley, and two end points. The valley represents the lag in information or commitment, which hinders the development of the project. Formula 2, *The crucial point formula for bimodal curves,* allows us to determine the value of point "B." Once "B" is known, the values of the remaining crucial points can be found.

As shown on the conventional X-Y graph system (see Fig. 4) the bi-modal curve is described by five crucial points. Time is measured along the X, or horizontal axis. The five crucial points along the horizontal axis are labeled X_{origin} through X_4. The relationships of these points to X_4 are:

Point	Relationship
X_{origin}	0
X_1	0.16
X_2	0.35
X_3	0.56
X_4	1.00

Therefore, when X_4, the total number of weeks required to engineer the project, is known, the remaining points can be found by multiplying X_4 by the appropriate fraction. Manpower requirements are measured along the vertical, or Y, axis. The four points along the vertical axis are labeled X origin, A, B, and C. The relationships of these points to "B" are:

Point	Relationship
X_{origin}	0
A	2.49
B	1.0
C	3.91

As before, these points are expressed in terms of one point, namely "B." When "B," the man-hours required at X_1, is known, the remaining points along the vertical axis can be determined by multiplying "B" by the appropriate ratio.

All the relationships for both types of curves were derived from one medium-size engineering company's historical data. The concept can be wholly transferred to any other similar company. However, the specific relationships must be altered to fit the circumstances.

Refinement methods. Refinements of the scheduling method may be obtained by modifying the inputs using the factors shown in Fig. 5, 6, and 7.

- **Manhour factors.** The three factors in Fig. 5 are used to modify the total manhours required to engineer the project. The first factor relates to the *degree of difficulty* of the project, with the typical project being rated 1. A project that requires special engineering can be rated as high as 1.3, and an extremely simple, straightforward project as low as 0.7.

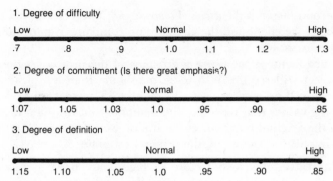

1. Degree of difficulty

Low			Normal			High
.7	.8	.9	1.0	1.1	1.2	1.3

2. Degree of commitment (Is there great emphasis?)

Low			Normal			High
1.07	1.05	1.03	1.0	.95	.90	.85

3. Degree of definition

Low			Normal			High
1.15	1.10	1.05	1.0	.95	.90	.85

Figure 5—Manhour consumption factors.

1. Degree of manpower available

Low			Normal			High
1.15	1.10	1.05	1.0	.95	.90	.85

2. Availability of vendor data

Poor				Complete
1.5	1.25	1.0	.90	.80

Figure 6—Time consumption factors.

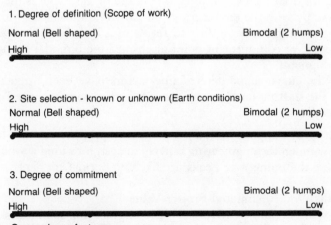

1. Degree of definition (Scope of work)

Normal (Bell shaped)   Bimodal (2 humps)
High   Low

2. Site selection - known or unknown (Earth conditions)
Normal (Bell shaped)   Bimodal (2 humps)
High   Low

3. Degree of commitment
Normal (Bell shaped)   Bimodal (2 humps)
High   Low

Figure 7—Curve shape factors.

The second factor is the *degree of commitment*. This commitment would include both the client and the engineering company. Again, modifying factors are as shown.

The third factor is the *degree of definition* of the project. A poorly defined project will require 1.15 more manhours than a typical project, and a very well-defined project will require 85 percent of the hours.

Once the values that represent the manhour consumption factors are selected, the original manhour consumption estimate may be refined by multiplying all the factors by the original estimate.

Calendar time. The two factors in Fig. 6 are used to modify the amount of calendar time required for the engineering portion of the project. The first factor selected is the degree of *manpower available*, with the judgment factor ranging from 1.5 for low manpower availability to 0.85 for high manpower availability. The second factor to be considered is the *availability of vendor data*, and the range here is from 1.5 to 0.8. These selected factors are multiplied by the calendar time for a typical project to yield a refined notion of the actual calendar time to be consumed during the engineer phase.

Curve shape. The third area to be considered for refinement is the set of curve shape factors.

The first determining factor (Fig. 7) is the *degree of definition*, or the Scope of Work, where a well-defined project will most likely be represented by a bell-shaped curve. Likewise, an ill-defined project will tend to be bimodal.

The second item to consider is *site selection* (if known or unknown) and the amount of difficulty with the site, ranging again from a clearly defined selected site to a poorly defined or unselected site.

The third area which will affect the shape of the curve is the *degree of commitment* by both the engineering company and the client; with a high degree of commitment tending to result in a bell-shaped curve and a lesser degree of commitment pointing toward the bimodal-shaped project development.

After the curve shape determining factors have been applied to the project, the staffing for the project can be calculated from the Formulas shown earlier.

An example. Suppose you have a $1 million project and want to determine how much the engineering is likely to cost, how long it would take, and where the manpower peaks are likely to occur (see Fig. 8).

$1,000,000 Total Estimated Project Value

($1,000,000) ÷ ($160) = 6250 engineering manhours
Duration should be 30 to 40 weeks

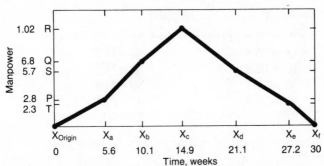

Total area = (Preliminary buildup manpower) (Constant determined thru
historical data) (Length of project, weeks) / 2

Figure 8—Example problem, manpower vs. calendar time.

Adjusting Factors:
- **Manhours**
  (1.1) degree of difficulty
  (.95) degree of commitment
  (.90) degree of definition
  (6250)(1.1)(.95)(.90) = 5900 manhours
- **Time**
  (.85) degree of manpower available
  (.85)(30) = 26
  (.85)(40) = 34
  Engineering time should range between 26 and 34 weeks.
- **Curve Shape Factor**
  1. Job is reasonably well defined
  2. Site conditions are clearly known
  3. Job has a high degree of commitment (from the client's point of view)

  The project will very likely have a normal (bell-shaped) manpower distribution.
  Based on calculations below; and Fig. 8.
  Manpower should peak at 10.2 people.
  Manpower peak should occur at the 15th week.
  The project will take 30 weeks to engineer.
  $$5900 = \frac{(P)(3.5)(30)}{2}$$
  Solving for P: P = 112.4 hours or divided by 40 hrs/wk, 2.8 men

Using the ratios:

$$
\begin{array}{llll}
P & = & 2.8 & \text{People — and } X_a = 5.6 \quad \text{Weeks} \\
Q & = & 6.8 & \qquad\qquad\quad\; '' \qquad X_b = 10.0 \qquad\quad '' \\
R & = & 10.2 & \qquad\qquad\quad\; '' \qquad X_c = 14.9 \qquad\quad '' \\
S & = & 5.7 & \qquad\qquad\quad\; '' \qquad X_d = 21.1 \qquad\quad '' \\
T & = & 2.3 & \qquad\qquad\quad\; '' \qquad X_e = 27.2 \qquad\quad '' \\
& & & \qquad\qquad\qquad\qquad\; X_f = 30 \qquad\quad\;\; ''
\end{array}
$$

The peak manpower needed will be 10.2 people and will occur about the 15th week.

Application. A significant application of this system has been its adaptation to multiple projects and to computer technology. One computerized application permits management to vary the factors and to actually plot backlog curves. By using a computer, management can easily experiment with the effects on backlog of delaying a project or projects, of varying the duration of a project or projects, and of subcontracting portions of the work.

Furthermore, the system is being developed to represent the various engineering and design disciplines required to execute a project. This will permit the production of discipline-backlog curves and provide management with an even more powerful decision-making tool.

Chapter 16

Develop Project Scope Early

Marvin Datz

	SUBJECTS	1 PREAWARD	2 INITIATION	3 ENGINEERING	4 PROCUREMENT	5 CONSTRUCTION
A	FINANCIAL/CONTRACTUAL					
B	ORGANIZATION/EXECUTION PLANNING					
C	MANAGING PEOPLE/COMMUNICATION					
D	ESTIMATING/COST CONTROL					
E	RISK ANALYSIS					
F	SCHEDULING		●	●	●	●
G	TRACKING/TRENDING					
H	PROGRESS/PRODUCTIVITY MEASUREMENT					
I	MATERIAL MANAGEMENT					

SUBJECT-PROJECT PHASE MATRIX — PROJECT PHASE

Standard pre-printed Critical Path Method (CPM) networks can be used to establish quickly a detailed project scope. I have developed 10 such networks designed along functional lines that will define about 85 percent of the engineering, procurement and construction activities.

Advantages. Use of the pre-printed networks offer these benefits:

- Network drafting is practically eliminated.
- Unique descriptions, durations, and restraints can be typed on the 11 inch × 17 inch network.
- It requires less than half the staff of scheduling engineers required for manually drawn networks.
- Level of detail is standardized, reportable, and compatible with a standard code of accounts.
- Standardized logic eliminates the continuing need to re-familiarize oneself with the artistic one-of-a-kind wallpaper network.
- The unique page and grid node numbering system practically eliminates accidental duplicates.
- Standard strings with standardized node numbers can be stored on tape or disk and quickly retrieved to produce a plan for a new project.
- Standard appearance and standard node numbers simplify the updating procedure.
- Standard networks can be developed for any type of project.

PLANNING

Planning is the key mechanism for effective project control of problems caused by inadequate performance. The planning and scheduling effort (two separate functions) that makes intelligent use of the computer is one way of exercising control over cost and schedule. Excluding GIGO (Garbage In—Garbage Out), the computer's ability to quickly and accurately process data offers the project manager an infinitely better opportunity to make a wiser decision. When the project manager tries to do these things mentally and manually he usually gets into trouble, stays there, and wishfully thinks he'll catch up later. The purpose of the project plan is to provide the client and contractor with an early-warning-system. It allows them to address and solve potential problems in an orderly fashion.

Tools of the trade. To perform more effectively, the project manager needs a reliable computer assisted CPM (Critical Path Method) technique. Of course, everyone knows that CPM doesn't work (*"Why CPM Schedules Sometimes Don't Work,"* H. Murray Hohns, 1977 PMI Proceedings). Clients want it to work but often don't know how. Some contractors don't want it to work and make sure it doesn't. My technique won't work either, unless you want it to.

In my standard *pre-printed* CPM networks, standard strings are linked by customized restraints which result in a project plan that accurately reflects the logical relationships within the project. To demonstrate this technique I will use these networks, along with some poetic license to violate some of my own rules, for illustration.

The following is the list of the 10 networks:

1. AAA-Engineering Drawing Packages
2. BBB-Procurement Cycle For Engineered Items
3. CCC-Piling Installation
4. DDD-Piperack Foundations, Concrete & Steel Erection
5. EEE-Equipment Erection
6. FFF-Underground Piping
7. GGG-Underground Electrical
8. HHH-Pipe Fabrication, Erection, Painting & Insulation
9. JJJ-Electrical Power & Instrumentation
10. KKK-Process Engineering Design

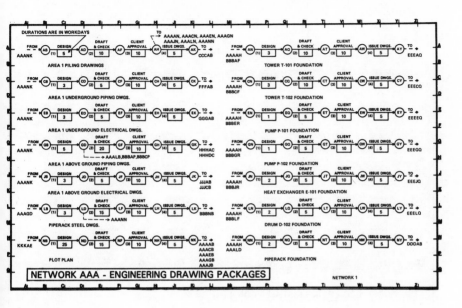

NETWORK AAA - ENGINEERING DRAWING PACKAGES   NETWORK 1

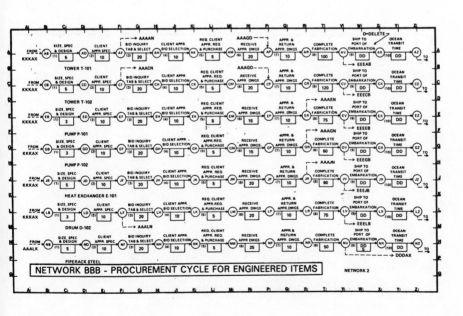

NETWORK BBB - PROCUREMENT CYCLE FOR ENGINEERED ITEMS   NETWORK 2

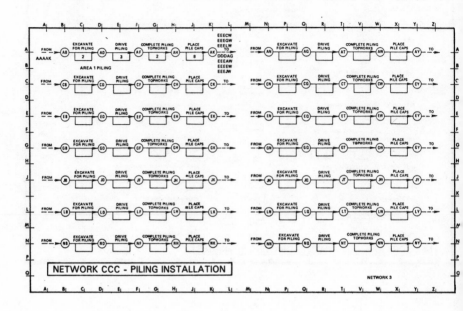

NETWORK CCC - PILING INSTALLATION

NETWORK 3

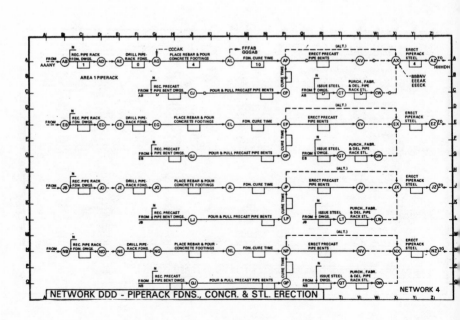

NETWORK DDD - PIPERACK FDNS., CONCR. & STL. ERECTION

NETWORK 4

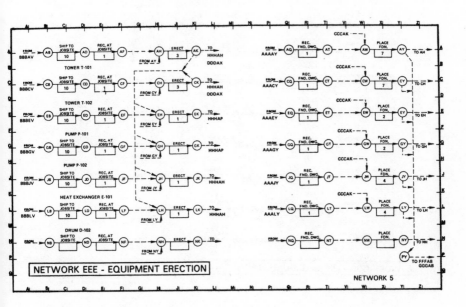

NETWORK EEE - EQUIPMENT ERECTION

NETWORK 5

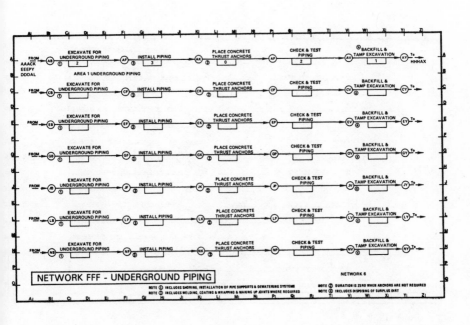

NETWORK FFF - UNDERGROUND PIPING

NETWORK 6

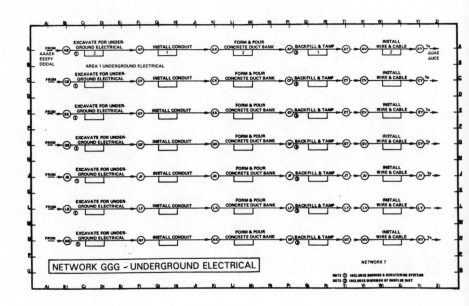

NETWORK GGG - UNDERGROUND ELECTRICAL

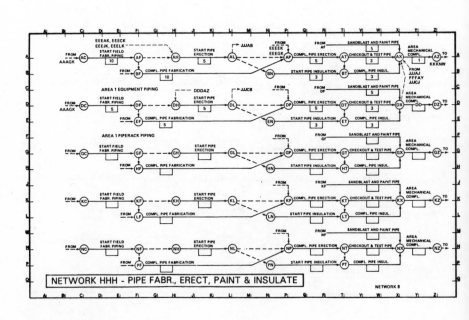

NETWORK HHH - PIPE FABR., ERECT, PAINT & INSULATE

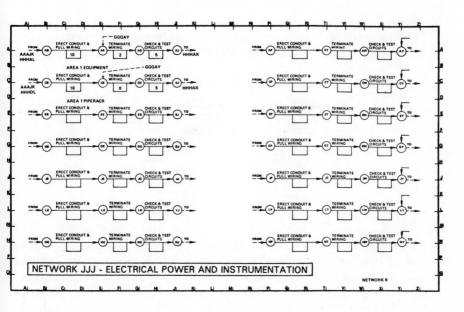

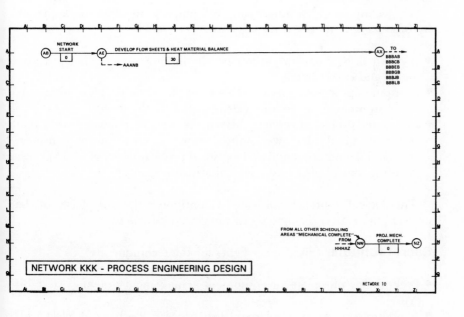

SUMMARIZE UP OR DETAIL DOWN?

Some "scheduling experts" start with a summary level "CPM." (This really is a bar chart dressed up with bubbles and arrows to fool the client into thinking he really has a CPM.)

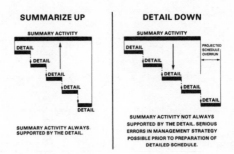

This summary level "CPM" is claimed to be the basis for producing three or four layers of networks, each more detailed than its predecessor. I call this technique "detailing down." This procedure misleads everyone on the project. *It uses prejudiced summary blobs to produce even more prejudiced blobettes.* Detailing down produces a schedule of limited integrity. It is not a Logic Plan.

My technique of "summarizing up" employs the opposite approach by producing at a very early stage:

• A detailed logic network automatically linking engineering, procurement, and construction
• Computer processed reports, based on the detailed logic, that correctly summarize up to all levels required by the project
• Computer processed reports, bar charts, and manpower curves that consider limited manpower, limited allowable area working densities, and special environmental and logistical problems—all of which transform the logical plan into a logical schedule

This logical approach cultivates a confidence that all phases of the project plan reflect a single set of integrated priorities.

Secret formula. Initial ingredients for the technique are:

• Preliminary plot plans or equipment arrangement drawings (Exhibit A)
• A preliminary major equipment list: process, mechanical, electrical, and instrumentation (Exhibit B)

- Standard pre-printed CPM logic networks (11 inch × 17 inch) (See networks AAA through KKK)
- The alpha grid systems of node numbering (See networks AAA through KKK)
- The Construction Scheduling Area Concept (Exhibits A & C)
- The use of my sophisticated SWG estimating system before detailed drawings or detailed quantity estimates are available (SWG = Scientific Wild Guess).

The Construction Scheduling Area Concept is not fully understood nor used for its many potential advantages. A Scheduling Area is usually square or rectangular, and sometimes round, oval, or amorphous, but always three-dimensional. It permits you to think of a project as a group of modules. It permits you to develop a standardized approach to project control whereby a $10-billion project can be handled in the same way as a small project, the only difference being in the number of modules.

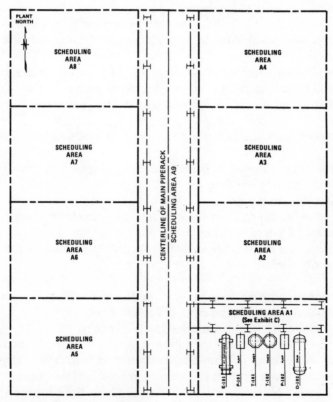

Exhibit A—Equipment location drawing.

Cost area. One or more whole Scheduling Areas constitute a Cost Area. A Scheduling Area cannot be in more than one Cost Area. In other words, Scheduling Areas can be summed up into a Cost Area. Boundaries for a Scheduling Area are based on geography and never on systems or accounting codes. (Towards the end of the project, the area schedule is replaced by a Systems Commissioning Schedule.)

Each Scheduling area is considered as a project that can be engineered, procured, and constructed independently of the next area. To add realism, necessary restraints from one area to another are added prior to computer processing.

Some of the key advantages to using the construction-scheduling-area concept are that it:

- Permits use of pre-printed standard networks
- Makes possible better network logic
- Allows a standard approach for large or small projects
- Permits each area to have its own mechanical completion date as required by the start-up sequence
- Makes it possible to establish a resource leveled schedule by permitting each Scheduling Area to have its own maximum manpower density limits
- Improves material control logistics by identifying, reserving, and grouping bulk material by Scheduling Area number
- Makes it easier to monitor, status, and control the project

Scheduling area. Some typical examples of a Scheduling Area are:

- Geographical grouping of process related equipment at grade
- One story control building
- One story warehouse
- Long straight run of piperack (not including street crossing)
- Piperack at a street crossing
- Each floor of a multi-story structure (to properly utilize maximum labor density limitations)

The Scheduling Area used in our sample project does not truly follow my Construction Scheduling Area definition since intentional deviations have been made to better illustrate the technique.

Once the Construction Scheduling Areas have been defined on the plot plan, we develop the Shopping List which in turn is used to produce the Scorecard. Data from the Scorecard are fed into the computer, usually on a monthly basis, and produces the Ouija Board projections for the balance of the project.

CLIENT:

BI:

UNIT_____

EFFECTIVE DATE_____

PAGE   OF

EQUIPMENT PROCUREMENT STATUS REPORT

SEQ. NO.	ITEM NO./ DESCRIPTION	INQ. SPECS AND DESIGN	① INQUIRY PACKAGE TO CLIENT	APMT APPROVE PACKAGE	② INQUIRY OUT	③ BIDS REC'D	④ BID TAB TO CLIENT	⑤ CLIENT APP. BID SELECT.	PREP. PO APP. & APMT SIGN	⑥ P. O. ISSUED	⑦ REC'D APP. DWGS.	APP. & RETURN APP. DWGS.	⑧ COMP FAB	⑨ SHIP TO PORT OF EXIT	SHIP TO PORT OF ENTRY	⑩ REC'D IN FIELD
1	T-101 TOWER															
2	T-102 TOWER															
3	P-101 PUMP															
4	P-102 PUMP															
5	E-101 HEAT EXCHANGER															
6	D-102 DRUM															

Exhibit B—Preliminary equipment list.

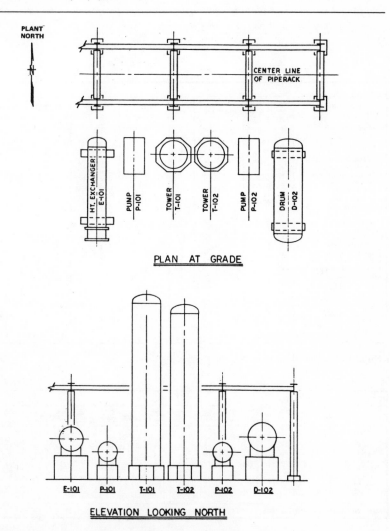

PLANT NORTH

N

CENTER LINE OF PIPERACK

HT. EXCHANGER E-101   PUMP P-101   TOWER T-101   TOWER T-102   PUMP P-102   DRUM D-102

PLAN AT GRADE

E-101   P-101   T-101   T-102   P-102   D-102

ELEVATION LOOKING NORTH

Exhibit C—Construction scheduling area.

SHOPPING LIST, SCORECARD, OUIJA BOARD

A Shopping List is prepared for each Construction Scheduling Area. It consists of a preprinted master list of engineering, procurement, and construction activities that could occur in that area. Using people experienced in each discipline, a guesstimated duration and manpower loading is recorded for each applicable activity. Keep in mind that at this time only preliminary equipment lists and equipment location drawings are available. Detailed drawings and quantities are yet to be developed. *The Shopping List therefore provides the earliest detailed definition of project scope and order of magnitude manpower curves for direct labor. See Exhibits D.1, D.2, and D.3.*

ENGINEERING WORK PACKAGE	SCHEDULING AREA NO	DESIGN		DRAFT & CHECK		CLIENT APPROVAL DURATION	ISSUE DURATION	PROCURE MATERIALS DURATION	ENGINEERING MAN DAYS
		DURATION	PEOPLE	DURATION	PEOPLE				
1) PROCESS & INSTRUMENT FLOW DIAGRAMS	A1	15	3	15	3	10	5		90
2) SITEWORK	A1								
3) PILING	A1	5	1	10	2	10	5	20	25
4) UNDERGROUND PIPE	A1	3	1	5	2	10	5	45	13
5) UNDERGROUND ELECTRICAL	A1	3	1	5	2	10	5	50	13
6) STEEL STRUCTURES - PIPERACK	A1	3	1	15	2	10	5		33
7) CONCRETE STRUCTURES	A1								1
8) ABOVE GROUND PIPING	A1	5	1	20	2	10	5	45	45
9) ELECTRICAL POWER	A1	3	1	5	2	10	5	70	13
10) ELECTRICAL LIGHTING	A1								
11) ELECTRICAL INSTRUMENTATION	A1								
12) INSTRUMENTATION	A1								
13) HVAC	A1								
14) FIRE PROTECTION	A1								
15) LADDERS & PLATFORMS	A1								
16) CONCRETE FOUNDATIONS - T-101	A1	3	1	10	2	10	5		23
17) CONCRETE FOUNDATIONS - T-102	A1	3	1	10	2	10	5		23
18) CONCRETE FOUNDATIONS - P-101	A1	1	1	5	2	10	5		11
19) CONCRETE FOUNDATIONS - P-102	A1	1	1	5	2	10	5		11
20) CONCRETE FOUNDATIONS - E-101	A1	2	1	5	2	10	5		12
21) CONCRETE FOUNDATIONS - D-102	A1	2	1	6	2	10	6		12
22) CONCRETE FOUNDATIONS - PIPERACK	A1	2	1	5	2	10	5		12
23) PLOT PLAN	A1	25	1	15	2	10	5		55
									391 MAN DAYS

PROJECT SCOPE DETAILS ENGINEERING WORK PACKAGES   EXHIBIT D   1 OF 3

Exhibit D.1—One of a series of three "shopping lists."

DESCRIPTION OF MAJOR PURCHASED EQUIPMENT	SCHEDULING AREA NO	DESIGN SPEC		CLIENT APPROVAL DURATION	BID INQUIRY TABULATE & SELECT OUR	CLIENT APPROVAL DURATION	ISSUE REQUISITION & P O DURATION	RECEIVE VENDOR DRAWINGS DURATION	APPROVE VENDOR DRAWINGS DURATION	COMPLETE FABRICATION DURATION	SHIP TO PORT OF ENTRY DURATION	WATER TRANSIT TIME DURATION	ENGINEERING MAN DAYS
		DURATION	PEOPLE										
1) TOWER T-101	A1	5	1	10	20	10	5	20	10	100	0	0	5
2) TOWER T-102	A1	5	1	10	20	10	5	20	10	120	0	0	5
3) PUMP P-101	A1	3	1	10	20	10	5	15	10	75	0	0	3
4) PUMP P-102	A1	3	1	10	20	10	5	15	10	60	0	0	3
5) HEAT EXCHANGER E-101	A1	5	1	10	20	10	5	20	10	90	0	0	5
6) DRUM D-102	A1	3	1	10	20	10	5	20	10	75	0	0	3
7) STEEL PIPERACK	A1	5	1	10	20	10	5	25	10	50	0	0	5
													29 MAN DAYS

PROJECT SCOPE DETAILS MAJOR EQUIPMENT PROCUREMENT

Exhibit D.2—One of a series of three "shopping lists."

	Duration	People	Construction Mandays		Duration	People	Construction Mandays		Duration	People	Construction Mandays		Duration	People	Construction Mandays
1 PILING				31 ELECTRICAL POWER WIRING				64 EQUIPMENT FOUNDATION & ERECTION				95 ITEM NO			
2 EXCAVATE FOR DRIVEN PILING	2	8	16	32 ERECT CONDUIT & PULL WIRE	10	2	20	65 ITEM NO T 101				96 ERECT EQUIPMENT			
3 DRIVE PILING	3	4	12	33 TERMINATE WIRING	2	2	4	66 ERECT EQUIPMENT	3	8	24	97 PLACE FOUNDATION			
4 COMPLETE PILING TOPWORKS	2	8	16	34 CHECK & TEST CIRCUITS	5	2	10	67 PLACE FOUNDATION	7	12	84	98 FOUNDATION CURE TIME			
5 PLACE PILE CAPS	8	8	64	35 MANDAY SUB TOTAL			34	68 FOUNDATION CURE TIME	20	0	0	99 MANDAY SUB TOTAL			
6 MANDAY SUB TOTAL			108	36 (EQUIPMENT)				69 MANDAY SUB TOTAL			108				
												100 ITEM NO			
7 PIPERACKS STEEL OR PRECAST				37 ERECT CONDUIT & PULL WIRE	10	2	20	70 ITEM NO T 102				101 ERECT EQUIPMENT			
8 DRILL PIPERACK FOUNDATIONS	0	0	0	38 TERMINATE WIRING	0	0	0	71 ERECT EQUIPMENT	3	8	24	102 PLACE FOUNDATION			
9 PLACE REBAR & POUR CONCRETE	4	12	48	39 CHECK & TEST CIRCUITS	5	2	10	72 PLACE FOUNDATION	7	12	84	103 FOUNDATION CURE TIME			
10 FOUNDATION CURE TIME	10	0	0	40 MANDAY SUB TOTAL			30	73 FOUNDATION CURE TIME	20	0	0	104 MANDAY SUB TOTAL			
11 ERECT PRECAST PIPE BENTS	0	0	0	41 (PIPERACK)				74 MANDAY SUB TOTAL			108				
12 ERECT PIPERACK STEEL	4	6	24												
13 POUR & PULL PRECAST PIPE BENTS	0	0	0	42 FABRICATE & ERECT PIPE				75 ITEM NO P 101							
14 PRECAST PIPE BENT CURE TIME	0	0	0	43 START FIELD FAB PIPING	10	8	80	76 ERECT EQUIPMENT	1	2	2				
15 PURCH, FAB & DEL PIPE RACK STEEL	0	0	0	44 COMPLETE FIELD FAB PIPING	10	8	80	77 PLACE FOUNDATION	2	4	8				
16 MANDAY SUB TOTAL			72	45 START PIPE ERECTION	5	10	50	78 FOUNDATION CURE TIME	5	0	0				
				46 COMPLETE PIPE ERECTION	5	10	50	79 MANDAY SUB TOTAL			10				
17 UNDERGROUND PIPING				47 SANDBLAST & PAINT PIPE	5	4	20								
18 EXCAVATE	2	4	8	48 START PIPE INSULATION	3	4	12	80 ITEM NO P 102							
19 INSTALL PIPING	3	6	18	49 COMPLETE PIPE INSULATION	3	4	12	81 ERECT EQUIPMENT	1	2	2				
20 PLACE CONCRETE THRUST ANCHORS	0	0	0	50 CHECK & TEST PIPE	3	2	6	82 PLACE FOUNDATION	2	4	8				
21 CHECK & TEST PIPE	2	2	4	51 MANDAY SUB TOTAL			310	83 FOUNDATION CURE TIME	5	0	0				
22 BACKFILL & TAMP EXCAVATION	1	4	4	52 (EQUIPMENT PIPING)				84 MANDAY SUB TOTAL			10				
23 MANDAY SUB TOTAL			34												
				53 FABRICATE & ERECT PIPE				85 ITEM NO E 101							
24 UNDERGROUND ELECTRICAL				54 START FIELD FAB PIPING	5	8	40	86 ERECT EQUIPMENT	1	2	2				
25 EXCAVATE	2	4	8	55 COMPLETE FIELD FAB PIPING	5	8	40	87 PLACE FOUNDATION	4	4	16				
26 INSTALL CONDUIT	1	2	2	56 START PIPE ERECTION	5	10	50	88 FOUNDATION CURE TIME	5	0	0				
27 FORM & POUR CONCRETE DUCT	2	4	8	57 COMPLETE PIPE ERECTION	5	10	50	89 MANDAY SUB TOTAL			18				
28 BACKFILL & TAMP	1	2	2	58 SANDBLAST & PAINT PIPE	5	4	20								
29 INSTALL WIRE & CABLE	2	2	4	59 START PIPE INSULATION	3	4	12	90 ITEM NO D-102							
30 MANDAY SUB TOTAL			24	60 COMPLETE PIPE INSULATION	3	4	12	91 ERECT EQUIPMENT	1	2	2				
				61 CHECK & TEST PIPE	3	2	6	92 PLACE FOUNDATION	4	4	16				
				62 MANDAY SUB TOTAL			230	93 FOUNDATION CURE TIME	5	0	0	CONSTRUCTION SCHEDULING AREA			
				63 (PIPERACK PIPING)				94 MANDAY SUB TOTAL			18	TOTAL MANDAYS			1114

PROJECT SCOPE DETAILS CONSTRUCTION WORK PACKAGES — EXHIBIT D 3 OF 3

Exhibit D.3—One of a series of three "shopping lists."

The Scorecard is a graphic portrayal and audit trail of the activity information originating from the Shopping List. It also illustrates the logical sequences being used, along with the current status of each activity. Activity status becomes the basis for a project progress report and a delineator of ahead or behind situations. The Scorecards consist of the standard pre-printed logic networks AAA through KKK.

These standard networks, plus some specials as required by the uniqueness of the project, can produce project control plans and schedules for 90 percent of all heavy construction projects anywhere in the world. Note that networks AAA through JJJ require no drafting effort. The standard strings and standard descriptions are preprinted. The special descriptions, durations, and restraint references require only a secretary and a typewriter. Standard networks can be considered a working tool, check list, or finished product, depending on the user's viewpoint and experience with logic networks.

The Ouija Board represents the various look-into-the-future reports produced by the computer and our CPM software program. To many people this is the mysterious black box which devours thousands of cards with weird rectangular holes, producing reams of strange messages on a paper form having equidistant holes on each side.

When the sum of the durations in a series chain of activities are such that projected dates exceed target dates, and the time phased manpower totals and manpower peaks exceed acceptable limits, we produce management-by-exception reports that highlight:

• Projected schedule overruns for specific drawings packages, major equipment items, and construction activities
• Projected schedule overruns for specific construction areas and project completion dates
• Projected overruns to the remaining direct man-hour budget
• Projected man-hour curves that exceed maximum area density limits or recruiting potential

The Ouija Board not only produces reports of projected potential problems, it also generates special reports and detailed work schedules that permit day-to-day monitoring and control of the project by supervisors of every discipline. Armed with exception reports and work schedules developed from one data base, the project manager now has all the information he needs to properly manage and control the project.

Early warning. To a knowledgeable and receptive project manager, the dire predictions highlighted in the exception reports represent a welcome early warning system that offers him a comfortable lead time to address and correct potential problems. The bottom line result of ignored warnings is a project running out of control and often beyond the point of effective corrective action. At this stage the project manager is overwhelmed, unable to cope with problems, and visibly in a state of "future shock."

20 STEPS TO PROJECT CONTROL

Exhibits A, B, C, D and networks AAA through KKK, form the basis for illustrating the Shopping List/Scorecard/Ouija Board technique. Procedural sequences, shown here, depict the methodology for the Construction Scheduling Area. Once these sequences are understood for one area it is a simple matter of repetition and duplication to develop a project plan for 10, 20, or even 100 areas. The sample project used is predicated on one contractor performing engineering, procurement, and construction. In chronological order, let us proceed:

Step 1 Starting point is contract award or letter of intent and the assignment of the project manager.

Step 2 Project planning manager is assigned to the project.

Step 3 The project planning manager, operating within the appropriate corporate procedures and guidelines adopted by the project manager, reviews all project correspondence, drawings, and specifications to confirm all prior or pending contractual commitments to subcontractors and equipment and bulk material vendors. Review includes contractor/client agreements related to project control systems.

Step 4 The project planning manager, in coordination with the project cost engineering manager, defines the boundaries of the Construction Scheduling Areas (CSA) on a reproducible copy of the plot plan. A CSA must lie completely within a project cost area.

Step 5 Client is requested to furnish a mechanical completion date for each Construction Scheduling Area.

Step 6 The project planning manager develops one Engineering Shopping List (Exhibit D.1) for each Construction Scheduling Area. Other engineering work packages may be added to the standard list as required.

Step 7 Using experience, intuition, existing information, and SWG, a senior representative of each discipline guesstimates the number of drawings and drawing manhours for each work package. These he will translate into the number of men needed for a number of work days. Without detail drawings and specific quantities, the SWG method develops an astonishingly valid and detailed job scope and engineering manhour estimate. (It is also the only game in town at this point.) Manpower curves are produced during Step 17.

Step 8 Since there is a one-to-one relationship, data on each Engineering Shopping List (Exhibit D.1) can be directly transferred to its Engineering Scorecard (network AAA).

At this point consider the standard network concept. Standard fragnets are pre-printed on an 11 inch × 17 inch form along with standard descriptions for each activity. The two letters within each node result from the intersection of the horizontal and vertical pre-printed alpha grid (letters i, o, s, and u are omitted to lessen computer entry errors). Thus, the page number AAA and the grid intersection AB form a unique five digit node number AAAAB. Adding pages AAB, AAC, AAD, etc., provides an almost limitless supply of unique node numbers. Restraints to other nodes on other sheets such as AAAAK-CCCAB indicate the restraint goes to page CCC and grid intersection AB. *Actual network drafting hours are close to zero.*

Back to Step 8. Durations are transferred from the Shopping List to the Scorecard. Manpower quantities are not shown on AAA. They are written up separately, and entered into the computer file along with other data.

Step 9 Project planning manager obtains a preliminary major equipment list (Exhibit B) from engineering or develops it himself from existing information.

Step 10 Equipment numbers and descriptions are transferred to the Procurement Shopping List (Exhibit D.2). Durations and manpower are developed and added to the pre-printed procurement cycle Shopping List using the same philosophy as in Step 7. Additional items may be added to this list as needed.

Step 11 Data on each Procurement Shopping List can be directly transferred to the Procurement Scorecard (network BBB) using the same philosophy as Step 8.

Step 12 Each Construction Scheduling Area number and its description are transferred to its corresponding Construction Shopping List (Exhibit D.3). Durations and manpower are added to the pre-printed construction activity checklist using the same philosophy again as in Step 7. Additional items may be added to this list as needed.

Step 13 Data on each Construction Shopping List can be directly transferred to the Construction Scorecards (networks CCC, DDD, EEE, FFF, GGG, HHH, and JJJ) using the same philosophy again as in Step 8.

Step 14 Nonstandard CPM networks can be developed parallel with Steps 1–13.

Step 15 At this point all CPM networks have been developed with each activity having a specific description, duration, and manpower load. The only remaining effort is to tie all fragnets together. The total network then truly reflects the individuality and peculiarity of the specific project. The project planning manager and his senior staff members add the restraints to all networks. Other members of the project team supply logic as required for special situations. These restraints include those within each Construction Scheduling Area as well as special restraints between areas. Some special restraints include:

- Pulling electrical wire through several areas
- Area sterilization required for setting very large pieces of equipment
- Forced sequences due to limited access and restrictive equipment location configurations.

Step 16 All network data are written up and keypunched. All prior or pending commitment dates (Step 3) and all client-furnished Construction Scheduling Area mechanical completion dates (Step 5) are keypunched and plugged into the computer as mandatory target dates.

Step 17 All data are computer processed. All system, program, and data errors are analyzed and debugged. When all corrections are made, the master file is reprocessed. Various project reports and manpower curves are then generated and distributed to the levels of management they are designed to serve. Imaginative and innovative applications of our CPM program allow us to produce schedules that consider very special conditions and limitations:

- Multiple calendars for different nationalities and different work weeks
- Limitations to maximum labor densities in each Construction Scheduling Area
- Limited availability of specific crafts at the project site
- Seasonal weather conditions that suspend certain construction activities
- Environmental regulations that prohibit certain construction activities during certain parts of the year
- Special schedules based on cash flow limitations.

Step 18 On a daily basis the project planning manager records progress on the CPM networks and carefully monitors progress on the critical items. The success of this system is dependent on:

- Updating and issuing all reports on a monthly basis
- Delegating authority and responsibility to each supervisor so that he may successfully complete his assignments
- Ensuring mandatory accountability and feedback by the supervisor to his manager.

Step 19 The project reports referred to in Step 18 require an expanded definition so that their purpose, content, and distribution are better understood. Exhibit E is a report distribution matrix listing the maximum number of standard reports required for any project. These are issued on a *need to know* basis to members of the client's and contractor's project management team. Exhibit F is a detailed description of the reports listed in Exhibit E. Examples of these computer reports are shown in Exhibits G through S. Certain reports can be consolidated or eliminated according to the experience of the project team with computerized project control systems. The CPM networks are updated monthly.

These reports furnish the project management team with much of the information necessary to effectively control the project.

Step 20 The previous 19 Steps define the initial creation of the project plan. Thereafter, on a monthly basis:

- The project plan is updated. (Completions, additions, deletions, and revisions are posted on the networks.)
- All data is written up and keypunched

ITEM NO.	REPORT DESCRIPTION	Corporate Management	Project Manager	Project Engineering Manager	Project Engineering Area Manager	Project Engineering Discipline Manager	Project Construction Manager	Project Construction Area Manager	Project Construction Discipline Manager	Project Planning Manager	Project Cost Engineering Manager	Project Estimating Manager	Project Material Control Manager	Project Procurement Manager	Project Inspection Manager	Project Expediting Manager	Project Documentation Manager
1)	Narrative Report	X	X	X	X	X	X	X	X	X	X	X	X	X	X	X	X
2)	Construction Scheduling Area Plot Plans (Exhibit A)	X	X	X	X	X	X	X	X	X	X	X	X	X			
3)	Milestone Report (Exhibit G)	X	X	X	X	X	X	X	X	X	X	X	X			X	
4)	Hotline Report (Exhibit H)	X	X	X	X	X	X	X	X		X	X					
5)	Criticality Reports - Drawing Issue Dates, Equipment and Bulk Material Delivery Dates, and Construction Milestones Dates (Exhibits I & J)		X	X	X	X	X	X	X			X	X	X	X	X	
6)	Slippage Reports - Drawing Issue Dates, Equipment and Bulk Material Delivery Dates, and Construction Milestone Dates	X	X	X	X	X	X	X	X			X	X	X	X	X	
7)	Manpower Distribution Curves by Discipline (Exhibit K)	X	X	X	X	X	X	X	X	X	X					X	
8)	Manpower "S" Curves by Discipline (Exhibit L)	X	X	X	X	X	X	X	X	X	X	X				X	
9)	Remaining Manday Labor Totals by Discipline (Exhibit M)	X	X	X	X	X	X	X	X	X	X					X	
10)	Milestones in Chronological Order - Drawing Issue Dates, Equipment and Bulk Material Delivery Dates, and Construction Milestone Dates (Exhibits N & O)	X	X	X	X	X	X	X	X			X	X	X	X		
11)	Engineering and Construction Work Schedules by Discipline (Exhibit P)	X		X	X		X	X		X							
12)	Engineering and Construction Work Schedules by Scheduling Area (Exhibit Q)	X	X		X	X		X									
13)	Major Equipment by Item Number (Exhibit R)							X			X	X	X				
14)	Bulk Material by Requisition Number							X			X		X				
15)	Major Equipment by Scheduling Area (Exhibit S)							X			X						

Exhibit E—Project planning reports distribution matrix.

EXHIBIT F
DETAILED DESCRIPTION OF PROJECT REPORTS
(See Exhibit E)

ITEM 1 - NARRATIVE REPORT

- A non-computer report prepared entirely by humans.
- Content includes an analysis of the overall project goals, specific critical items needing management action, manpower curve analysis, progress trends, and special forms of progress reporting.
- Essentially a management-by-exception report. Whenever possible, the project planning manager lists the various options and solutions available for project management consideration. It is distributed to the highest levels of client and contractor management so that decisions and corrective action may be initiated at the earliest possible time.

ITEM 2 - CONSTRUCTION SCHEDULING AREA PLAN (EXHIBIT A)

- A reproducible drawing made from a project plot plan, or equipment location drawing and elevation, on which we draw the physical boundaries for each Construction Scheduling Area.
- Each Scheduling Area is assigned a unique number. Each Cost Area contains a whole number of Scheduling Areas.
- This drawing is issued with each project report as a tangible frame of reference of the amount of work contained within each Scheduling Area.

ITEM 3 - MILESTONE REPORT (EXHIBIT G)

- Tabular report listing Target Dates, Latest Allowable Dates, and Priority (Total Float) for every activity coded as a milestone. Bar chart format is available. Plus (+) 20 days of total float, or less, should be considered critical.
- Typical milestones are: project mechanical completion dates, project start-up dates, scheduling area mechanical completion dates, sub-contractor commitment dates, client mandated dates, delivery of key equipment, restrictions based on annual climatic conditions, etc.
- High level concise report intended as a project planning overview for client and contractor corporate and project management.

ITEM 4 - HOTLINE REPORT (EXHIBIT H)

- Tabular report listing Earliest and Latest Starts and Finishes, and Priority (Total Float) for each critical activity. Plus (+) 20 days of total float, or less, is defined as the area of criticality. Bar chart format is available.
- Second highest level report. Designed to provide a detailed explanation of each critical milestone in the Milestone Report (Item 3 - Exhibit G).
- Project management is provided with a detailed list of what the problems are and where. The project manager should base his corrective action on this report.
- Corporate Management should monitor this report to evaluate the results of action taken.

Exhibit F—Detailed description of project reports.

EXHIBIT F (Continued)
DETAILED DESCRIPTION OF PROJECT REPORTS
(See Exhibit E)

ITEM 5 - CRITICALITY REPORTS   (EXHIBITS I & J)

- Tabular report listing Target Dates, Latest Allowable Dates, and Total Float. Bar chart format is available.
- All critical activities are grouped by discipline or crew type and issued to specific supervisors.
- this is a working level report intended to focus attention and resources on the most critical problems.
- Continuous monitoring and implementation by first line supervisors will reveal the tangible results to project management.

ITEM 6 - SLIPPAGE REPORTS

- Tabular report listing Current Projected Date, Previous Month's Projected Date, and Baseline Projected Date. The slippage or improvement of each specified interface activity with respect to the previous month and baseline month is prominently displayed.
- This is a moment-of-truth report that specifically and numerically indicates which parts of the project are under control or out of control.

ITEM 7 - MANPOWER DISTRIBUTION CURVES   (EXHIBIT K)

- One Early Start and one Late Start manpower curve is generated for each resource code, area code, and summary code residing in the master file.
- Early and Late curves usually portray extremes in manpower distribution that are not always desirable or economical. They serve to provide valuable information concerning the two extreme boundaries of manpower distribution. When limitations of manpower availability and maximum practical labor densities are established and entered into the program, we can develop more realistic detailed activity schedules and manpower curves.
- The procedure of developing manpower curves based on imposed resource limitations is called "Resource Leveling" or "Scheduling to Limited Resources."
- Resource Leveling computer techniques offer unusual opportunities to produce schedules that consider some sophisticated limitations to project progress. Manual scheduling can never duplicate these results.

Exhibit F—Detailed description of project reports (continued).

EXHIBIT F (Continued)
DETAILED DESCRIPTION OF PROJECT REPORTS
(See Exhibit E)

ITEM 8 - MANPOWER "S" CURVES (EXHIBIT L)

● "S" curves are a cumulative representation of the manpower distribution curves.
● An "S" curve, consisting of an "envelope" formed by the Early Start-Late Start "S" curve, is generated for each resource code, area code, and summary code residing in the master file.
● The "envelope" resembles a hysteresis loop whereby both Early & Late "S" curves have the same start and end point.
● The horizontal and vertical spread between the Early and Late curves are a good indicator of the degree of criticality of that resource. The mean curve of each "envelope" is usually a sound basis for establishing a resource leveled schedule.

ITEM 9 - REMAINING MANDAY LABOR TOTALS (EXHIBIT M)

● A tabular report with column headings of Original Mandays, Remaining Mandays, and Original-Remaining Mandays (or Earned Mandays).
● Each network activity may have one or more resource codes (skill classifications). The computer calculates the mandays for each resource code for each activity and summarizes all mandays for the same resource code.
● Manday totals for each resource code change under each column heading as activities are added, deleted, revised, or completed.
● Manday totals are extremely useful for showing progress of each resource code and relative weighting of each resource code.

ITEM 10 - MILESTONE REPORT IN CHRONOLOGICAL ORDER
(EXHIBITS N & O)

● Tabular report listing Target Dates vs. Latest Allowable Dates. Bar chart format is available.
● Lists Drawing Issue Dates, and Equipment and Bulk Material Delivery Dates in chronological order.
● These milestones are grouped by specific types or disciplines and issued to specific supervisors.
● this report provides an automated updated early warning system at major interface points between engineering, procurement, and construction.

ITEM 11 - WORK SCHEDULES BY DISCIPLINE (EXHIBIT P)

● Tabular report listing Earliest and Latest Starts and Finishes, and Priority (Total Float) for each activity. Bar chart format is available.
● Lists all work activities in chronological Early Start order.
● These activities are grouped by type of work and issued to the responsible discipline and craft supervisors.
● This report prints complete descriptions, durations, and manpower for each activity. It is a working document for marking completions, revisions, additions, and deletions as well as serving as a vehicle for expressing clarifying remarks, comments, and specific problems.

Exhibit F—Detailed description of project reports (continued).

EXHIBIT F (Continued)
DETAILED DESCRIPTION OF PROJECT REPORTS
(See Exhibit E)

ITEM 12 - WORK SCHEDULES BY SCHEDULING AREA (EXHIBIT Q)

• Tabular report listing Earliest and Latest Starts and Finishes, and Priority (Total Float) for each activity. Bar chart format is available.
• Lists all network activities in chronological Early Start order.
• Activities are grouped by Scheduling Area and issued to the responsible area project managers.
• This report prints complete descriptions, durations, and manpower for each activity. It is a working document for marking completions, revisions, additions, and deletions as well as serving as a vehicle for expressing clarifying remarks, comments, and specific problems.

ITEM 13 - MAJOR EQUIPMENT BY ITEM NUMBER (EXHIBIT R)

• Tabular report containing the Target Shipping Date, Target Receiving Date, Vendor Name, Vendor Location, Requisition Number, and Purchase Order Number for every major tag-numbered piece of equipment on the project. Bar chart format is available.
• Serves as a reference status report for the projected or actual delivery of all major equipment in tag number sequence. This report could be produced in purchase order sequence, vendor sequence, or vendor location sequence for the inspection department.

ITEM 14 - BULK MATERIAL BY REQUISITION NUMBER

• Tabular report containing the Target Shipping Date, Target Receiving Date, Vendor Name, Vendor Location, Requisition Number, and Purchase Order Number for each bulk material requisition number on the project. Bar chart format is available.
• Serves as a reference status report for the projected or actual delivery of all bulk material in requisition number sequence. This report could be produced in purchase order sequence.

ITEM 15 - MAJOR EQUIPMENT BY SCHEDULING AREA (EXHIBIT S)

• Tabular report containing the Early and Late Start and Finish Equipment Shipping Dates and their Priority (Total Float). Includes vendor name and location, requisition and purchase order number. Bar chart format is available.
• All equipment shipping activities are grouped by Scheduling Area. This report was requested by an equipment erection superintendent. He said it helped him to logically establish the physical logistics for his work as well as determine the most efficient and economical application of heavy construction equipment.

Exhibit F—Detailed description of project reports (continued).

```
TARGET NETWORK REPORT     /03           *** ANY PRODUCT PRODUCTION PLANT***ALL PRODUCTS INC. ***                        PAGE   1
MGMT MILESTONE REPORT                              *** ANYPLACE IN THE WORLD ***                             DATA DATE  02JAN81
MASTER FILE NAME = ALLPRO   MASTER FILE NUMBER = 001                                     RUN DATE 27MAR80      RUN TIME 09.23
--------------------------------------------------------------------------------------------------------------------------
                                                                NEGATIVE TOTAL . *** PROJECTED *********    LATEST *********** TOTAL *
   I     J     ACTIVITY DESCRIPTION              B&R SCHEDULING  FLOAT INDICATES A*** EARLIEST ********* ALLOWABLE ***********FLOAT IN*
                                                 AREA NO.        TARGET OVERRUN   ***FINISH DATE*********FINISH DATE*********WORKDAYS*
--------------------------------------------------------------------------------------------------------------------------
HHHAX HHHAZ   AREA 1 MECHANICALLY COMPL.  A A1 CB PMX 72                          25JAN82            25JAN82              0.0
              SCHEDULING AREA 1  MX PROCESS UNIT C

KKKNW KKKNZ   PROJECT MECHANICALLY COMPL. A A1 CB PMX 72                          25JAN82            25JAN82              0.0

HHHGX KKKNW   AREA 2 MECHANICALLY COMPL.  A A2 CB PMX 72                          16DEC81            25JAN82             26.0
              SCHEDULING AREA 2  MX PROCESS UNIT B

HHHKX KKKNW   AREA 3 MECHANICALLY COMPL.  A A3 CB PMX 72                          02DEC81            25JAN82             36.0
              SCHEDULING AREA 3  MX PROCESS UNIT A

HHHNX KKKNW   AREA 4 MECHANICALLY COMPL.  A A4 CB PMX 72                          17NOV81            25JAN82             45.0
              SCHEDULING AREA 4  PROCESS CONTROL ROOM

HHJAX KKKNW   AREA 5 MECHANICALLY COMPL.  A A5 CB PMX 72                          03NOV81            25JAN82             55.0
              SCHEDULING AREA 5  INTERMEDIATE PRODUCT STORAGE

HHJDX KKKNW   AREA 6 MECHANICALLY COMPL.  A A6 CB PMX 72                          16OCT81            25JAN82             67.0
              SCHEDULING AREA 6  PRODUCT COOLING UNIT STORAGE

HHJGX KKKNW   AREA 7 MECHANICALLY COMPL.  A A7 CB PMX 72                          02OCT81            25JAN82             77.0
              SCHEDULING AREA 7  PRODUCT BLENDING UNITSTORAGE

HHJKX KKKNW   AREA 8 MECHANICALLY COMPL.  A A8 CB PMX 72                          16SEP81            25JAN82             89.0
              SCHEDULING AREA 8  DEMINERALIZATION UNITSTORAGE

HHJNX KKKNW   AREA 9 MECHANICALLY COMPL.  A A9 CB PMX 72                          02SEP81            25JAN82             98.0
              SCHEDULING AREA 9  MAIN NORTH SOUTH PIPERACK
```

Exhibit G—Milestone report.

```
TARGET NETWORK REPORT     /04           *** ANY PRODUCT PRODUCTION PLANT***ALL PRODUCTS INC. ***                        PAGE   1
MGMT HOTLINE REPORT                               *** ANYPLACE IN THE WORLD ***                              DATA DATE  02JAN81
MASTER FILE NAME = ALLPRO   MASTER FILE NUMBER = 001                                     RUN DATE 27MAR80      RUN TIME 09.23
--------------------------------------------------------------------------------------------------------------------------
   I     J    ACTIVITY DESCRIPTION        VARIABLE CODES      ORG     REM    EARLY    EARLY    LATE     LATE     TOTAL
                                                              DUR     DUR    START    FINISH   START    FINISH   FLOAT
--------------------------------------------------------------------------------------------------------------------------
KKKAB KKKAE   NETWORK START                                   0.0     0.0    02JAN81  02JAN81  02JAN81  02JAN81  0.0

KKKAE KKKAX   DEVELOP PROCESS DATA FOR    A A1 EB PPF 66      30.0    30.0    02JAN81  13FEB81  02JAN81  13FEB81  0.0
              SCHEDULING AREA 1 FLOW SHEETS AND HEAT AND MATERIAL BALANCE
        RES   02/03.0 12/03.0

KKKAX BBBCB   RESTRAINT                                       0.0     0.0    13FEB81  13FEB81  13FEB81  13FEB81  0.0

BBBCB BBBCD   PREPARE DESIGN SPEC. FOR    A A1 EB EQT 78       5.0     5.0    13FEB81  20FEB81  13FEB81  20FEB81  0.0
              SCHEDULING AREA 1 EQUIP.NO.T-102 TOWER
        RES   02/01.0 19/01.0

BBBCD BBBCF   CLIENT APPROVE SPEC. FOR    A A1 EC EQT 75      10.0    10.0    20FEB81  06MAR81  20FEB81  06MAR81  0.0
              SCHEDULING AREA 1 EQUIP.NO.T-102 TOWER

BBBCF BBBCH   OBTAIN BIDS,PICK VENDOR FOR A A1 EB EQT 62      20.0    20.0    06MAR81  03APR81  06MAR81  03APR81  0.0
              SCHEDULING AREA 1 EQUIP.NO.T-102 TOWER

BBBCH BBBCK   CLIENT APPROVE VENDOR FOR   A A1 EC EQT 61      10.0    10.0    03APR81  17APR81  03APR81  17APR81  0.0
              SCHEDULING AREA 1 EQUIP.NO.T-102 TOWER

BBBCK BBBCM   PREPARE&ISSUE REQ.&P.O. FOR A A1 EB EQT 73       5.0     5.0    17APR81  24APR81  17APR81  24APR81  0.0
              SCHEDULING AREA 1 EQUIP.NO.T-102 TOWER

BBBCM BBBCP   PREPARE VENDOR DRAWINGS FOR A A1 E3 EQT 74      20.0    20.0    24APR81  22MAY81  24APR81  22MAY81  0.0
              SCHEDULING AREA 1 EQUIP.NO.T-102 TOWER

BBBCP BBBCR   APPROVE VENDOR DRAWINGS FOR A A1 EB EQT 60      10.0    10.0    22MAY81  08JUN81  22MAY81  08JUN81  0.0
              SCHEDULING AREA 1 EQUIP.NO.T-102 TOWER

BBBCR BBBCV   VENDOR FABRICATION TIME FOR A A1 S3 EQT 63     120.0   120.0    08JUN81  25NOV81  08JUN81  25NOV81  0.0
              SCHEDULING AREA 1 EQUIP.NO.T-102 TOWER

BBBCV EEECB   RESTRAINT                                       0.0     0.0    25NOV81  25NOV81  25NOV81  25NOV81  0.0

EEECB EEECD   SHIPMENT TO JOBSITE FOR     A A1 PB EQT 00      10.0    10.0    25NOV81  11DEC81  25NOV81  11DEC81  0.0
              SCHEDULING AREA 1 EQUIP.NO.T-102 TOWER
              REQ.NO.        *P.O.NO.
              STATE,CITY     *VENDOR

EEECD EEECF   RECEIVE AT JOBSITE          A A1 PB EQT 01       1.0     1.0    11DEC81  14DEC81  11DEC81  14DEC81  0.0
              SCHEDULING AREA 1 EQUIP.NO.T-102 TOWER

EEECF EEECH   RESTRAINT                                       0.0     0.0    14DEC81  14DEC81  14DEC81  14DEC81  0.0
```

Exhibit H.1—Hotline report. See also Exhibit H.2.

TARGET NETWORK REPORT   /04   **** ANY PRODUCT PRODUCTION PLANT****ALL PRODUCTS INC. ****   PAGE   2
MGMT HOTLINE REPORT   **** ANYPLACE IN THE WORLD ****   DATA DATE 02JAN81
MASTER FILE NAME = ALLPRO   MASTER FILE NUMBER = 001   RUN DATE 27MAR80   RUN TIME 09.23

I	J	ACTIVITY DESCRIPTION	VARIABLE CODES	ORG DUR	REM DUR	EARLY START	EARLY FINISH	LATE START	LATE FINISH	TOTAL FLOAT
EEECH	EEECK	ERECT,LEVEL & ALIGN A A1 CB EQT XH		3.0	3.0	14DEC81	17DEC81	14DEC81	17DEC81	0.0
		SCHEDULING AREA 1 EQUIP.NO.T-102 TOWER								
	RES	A1/08.0 XH/08.0 ZX/08.0 ZZ/08.0								
EEECK	DDDAX	RESTRAINT		0.0	0.0	17DEC81	17DEC81	17DEC81	17DEC81	0.0
DDDAX	DDDAZ	ERECT PIPERACK STEEL A A1 CB SSP XF		4.0	4.0	17DEC81	23DEC81	17DEC81	23DEC81	0.0
		SCHEDULING AREA 1 PIPERACK								
	RES	A1/06.0 XF/06.0 ZX/06.0 ZZ/06.0								
DDDAZ	HHHDH	RESTRAINT		0.0	0.0	23DEC81	23DEC81	23DEC81	23DEC81	0.0
HHHDH	HHHDL	START ERECTING PIPE FOR A A1 CB PPA XK		5.0	5.0	23DEC81	31DEC81	23DEC81	31DEC81	0.0
		SCHEDULING AREA 1 PIPING IN PIPERACK								
	RES	A1/10.0 XK/10.0 ZX/10.0 ZZ/10.0								
HHHDL	JJJCB	RESTRAINT		0.0	0.0	31DEC81	31DEC81	31DEC81	31DEC81	0.0
JJJCB	JJJCE	ERECT CONDUIT & PULL WIRE A A1 CB ELA XL		10.0	10.0	31DEC81	15JAN82	31DEC81	15JAN82	0.0
		SCHEDULING AREA 1 POWER WIRING IN PIPERACK								
	RES	A1/02.0 XL/02.0 ZX/02.0 ZZ/02.0								
JJJCE	JJJCG	TERMINATE WIRING FOR A A1 CB ELA XL		0.0	0.0	15JAN82	15JAN82	15JAN82	15JAN82	0.0
		SCHEDULING AREA 1 POWER WIRING IN PIPERACK								
	RES	A1/02.0 XL/02.0 ZX/02.0 ZZ/02.0								
JJJCG	JJJCJ	CHECK & TEST CIRCUITS FOR A A1 CB ELA XL		5.0	5.0	15JAN82	22JAN82	15JAN82	22JAN82	0.0
		SCHEDULING AREA 1 POWER WIRING IN PIPERACK								
	RES	A1/02.0 XL/02.0 ZX/02.0 ZZ/02.0								
JJJCJ	HHHAX	RESTRAINT		0.0	0.0	22JAN82	22JAN82	22JAN82	22JAN82	0.0
HHHAX	HHHAZ	AREA 1 MECHANICALLY COMPL. A A1 CB PMX 72		1.0	1.0	22JAN82	25JAN82	22JAN82	25JAN82	0.0
		SCHEDULING AREA 1 MX PROCESS UNIT C								
HHHAZ	KKKHW	RESTRAINT		0.0	0.0	25JAN82	25JAN82	25JAN82	25JAN82	0.0
KKKHW	KKKHZ	PROJECT MECHANICALLY COMPL. A A1 CB PMX 72		0.0	0.0	25JAN82	25JAN82	25JAN82	25JAN82	0.0
KKKHZ	KKKPZ	NETWORK COMPLETE		0.0	0.0	25JAN82	25JAN82	25JAN82	25JAN82	0.0
EEECK	EEEJH	RESTRAINT		0.0	0.0	17DEC81	17DEC81	18DEC81	18DEC81	1.0
EEECK	EEELH	RESTRAINT		0.0	0.0	17DEC81	17DEC81	18DEC81	18DEC81	1.0

Exhibit H.2—Hotline report. See also Exhibit H.1.

TARGET NETWORK REPORT   /07   **** ANY PRODUCT PRODUCTION PLANT****ALL PRODUCTS INC. ****   PAGE   1
ENGRG.ISSUES-TOTAL FLOAT   **** ANYPLACE IN THE WORLD ****   DATA DATE 02JAN81
MASTER FILE NAME = ALLPRO   MASTER FILE NUMBER = 001   RUN DATE 27MAR80   RUN TIME 09.23

I	J	ACTIVITY DESCRIPTION	VARIABLE CODES	USE TARGET DATES IF TOTAL *** TARGET ********** LATEST * TOTAL * FLOAT IS PLUS,IF NEGATIVE,*** EHGRG. ***********ALLOWABLE *FLOAT IN* USE LATEST ALLOWABLE DATE ***ISSUE DATE**********ISSUE DATE*WORKDAYS*		
AAAHH	AAAHK	ISSUE DRAWINGS FOR A A1 EB PPP 65		13MAR81	23MAR81	6.0
		SCHEDULING AREA 1 EQUIPMENT ARRANGEMENT PLOT PLAN				
AAALH	AAALK	ISSUE DRAWINGS FOR A A1 EB SSP 65		06MAY81	14MAY81	6.0
		SCHEDULING AREA 1 PIPERACK STEEL				
AAAAH	AAAAK	ISSUE DRAWINGS FOR A A1 EB CIP 65		24APR81	08SEP81	94.0
		SCHEDULING AREA 1 PILING				
AAAGH	AAAGK	ISSUE DRAWINGS FOR A A1 EB PPA 65		08MAY81	24SEP81	96.0
		SCHEDULING AREA 1 ABOVE GROUND PIPING				
AAAJH	AAAJK	ISSUE DRAWINGS FOR A A1 EB ELA 65		15APR81	10SEP81	103.0
		SCHEDULING AREA 1 ABOVE GROUND ELECTRICAL				
AAAJW	AAAJY	ISSUE DRAWINGS FOR A A1 EB COF 65		01JUL81	25NOV81	103.0
		SCHEDULING AREA 1 EQUIP.NO. E-101 HEAT EXCHANGER FOUNDATION				
AAAAW	AAAAY	ISSUE DRAWINGS FOR A A1 EB COF 65		28MAY81	26OCT81	105.0
		SCHEDULING AREA 1 EQUIP.NO. T-101 TOWER FOUNDATION				
AAACW	AAACY	ISSUE DRAWINGS FOR A A1 EB COF 65		28MAY81	26OCT81	105.0
		SCHEDULING AREA 1 EQUIP.NO. T-102 TOWER FOUNDATION				
AAAEH	AAAEK	ISSUE DRAWINGS FOR A A1 EB ELB 65		15APR81	12OCT81	125.0
		SCHEDULING AREA 1 UNDERGROUND ELECTRICAL				
AAAEW	AAAEY	ISSUE DRAWINGS FOR A A1 EB COF 65		19JUN81	18DEC81	126.0
		SCHEDULING AREA 1 EQUIP.NO. P-101 PUMP FOUNDATION				
AAAGW	AAAGY	ISSUE DRAWINGS FOR A A1 EB COF 65		19JUN81	18DEC81	126.0
		SCHEDULING AREA 1 EQUIP.NO. P-102 PUMP FOUNDATION				
AAANW	AAANY	ISSUE DRAWINGS FOR A A1 EB COF 65		19MAY81	17NOV81	127.0
		SCHEDULING AREA 1 PIPERACK FOUNDATION				
AAALW	AAALY	ISSUE DRAWINGS FOR A A1 EB COF 65		19MAY81	25NOV81	133.0
		SCHEDULING AREA 1 EQUIP.NO. D-102 DRUM FOUNDATION				
AAACH	AAACK	ISSUE DRAWINGS FOR A A1 EB PPB 65		15APR81	28OCT81	137.0
		SCHEDULING AREA 1 UNDERGROUND PIPING				

Exhibit I—Engineering criticality report.

```
TARGET NETWORK REPORT    /10                *** ANY PRODUCT PRODUCTION PLANT***ALL PRODUCTS INC. ***                           PAGE    1
SHIP EQUIP.-TOTAL FLOAT                            *** ANYPLACE IN THE WORLD ***                               DATA DATE  02JAN81
MASTER FILE NAME = ALLPRO   MASTER FILE NUMBER = 001                                      RUN DATE 27MAR80        RUN TIME 09.23
--------------------------------------------------------------------------------------------------------------------------------
                                                             EQUIP & MATERIAL *********** TARGET *********** LATEST  * TOTAL  *
    I    J    ACTIVITY DESCRIPTION        VARIABLE CODES     ARRIVAL AT JOBSITE***********SHIPPING ***********ALLOWABLE*FLOAT IN*
                                                             BY TOTAL FLOAT  *********** DATE  ***********SHIP DATE*WORKDAYS*
--------------------------------------------------------------------------------------------------------------------------------
EEECB EEECD   SHIPMENT TO JOBSITE FOR     A A1 PB EQT 00
              SCHEDULING AREA 1 EQUIP.NO.T-102 TOWER                            25NOV81                25NOV81     0.0
              REQ.NO.            *P.O.NO.
              STATE,CITY         *VENDOR

BBBHV DDDAX   SHIPMENT TO JOBSITE FOR     A A1 PB SSP 00
              SCHEDULING AREA 1 PIPERACK STEEL                                  23NOV81                03DEC81     6.0
              REQ.NO.            *P.O.NO.
              STATE,CITY         *VENDOR

EEEAB EEEAD   SHIPMENT TO JOBSITE FOR     A A1 PB EQT 00
              SCHEDULING AREA 1 EQUIP.NO.T-101 TOWER                            28OCT81                25NOV81    20.0
              REQ.NO.            *P.O.NO.
              STATE,CITY         *VENDOR

EEEJB EEEJD   SHIPMENT TO JOBSITE FOR     A A1 PB EQE 00
              SCHEDULING AREA 1 EQUIP.NO.E-101 HEAT EXCHANGER                   14OCT81                03DEC81    34.0
              REQ.NO.            *P.O.NO.
              STATE,CITY         *VENDOR

EEELB EEELD   SHIPMENT TO JOBSITE FOR     A A1 PB EQD 00
              SCHEDULING AREA 1 EQUIP.NO.D-102 DRUM                             21SEP81                03DEC81    51.0
              REQ.NO.            *P.O.NO.
              STATE,CITY         *VENDOR

EEEEB EEEED   SHIPMENT TO JOBSITE FOR     A A1 PB EQP 00
              SCHEDULING AREA 1 EQUIP.NO.P-101 PUMP                             14SEP81                23DEC81    70.0
              REQ.NO.            *P.O.NO.
              STATE,CITY         *VENDOR

EEEGB EEEGD   SHIPMENT TO JOBSITE FOR     A A1 PB EQP 00
              SCHEDULING AREA 1 EQUIP.NO.P-102 PUMP                             21AUG81                23DEC81    85.0
              REQ.NO.            *P.O.NO.
              STATE,CITY         *VENDOR
```

Exhibit J—Equipment delivery criticality report.

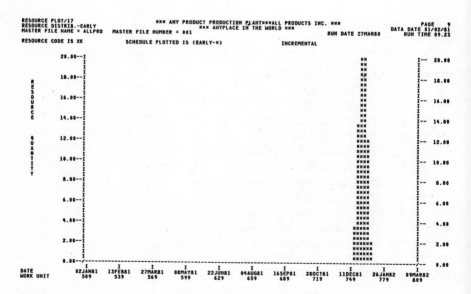

Exhibit K.1—Early start manpower curve for pipe erection crew.

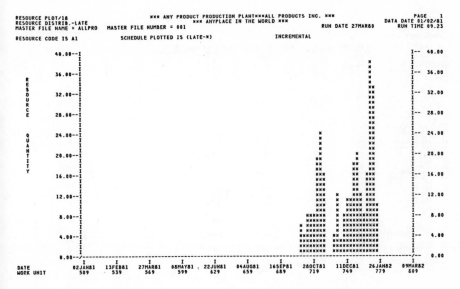

Exhibit K.2—Late start manpower curve for a construction scheduling area.

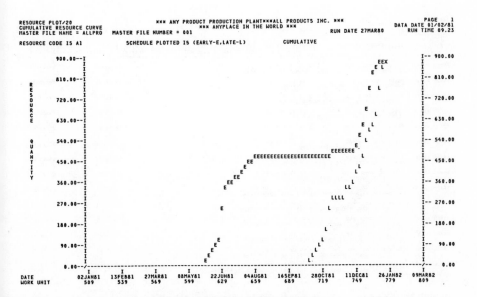

Exhibit L—Early-late manpower "S" curve for a scheduling area.

```
                          *** ANY PRODUCT PRODUCTION PLANT***ALL PRODUCTS INC. ***
                                *** ANYPLACE IN THE WORLD ***                          DATA DATE  02JAN81
MASTER FILE NAME = ALLPRO   MASTER FILE NUMBER = 001                    RUN DATE 27MAR80   RUN TIME 09.23
RESOURCE EDIT REPORT

CODE  RESOURCE NAME      MAX RESOURCE EDIT QTY   **** RESOURCE QUANTITY TIMES DURATION ****
                          SPECIFIED   ACTUAL      ORIGINAL      REMAINING    (ORG-REM)
A1    AREA A1 LABOR         99.9      12.0         874.0         874.0
XA    SITE WORK CREW        99.9       8.0          38.0          38.0
XB    UG PIPE CREW          99.9       6.0          22.0          22.0
XC    UG ELECTR.CREW        99.9       2.0           6.0           6.0
XD    CONCR.PL.CREW         99.9      12.0         352.0         352.0
XE    F.F.STEEL CREW        99.9
XF    STL.ERECT CREW        99.9       6.0          24.0          24.0
XG    BLD ERECT CREW        99.9
XH    EQUIP.SET CREW        99.9       8.0          56.0          56.0
XJ    PIPE FAB CREW         99.9       8.0         240.0         240.0
XK    PIPE ERECT CRU        99.9      10.0         212.0         212.0
XL    ELECTR.CREW           99.9       2.0          64.0          64.0
XM    INSTRUMENT CRU        99.9
XN    INSULATION CRU        99.9       4.0          48.0          48.0
XO    PLANT OPERATOR        99.9
XP    SANDBLST&PNT          99.9       4.0          40.0          40.0
XQ    SUBCHTRCT.CREW        99.9       4.0          60.0          60.0
XR    BOILERMKR CREW        99.9
XS    SCAFFOLD CREW         99.9
XT    PILE DR. CREW         99.9       4.0          12.0          12.0
XU    VHDR.ERECT CRU        99.9
XV    REFRACTRY CREW        99.9
XW    MTRL.RCV. CREW        99.9
XX    DRILLED FTG.CR        99.9
XY    CLG.TWR.ER.CRU        99.9
XZ    ERECT DUCTS CR        99.9
ZX    B&R DIR.LABOR         99.9      12.0        1,054.0       1,054.0
ZZ    B&R & SUB LABR        99.0      12.0        1,114.0       1,114.0
02    ALL DESIGNERS         99.9       3.0         420.0         420.0
06    CONCR.DESIGN          99.9       2.0         104.0         104.0
07    ARCH.DESIGNERS        99.9
08    HVAC DESIGNERS        99.9
09    ELEC.DESIGNERS        99.9       2.0          13.0          13.0
10    INSTR.DESIGN          99.9
11    MODELERS              99.9
12    PIPE DESIGNERS        99.9       3.0         190.0         190.0
13    PIPE ISO DRAFT        99.9
14    CIVIL DESIGN          99.9
15    STRUCT.DESIGN         99.9       2.0          38.0          38.0
16    UG PIPE DESIGN        99.9       2.0          13.0          13.0
17    PILING DESIGN         99.9       2.0          25.0          25.0
18    UG ELECT.DES.         99.9       2.0          13.0          13.0
19    EQUIP.DESIGN          99.9       1.0          24.0          24.0
```

Exhibit M—Remaining man-day labor totals.

```
TARGET NETWORK REPORT    /06           *** ANY PRODUCT PRODUCTION PLANT***ALL PRODUCTS INC. ***            PAGE   1
ENGRG.ISSUE-CHRONOLOGICAL                    *** ANYPLACE IN THE WORLD ***                        DATA DATE 01/02/81
MASTER FILE NAME = ALLPRO   MASTER FILE NUMBER = 001                       RUN DATE 03/27/80      RUN TIME 09.23

                                                          A TARGET ISSUE DATE EQUAL TO THE********  TARGET    **********EXPECTED*
  I    J    ACTIVITY DESCRIPTION      VARIABLE CODES      DATA DATE INDICATES ITEM IS PAST******** ENGRG. **********RECEIPT *
                                                          DUE OR TARGET DATE NOT FURNISHED********ISSUE DATE**********AT SITE *

AAANH AAANK  ISSUE DRAWINGS FOR        A A1 EB PPP 65                                    03/13/81             03/20/81
             SCHEDULING AREA 1 EQUIPMENT ARRANGEMENT PLOT PLAN

AAAJH AAAJK  ISSUE DRAWINGS FOR        A A1 EB ELA 65                                    04/15/81             04/22/81
             SCHEDULING AREA 1 ABOVE GROUND ELECTRICAL

AAAEH AAAEK  ISSUE DRAWINGS FOR        A A1 EB ELB 65                                    04/15/81             04/22/81
             SCHEDULING AREA 1 UNDERGROUND ELECTRICAL

AAACH AAACK  ISSUE DRAWINGS FOR        A A1 EB PPB 65                                    04/15/81             04/22/81
             SCHEDULING AREA 1 UNDERGROUND PIPING

AAAAH AAAAK  ISSUE DRAWINGS FOR        A A1 EB CIP 65                                    04/24/81             05/01/81
             SCHEDULING AREA 1 PILING

AAALH AAALK  ISSUE DRAWINGS FOR        A A1 EB SSP 65                                    05/06/81             05/13/81
             SCHEDULING AREA 1 PIPERACK STEEL

AAAGH AAAGK  ISSUE DRAWINGS FOR        A A1 EB PPA 65                                    05/08/81             05/15/81
             SCHEDULING AREA 1 ABOVE GROUND PIPING

AAANW AAANY  ISSUE DRAWINGS FOR        A A1 EB COF 65                                    05/19/81             05/27/81
             SCHEDULING AREA 1 PIPERACK FOUNDATION

AAALW AAALY  ISSUE DRAWINGS FOR        A A1 EB COF 65                                    05/19/81             05/27/81
             SCHEDULING AREA 1 EQUIP.NO. D-102 DRUM FOUNDATION

AAAAW AAAAY  ISSUE DRAWINGS FOR        A A1 EB COF 65                                    05/28/81             06/04/81
             SCHEDULING AREA 1 EQUIP.NO. T-101 TOWER FOUNDATION

AAACW AAACY  ISSUE DRAWINGS FOR        A A1 EB COF 65                                    05/28/81             06/04/81
             SCHEDULING AREA 1 EQUIP.NO. T-102 TOWER FOUNDATION

AAAEW AAAEY  ISSUE DRAWINGS FOR        A A1 EB COF 65                                    06/19/81             06/26/81
             SCHEDULING AREA 1 EQUIP.NO. P-101 PUMP FOUNDATION

AAAGW AAAGY  ISSUE DRAWINGS FOR        A A1 EB COF 65                                    06/19/81             06/26/81
             SCHEDULING AREA 1 EQUIP.NO. P-102 PUMP FOUNDATION

AAAJW AAAJY  ISSUE DRAWINGS FOR        A A1 EB COF 65                                    07/01/81             07/09/81
             SCHEDULING AREA 1 EQUIP.NO. E-101 HEAT EXCHANGER FOUNDATION
```

Exhibit N—Engineering issue milestones in chronological order.

```
TARGET NETWORK REPORT    /89        ××× ANY PRODUCT PRODUCTION PLANT×××ALL PRODUCTS INC. ×××                    PAGE    1
SHIP EQUIP.-CHRONOLOGICAL                    ××× ANYPLACE IN THE WORLD ×××                         DATA DATE  02JAN81
MASTER FILE NAME = ALLPRO    MASTER FILE NUMBER = 001                         RUN DATE 27MAR80        RUN TIME 09.23
---------------------------------------------------------------------------------------------------------------------
                                                ××× EQUIPMENT & MATERIAL ×××    VENDOR  ××××××    JOBSITE  ××××××
   I    J    ACTIVITY DESCRIPTION    VARIABLE CODES  ××× PROCUREMENT DATES  ×××    TARGET  ××××××    TARGET  ××××××
                                                ×××IN CHRONOLOGICAL ORDER×××SHIPPING DATE××××××RECEIVING DATE××××××
---------------------------------------------------------------------------------------------------------------------

EEEGB EEEGD   SHIPMENT TO JOBSITE FOR     A A1 PB EQP 00                         21AUG81            04SEP81
              SCHEDULING AREA 1 EQUIP.NO.P-102 PUMP
              REQ.NO.           ×P.O.NO.
              STATE,CITY        ×VENDOR

EEEEB EEEED   SHIPMENT TO JOBSITE FOR     A A1 PB EQP 00                         14SEP81            28SEP81
              SCHEDULING AREA 1 EQUIP.NO.P-101 PUMP
              REQ.NO.           ×P.O.NO.
              STATE,CITY        ×VENDOR

EEELB EEELD   SHIPMENT TO JOBSITE FOR     A A1 PB EQD 00                         21SEP81            05OCT81
              SCHEDULING AREA 1 EQUIP.NO.D-102 DRUM
              REQ.NO.           ×P.O.NO.
              STATE,CITY        ×VENDOR

EEEJB EEEJD   SHIPMENT TO JOBSITE FOR     A A1 PB EQE 00                         14OCT81            28OCT81
              SCHEDULING AREA 1 EQUIP.NO.E-101 HEAT EXCHANGER
              REQ.NO.           ×P.O.NO.
              STATE,CITY        ×VENDOR

EEEAB EEEAD   SHIPMENT TO JOBSITE FOR     A A1 PB EQT 00                         28OCT81            11NOV81
              SCHEDULING AREA 1 EQUIP.NO.T-101 TOWER
              REQ.NO.           ×P.O.NO.
              STATE,CITY        ×VENDOR

BBBNV DDDAX   SHIPMENT TO JOBSITE FOR     A A1 PB SSP 00                         23NOV81            09DEC81
              SCHEDULING AREA 1 PIPERACK STEEL
              REQ.NO.           ×P.O.NO.
              STATE,CITY        ×VENDOR

EEECB EEECD   SHIPMENT TO JOBSITE FOR     A A1 PB EQT 00                         25NOV81            11DEC81
              SCHEDULING AREA 1 EQUIP.NO.T-102 TOWER
              REQ.NO.           ×P.O.NO.
              STATE,CITY        ×VENDOR
```

Exhibit O—Equipment delivery milestones in chronological order.

```
TARGET NETWORK REPORT    /85        ××× ANY PRODUCT PRODUCTION PLANT×××ALL PRODUCTS INC. ×××                    PAGE    9
CONSTR.SCHED-CREW/AREA/ES                    ××× ANYPLACE IN THE WORLD ×××                         DATA DATE  02JAN81
MASTER FILE NAME = ALLPRO    MASTER FILE NUMBER = 001                         RUN DATE 27MAR80        RUN TIME 09.23
---------------------------------------------------------------------------------------------------------------------
                                                ×USE LS  ×REMAINING×EARLIEST ×EARLIEST × LATEST × LATEST × TOTAL ×
   I    J    ACTIVITY DESCRIPTION    VARIABLE CODES  ×IF FLOAT× TIME IN × CONSTR. × CONSTR. × CONSTR. × CONSTR. ×FLOAT IN×
                                                ×IS NEG. ×WORKDAYS × START  × FINISH × START × FINISH ×WORKDAYS×
---------------------------------------------------------------------------------------------------------------------

HHHAH HHHAL   START ERECTING PIPE FOR     A A1 CB PPA XK        5.0    18DEC81  28DEC81  21DEC81  29DEC81    1.0
              SCHEDULING AREA 1 PIPING AT EQUIPMENT
         RES  A1/10.0  XX/10.0  ZX/10.0  ZZ/10.0

HHHDH HHHDL   START ERECTING PIPE FOR     A A1 CB PPA XK        5.0    23DEC81  31DEC81  23DEC81  31DEC81    0.0
              SCHEDULING AREA 1 PIPING IN PIPERACK
         RES  A1/10.0  XX/10.0  ZX/10.0  ZZ/10.0

HHHAP HHHAT   COMPL.ERECTING PIPE FOR     A A1 CB PPA XK        5.0    28DEC81  05JAN82  12JAN82  19JAN82   10.0
              SCHEDULING AREA 1 PIPING AT EQUIPMENT
         RES  A1/10.0  XX/10.0  ZX/10.0  ZZ/10.0

HHHDP HHHDT   COMPL.ERECTING PIPE FOR     A A1 CB PPA XK        5.0    31DEC81  08JAN82  12JAN82  19JAN82    7.0
              SCHEDULING AREA 1 PIPING IN PIPERACK
         RES  A1/10.0  XX/10.0  ZX/10.0  ZZ/10.0

HHHAT HHHAX   CHECKOUT & TEST PIPE FOR    A A1 CB PPA XK        3.0    05JAN82  08JAN82  19JAN82  22JAN82   10.0
              SCHEDULING AREA 1 PIPING AT EQUIPMENT
         RES  A1/02.0  XX/02.0  ZX/02.0  ZZ/02.0

HHHDT HHHDX   CHECKOUT & TEST PIPE FOR    A A1 CB PPA XK        3.0    08JAN82  13JAN82  19JAN82  22JAN82    7.0
              SCHEDULING AREA 1 PIPING IN PIPERACK
         RES  A1/02.0  XX/02.0  ZX/02.0  ZZ/02.0
```

Exhibit P—Chronological work schedule by discipline.

```
NETWORK REPORT        /28           *** ANY PRODUCT PRODUCTION PLANT***ALL PRODUCTS INC. ***                    PAGE   5
PROJ.SCHED.-AREA/ES-TAB                       *** ANYPLACE IN THE WORLD ***                          DATA DATE  02JAN81
MASTER FILE NAME = ALLPRO    MASTER FILE NUMBER = 001                              RUN DATE 27MAR80    RUN TIME 09.23
-----------------------------------------------------------------------------------------------------------------------
  I    J                                ORG   REM                        EARLY     EARLY     LATE      LATE     TOTAL
NODE  NODE   ACTIVITY DESCRIPTION        DUR   DUR CODES                 START     FINISH    START     FINISH   FLOAT
-----------------------------------------------------------------------------------------------------------------------
EEELH EEELK  ERECT,LEVEL & ALIGN          1.0    1.0 A A1C B EQD XH       17DEC81   18DEC81   18DEC81   21DEC81   1.0
             SCHEDULING AREA 1 EQUIP.NO.D-102 DRUM
       RES   A1/ 2.0  XH/ 2.0  ZX/ 2.0  ZZ/ 2.0

EEEEH EEEEK  ERECT,LEVEL & ALIGN          1.0    1.0 A A1C B EQP XH       17DEC81   18DEC81   11JAN82   12JAN82   15.0
             SCHEDULING AREA 1 EQUIP.NO.P-101 PUMP
       RES   A1/ 2.0  XH/ 2.0  ZX/ 2.0  ZZ/ 2.0

EEEGH EEEGK  ERECT,LEVEL & ALIGN          1.0    1.0 A A1C B EQP XH       17DEC81   18DEC81   11JAN82   12JAN82   15.0
             SCHEDULING AREA 1 EQUIP.NO.P-102 PUMP
       RES   A1/ 2.0  XH/ 2.0  ZX/ 2.0  ZZ/ 2.0

HHHAH HHHAL  START ERECTING PIPE FOR      5.0    5.0 A A1C B PPA XK       18DEC81   28DEC81   21DEC81   29DEC81   1.0
             SCHEDULING AREA 1 PIPING AT EQUIPMENT
       RES   A1/10.0  XK/10.0  ZX/10.0  ZZ/10.0

HHHDH HHHDL  START ERECTING PIPE FOR      5.0    5.0 A A1C B PPA XK       23DEC81   31DEC81   23DEC81   31DEC81   0.0
             SCHEDULING AREA 1 PIPING IN PIPERACK
       RES   A1/10.0  XK/10.0  ZX/10.0  ZZ/10.0

JJJAB JJJAE  ERECT CONDUIT & PULL WIRE   10.0   10.0 A A1C B ELA XL       28DEC81   12JAN82   29DEC81   13JAN82   1.0
             SCHEDULING AREA 1 POWER WIRING AT EQUIPMENT
       RES   A1/ 2.0  XL/ 2.0  ZX/ 2.0  ZZ/ 2.0

HHHAP HHHAT  COMPL.ERECTING PIPE FOR      5.0    5.0 A A1C B PPA XK       28DEC81   05JAN82   12JAN82   19JAN82   10.0
             SCHEDULING AREA 1 PIPING AT EQUIPMENT
       RES   A1/10.0  XK/10.0  ZX/10.0  ZZ/10.0

HHHBH HHHBT  START INSULATION FOR         3.0    3.0 A A1C 2 TIP XH       28DEC81   31DEC81   14JAN82   19JAN82   12.0
             SCHEDULING AREA 1 PIPING AT EQUIPMENT
       RES   A1/ 4.0  XH/ 4.0  XQ/ 4.0  ZX/        ZZ/ 4.0

JJJCB JJJCE  ERECT CONDUIT & PULL WIRE   10.0   10.0 A A1C B ELA XL       31DEC81   15JAN82   31DEC81   15JAN82   0.0
             SCHEDULING AREA 1 POWER WIRING IN PIPERACK
       RES   A1/ 2.0  XL/ 2.0  ZX/ 2.0  ZZ/ 2.0

HHHDP HHHDT  COMPL.ERECTING PIPE FOR      5.0    5.0 A A1C B PPA XK       31DEC81   08JAN82   12JAN82   19JAN82   7.0
             SCHEDULING AREA 1 PIPING IN PIPERACK
       RES   A1/10.0  XK/10.0  ZX/10.0  ZZ/10.0

HHHEH HHHET  START INSULATION FOR         3.0    3.0 A A1C 2 TIP XH       31DEC81   06JAN82   14JAN82   19JAN82   9.0
             SCHEDULING AREA 1 PIPING IN PIPERACK
       RES   A1/ 4.0  XH/ 4.0  XQ/ 4.0  ZX/        ZZ/ 4.0
```

Exhibit Q—Work schedules by scheduling area.

```
TARGET NETWORK REPORT    /12           *** ANY PRODUCT PRODUCTION PLANT***ALL PRODUCTS INC. ***                    PAGE   1
EQUIPMENT BY ITEM NO.                          *** ANYPLACE IN THE WORLD ***                          DATA DATE  02JAN81
MASTER FILE NAME = ALLPRO    MASTER FILE NUMBER = 001                              RUN DATE 27MAR80    RUN TIME 09.23
-----------------------------------------------------------------------------------------------------------------------
                                                          A TARGET SHIPPING DATE EQUAL TO ********    TARGET **********EXPECTED*
  I    J     ACTIVITY DESCRIPTION        VARIABLE CODES   DATA DATE INDICATES ITEM IS PAST*********SHIPPING **********RECEIPT *
                                                          DUE OR TARGET DATE NOT FURNISHED********  DATE     **********AT SITE *
-----------------------------------------------------------------------------------------------------------------------
EEELB EEELD  SHIPMENT TO JOBSITE FOR       A A1 PB EQD 00                                           21SEP81           05OCT81
             SCHEDULING AREA 1 EQUIP.NO.D-102 DRUM
             REQ.NO.              *P.O.NO.
             STATE,CITY           *VENDOR

EEEJB EEEJD  SHIPMENT TO JOBSITE FOR       A A1 PB EQE 00                                           14OCT81           28OCT81
             SCHEDULING AREA 1 EQUIP.NO.E-101 HEAT EXCHANGER
             REQ.NO.              *P.O.NO.
             STATE,CITY           *VENDOR

EEEEB EEEED  SHIPMENT TO JOBSITE FOR       A A1 PB EQP 00                                           14SEP81           28SEP81
             SCHEDULING AREA 1 EQUIP.NO.P-101 PUMP
             REQ.NO.              *P.O.NO.
             STATE,CITY           *VENDOR

EEEGB EEEGD  SHIPMENT TO JOBSITE FOR       A A1 PB EQP 00                                           21AUG81           04SEP81
             SCHEDULING AREA 1 EQUIP.NO.P-102 PUMP
             REQ.NO.              *P.O.NO.
             STATE,CITY           *VENDOR

BBBNV DDDAX  SHIPMENT TO JOBSITE FOR       A A1 PB SSP 00                                           23NOV81           09DEC81
             SCHEDULING AREA 1 PIPERACK STEEL
             REQ.NO.              *P.O.NO.
             STATE,CITY           *VENDOR

EEEAB EEEAD  SHIPMENT TO JOBSITE FOR       A A1 PB EQT 00                                           28OCT81           11NOV81
             SCHEDULING AREA 1 EQUIP.NO.T-101 TOWER
             REQ.NO.              *P.O.NO.
             STATE,CITY           *VENDOR

EEECB EEECD  SHIPMENT TO JOBSITE FOR       A A1 PB EQT 00                                           25NOV81           11DEC81
             SCHEDULING AREA 1 EQUIP.NO.T-102 TOWER
             REQ.NO.              *P.O.NO.
             STATE,CITY           *VENDOR
```

Exhibit R—Major equipment by item number.

```
NETWORK REPORT        /27            *** ANY PRODUCT PRODUCTION PLANT***ALL PRODUCTS INC. ***                        PAGE   1
MAJOR EQP.-AREA/ITEM NO.                      *** ANYPLACE IN THE WORLD ***                          DATA DATE  02JAN81
MASTER FILE NAME = ALLPRO   MASTER FILE NUMBER = 001                            RUN DATE 27MAR80   RUN TIME 09.23
------------------------------------------------------------------------------------------------------------------
  I    J                             ORG   REM                          EARLY     EARLY     LATE      LATE    TOTAL
NODE  NODE  ACTIVITY DESCRIPTION      DUR   DUR CODES                    START    FINISH    START    FINISH   FLOAT
------------------------------------------------------------------------------------------------------------------
EEELB EEELD  SHIPMENT TO JOBSITE FOR       10.0   10.0 A A1 PB EQD 00    21SEP81   05OCT81   03DEC81  17DEC81   51.0
             SCHEDULING AREA 1 EQUIP.NO.D-102 DRUM
             REQ.NO.              *P.O.NO.
             STATE,CITY           *VENDOR

EEEJB EEEJD  SHIPMENT TO JOBSITE FOR       10.0   10.0 A A1 PB EQE 00    14OCT81   28OCT81   03DEC81  17DEC81   34.0
             SCHEDULING AREA 1 EQUIP.NO.E-101 HEAT EXCHANGER
             REQ.NO.              *P.O.NO.
             STATE,CITY           *VENDOR

EEEEB EEEED  SHIPMENT TO JOBSITE FOR       10.0   10.0 A A1 PB EQP 00    14SEP81   28SEP81   23DEC81  08JAN82   70.0
             SCHEDULING AREA 1 EQUIP.NO.P-101 PUMP
             REQ.NO.              *P.O.NO.
             STATE,CITY           *VENDOR

EEEGB EEEGD  SHIPMENT TO JOBSITE FOR       10.0   10.0 A A1 PB EQP 00    21AUG81   04SEP81   23DEC81  08JAN82   85.0
             SCHEDULING AREA 1 EQUIP.NO.P-102 PUMP
             REQ.NO.              *P.O.NO.
             STATE,CITY           *VENDOR

BBBNV DDDAX  SHIPMENT TO JOBSITE FOR       10.0   10.0 A A1 PB SSP 00    23NOV81   09DEC81   03DEC81  17DEC81    6.0
             SCHEDULING AREA 1 PIPERACK STEEL
             REQ.NO.              *P.O.NO.
             STATE,CITY           *VENDOR

EEEAB EEEAD  SHIPMENT TO JOBSITE FOR       10.0   10.0 A A1 PB EQT 00    28OCT81   11NOV81   25NOV81  11DEC81   20.0
             SCHEDULING AREA 1 EQUIP.NO.T-101 TOWER
             REQ.NO.              *P.O.NO.
             STATE,CITY           *VENDOR

EEECB EEECD  SHIPMENT TO JOBSITE FOR       10.0   10.0 A A1 PB EQT 00    25NOV81   11DEC81   25NOV81  11DEC81    0.0
             SCHEDULING AREA 1 EQUIP.NO.T-102 TOWER
             REQ.NO.              *P.O.NO.
             STATE,CITY           *VENDOR
```

Exhibit S—Major equipment by scheduling area.

SUCCESS POTENTIAL

The potential for project success is:

- Directly proportional to the credentials and track records of the Project Manager and the Project Management Team. No project can afford the luxury of limiting excellence by inadequate compensation, motivation, and home office support.
- Inversely proportional to the number of intermediate supervisors placed between the Project Manager and the Management Specialists.
- Highly dependent on the quality, the accuracy, the data handling speed, and the dedication to implementation of the project control systems. Schedules must be computer integrated to eliminate the hazards of manual interfaces.
- Usually greatly diminished when 1950 concepts are used on today's fast track projects.
- Usually decreased when the Project Manager is unfamiliar with his own project control systems.
- Greatly enhanced when unconditional corporate management support exists for all project control systems.

The Contractor's demonstrated ability to control both schedule and budget has become the most important single consideration influencing contract awards.

ADVANTAGES

• A preliminary plot plan and equipment list form basis for early development of a detailed project scope with respect to work package definition and manhour estimates for engineering, procurement, and construction. These work packages are illustrated on the Shopping List (Exhibit D).

• The Scorecard (networks AAA-KKK) portrays the sequential logic of all work packages on the Shopping List and offers a logical graphical basis for showing work package status. Logical time-phased relationships furnish all necessary information for computer-produced manpower curves.

• The Construction Scheduling Area concept allows a standardized modular approach to any project. Once you've done one, you've done them all. A large project simply has more modules than a smaller one.

• The computer software and hardware (the Ouija Board) provide the black box that handles data with speed and efficiency.

• The various types of computer reports provide a timely reservoir of work schedules, manpower curves, and early warning signals on potential problems.

• The 20-Step procedure offers a cookbook recipe for the control of projects, regardless of size or complexity.

• Once adopted, the standardized approach to problem solving has the psychological effect of reducing the stress-producing situations that are responsible for "future shock."

(This article originally presented as a paper at Project Management Institute annual project management institute seminar and symposium, Phoenix, Ariz., Oct. 28, 1980).

ACKNOWLEDGMENT

Many thanks to those at Brown & Root who helped with preparation of this article: Craig Overbeck (editor), Chuck Guy (senior editor), Thomas Palermo (graphics coordinator) and Faye McFerrin (text processing supervisor).   ∎

Part 5: Estimating

Chapter 17

Evaluate Project Cost Factors

A. E. Kerridge

SUBJECT–PROJECT PHASE MATRIX	PROJECT PHASE				
SUBJECTS	1 PREAWARD	2 INITIATION	3 ENGINEERING	4 PROCUREMENT	5 CONSTRUCTION
A FINANCIAL/CONTRACTUAL					
B ORGANIZATION/EXECUTION PLANNING					
C MANAGING PEOPLE/COMMUNICATION					
D ESTIMATING/COST CONTROL	●	●	●		
E RISK ANALYSIS					
F SCHEDULING					
G TRACKING/TRENDING					
H PROGRESS/PRODUCTIVITY MEASUREMENT					
I MATERIAL MANAGEMENT					

The cost of a project is initially set during the conceptual design phase. Each equipment item adds three to five times its purchased cost to the total project cost. Foundations, piping, structures, other facilities and services automatically come with each equipment item. To control costs at this stage, an early estimate is essential, together with a good understanding of the anatomy of project costs, their relationships and interdependencies. Early project cost estimates usually use cost ratios or factors. The accuracy of these estimates is dependent upon the methods used to derive the factors and the validity of the source data.

Estimating methods. There are five basic methods of preparing capital cost estimates for process plants.
1. Cost per unit of product produced
2. Capacity curves or the six-tenth-factor rule
3. Adjust known costs from a previous project
4. Estimate equipment items, and factor bulk materials, labor and indirects
5. Estimate in detail, with take-offs from drawings and specifications.
   The accuracy of the estimate will, in general, increase from methods 1 through 5, and will require a corresponding increase in the effort and time expended.

- **Method 1** assumes a linear relationship between the cost of the plant and its capacity (See Fig. 1). This would assume, for example, that a 1,500-tpd ammonia plant would cost three times a 500-tpd ammonia plant.

217

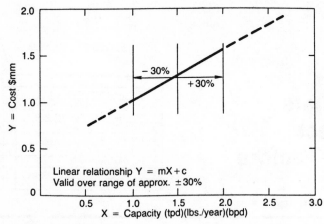

Figure 1—Cost per unit of product.

Method 1 only has value when comparing similar plants having capacities within a fairly narrow range, say, plus or minus 30 percent.

• **Method 2** is also an approximate method which takes into account the effect of scale. According to this rule, if the cost of plant A having capacity A is known, then the cost of a similar plant B will be approximately the cost of Plant A times the ratio of the capacities raised to the power 0.6. This is expressed in the following equation.

Cost Plant A = Cost Plant B × (Capacity Plant A/Capacity Plant B)$^{0.6}$

This equation generates the curve shape shown in Fig. 2. Capacity/cost curves are available for most types of process plants, and are used for approximate capital cost estimates.

• **Method 3** is the best method of preparing a preliminary estimate, when a cost return is available from a similar plant, completed recently. The existing cost return may then be adjusted on an overall basis or in detail by using one or more of the other methods. When working up a new estimate from a previous cost return, care should be taken to identify the major differences between the proposed new plant and the previous plant. Corrections and adjustments should also be made for cost escalation that will have occurred over the intervening time period.

• **Method 4** is the most accurate method of preparing a preliminary estimate for a new plant without going to the time and expense of Method 5, if there is no recent cost return available for a plant of the same size and type. With Method 4, preliminary process design must proceed to the point where equipment items can be defined and sized. Equip-

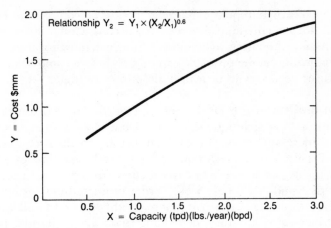

Figure 2—Six-tenth-factor curve.

Component	Cost factor		
	Low	Median	High
Purchased cost of equipment	100	100	100
Purchased cost of bulk materials	76	95	152
*Labor associated with equipment	10	13	21
*Labor associated with bulk materials	62	77	123
*Total labor	72	90	144
Construction supervision	8	10	16
Construction indirects	16	20	32
Home office engineering & design)	28	35	56
Total project cost	300	350	500

*Includes labor benefits

Figure 3—Typical equipment factors.

ment items are then estimated individually and all other costs are factored from the equipment costs. Fig. 3 shows, in tabular form, a typical range of factors for bulk materials, labor, and indirects related to the total cost of purchased equipment.

• **Method 5** requires that engineering be completed to the point where definitive bulk material quantities can be generated from piping and instrumentation diagrams and plant arrangement drawings showing piping, civil, electrical and instrumentation details. With a detailed definitive estimate, materials are taken off and priced at unit rates, labor hours are developed and costed at unit labor rates, and other indirect costs are estimated individually. The preparation of a detailed definitive estimate requires that engineering be complete to between 25 and 40 percent, and also requires a considerable investment in take-off and estimating manhours. Most owners will want to have a good indication of the probable capital cost before committing the expenditures necessary to develop a definitive estimate.

Value of methods. It is for this reason that Method 4 becomes an important estimating technique that is used both by owners and contractors to an increasing extent to arrive at an early realistic cost estimate. Method 4 is also a useful technique for spot checking estimates prepared by other means, or to predict or trend costs during project execution.

Methods 1 and 2 will only yield "order of magnitude" estimates for preliminary capital cost approximation. Methods 3 and 4 will yield estimates of increasing accuracy, depending upon the similarities between the process plant under consideration and the plant from which the cost factors or correlations have been developed. Corrections must be made for items such as the plant location, site conditions, material sources, design code and regulatory requirements, anticipated labor availability and productivity, and other variances which are specific for the project.

Methods 1 through 4, which are appropriate for the estimation of process plants within a process battery limit, cannot be applied with reliability to the estimation of offsite facilities. Process plants within battery limits have a typical mix and arrangement of equipment that is governed by the process requirements, which establishes generalized cost ratios. Offsite facilities, on the other hand are governed by the site location, topography and the utility economics of the location. Offsite facilities will service a mix of process units and will be quite different for each location. For this reason, it is difficult to establish any consistent cost factors for offsite facilities.

Total equipment factors. Within a process plant, there are certain logical cost relationships which always apply.

1. Total Installed Cost =
    $K1 \times$ Total Purchased Equipment
2. Total Purchased Bulk Material =
    $K2 \times$ Total Purchased Equipment
3. Total Equipment Field Labor =
    $K3 \times$ Total Purchased Equipment
4. Total Bulk Material Field Labor =
    $K4 \times$ Total Purchased Bulk Material
5. Total Field Supervision Cost =
    $K5 \times$ Total Field Labor

6. Total Field Indirects =
K6 × Total Field Labor

7. Total Home Office Cost =
K7 × Total Purchased Equipment or =
K8 × Total Installed Cost

The factors K1 to K8 can all be related to the Total Purchased Equipment Cost through their interlinking relationships. Although estimating factors normally relate component costs to total equipment costs, many cost ratios are more closely governed by the relationships shown above. The preparation of a factored estimate should proceed in the activity sequence shown in Fig. 4 in preference to factoring all components directly from total equipment costs.

Adjustments made to certain components because of known project variances will also affect those costs which are dependent upon the component cost that has been adjusted. The interrelated component cost is also adjusted if the directly related cost factors are used.

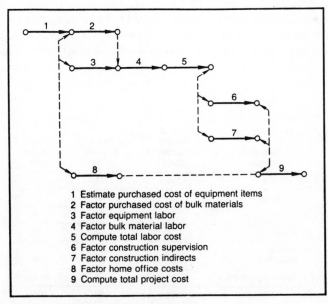

1 Estimate purchased cost of equipment items
2 Factor purchased cost of bulk materials
3 Factor equipment labor
4 Factor bulk material labor
5 Compute total labor cost
6 Factor construction supervision
7 Factor construction indirects
8 Factor home office costs
9 Compute total project cost

Figure 4—Activity sequence for factored estimates.

Validity. Total equipment cost relationships are valid only if the following conditions apply in general:

- The process plants are similar
- The mix of equipment items is approximately the same
- The same materials of construction and design codes are used
- The plant layout and arrangement is comparable
- The design philosophy on spareage, instrumentation, controls, maintenance, etc. is of the same order.

If the above conditions apply, then a set of factors will yield a reasonably good factored estimate, which may then still need adjustment to correct for site conditions and other local factors.

A single factor relating the total installed cost to the total purchased equipment cost may be adequate when a single overall cost figure is needed. In many cases, it is desirable to use individual factors to develop the component costs, since these can then be reviewed and adjusted independently. They also can be used to develop other data, such as home office and field labor manhours and material quantity figures, which are for preliminary planning purposes.

Individual equipment factors. The equipment cost factors in Fig. 3 refer to the total purchased equipment cost, which is the sum of all the equipment items purchased for a project. The mix of equipment items will vary for different process plants. One type of process plant may contain a high ratio of furnaces, whereas another may contain no furnaces, but have a high proportion of gas compression machinery. Fig. 5 lists

Equipment category	Typical refinery petrochemical plants	Typical ethylene plants	Typical aromatics plants
B Furnaces	15	34	3
C Exchangers	21	20	24
E Towers	19	12	29
F Vessels	13	10	27
J Rotating equipment	27	22	16
L Special equipment	5	2	1
Total	100	100	100

Figure 5—Equipment mixes for different types of process plants.

typical equipment mixes for different types of plants. The equipment mix that applies for the average refinery process plant may be very different from that which applies for a petrochemical or chemical plant.

Equipment cost factors are based on the assumption that each piece of equipment brings with it a share of the bulk materials (civil, structural, piping, electrical, instrumentation) and their attendant construction labor and indirects. Individual equipment items do not contribute equal shares of bulk materials. A distillation column will require more structural steel and piping but practically no electrical materials. A pump will contribute more to the electrical account, but less to the structural and piping account. Thus, cost factors which relate bulk materials to individual equipment items rather than the total purchased equipment will generate a more accurate factored estimate, which will reflect the specific mix of equipment items for the process plant under consideration.

Fig. 6 shows a cost matrix which illustrates graphically the varying contribution that different equipment items make to the total project cost. Fig. 7 is the same matrix expressed as cost factors.

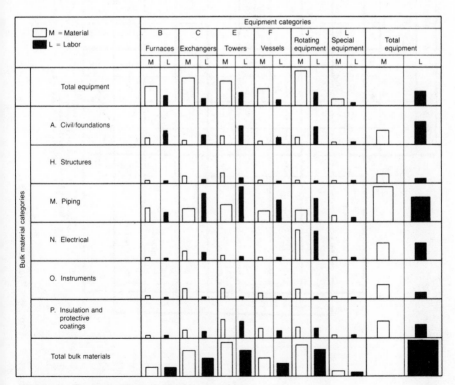

Figure 6—Equipment/bulk material cost matrix.

| | | EQUIPMENT CATEGORIES | | | | | | | | | | | | TOTAL EQUIPMENT | |
| | | B Furnaces | | C Exchangers | | E Towers | | F Vessels | | J Rotating Equipment | | L Special Equipment | | | |
		M	L	M	L	M	L	M	L	M	L	M	L	M	L
TOTAL EQUIPMENT	1	100	17.6	100	8.8	100	16.6	100	9.8	100	12.7	100	12.7	--	--
	2	15	2.6	21	1.8	19	3.2	13	1.3	27	3.4	5	0.7	100	13
A Civil/Foundations	1	10.3	(240)	4.3	(240)	10.8	(240)	6.0	(240)	6.9	(240)	5.8	(240)	--	(240)
	2	1.5	3.6	0.9	2.2	2.0	4.8	0.8	1.9	1.9	4.6	0.3	0.7	7.4	17.8
H Structures	1	2.8	(47)	8.4	(47)	12.5	(47)	6.6	(47)	2.1	(47)	6.7	(47)	--	(47)
	2	0.4	0.2	1.8	0.9	2.4	1.1	0.8	0.4	0.6	0.3	0.3	0.1	6.3	3.0
M Piping	1	22.6	(70)	48.9	(70)	68.4	(70)	61.8	(70)	31.9	(70)	27.1	(70)	--	(70)
	2	3.4	2.4	10.3	7.2	13.0	9.1	8.0	5.6	8.6	6.0	1.4	1.0	44.7	31.3
N Electrical	1	2.4	(93)	10.4	(93)	5.7	(93)	5.9	(93)	29.4	(93)	14.2	(93)	--	(93)
	2	0.4	0.4	2.2	2.0	1.1	1.0	0.8	0.7	7.9	7.4	0.7	0.7	13.1	12.2
O Instruments	1	6.1	(17)	13.5	(17)	14.4	(17)	10.7	(17)	8.6	(17)	13.4	(17)	--	(17)
	2	0.9	0.1	2.8	0.5	2.7	0.5	1.4	0.2	2.3	0.4	0.7	0.1	10.8	1.8
P Insulation & Protective Coatings	1	2.8	(86)	9.5	(86)	25.2	(86)	17.0	(86)	10.1	(86)	12.8	(86)	--	(86)
	2	0.4	0.4	2.0	1.7	4.8	4.1	2.2	1.9	2.7	2.3	0.6	0.5	12.7	10.9
TOTAL BULK MATERIALS	1	47	(101)	95	(73)	137	(79)	108	(76)	89	(83)	80	(78)	--	(81)
	2	7	7.1	20	14.5	26	20.6	14	10.7	24	21.0	4	3.1	95	77
TOTAL EQUIPMENT & BULK MATERIALS	1	147	(44)	195	(40)	237	(53)	208	(44)	139	(48)	180	(42)	195	(46)
	2	22.	9.7	41	16.3	45	23.8	27	12.0	51	24.4	9	3.8	195	90

M = Purchased Material Cost   L = Field Erection Labor Cost (Including Benefits)
Line 1 under M = Purchased Material Cost as a % of Individual Equipment Category (at top) = 100%
Line 1 under (L) = Field Erection Labor Cost as a % of Purchased Material Cost (Left Column) = 100%
Line 2 under M & L = All Costs expressed as a % of TOTAL EQUIPMENT = 100%

Figure 7—Equipment/bulk material factors.

Evaluating bulk material factors. The following letters represent the purchased cost of the more common equipment and bulk material categories.

Equipment categories

B = Furnaces
C = Exchangers
E = Towers
F = Vessels
J = Rotating equipment & drivers
L = Special equipment

Bulk material categories

A = Civil/foundations
H = Structures
M = Piping
N = Electrical
O = Instruments
P = Insulation & protective coatings

The purchased cost of each bulk material category may be related to the purchased cost of each individual equipment category by the following generalized equation.

Eq. 1: $B(kBX) + C(kCX) + E(kEX) + F(kFX)$
$$+ J(kJX) + L(kLX) \ = \ X$$

where:

B, C, E, F, J, L = *total purchased cost of each equipment category*

X = *total purchased cost of a bulk material category*

$kBX, kCX, kEX, etc.$ = *bulk material factors for the purchased cost of bulk material "X" associated with the specific equipment category*

Equation 1 is a simple linear equation in which the six bulk material factors are unknown. To obtain a value for these factors six simultaneous linear equations must be created from the actual return purchased costs from six similar projects. These then can be solved by the process of substitution and elimination.

A series of six simultaneous linear equations may be set up as follows:

(1) $B1(kBA) + C1(kCA) + E1(kEA) + F1(kFA)$
$$+ J1(kJA) + L1(kLA) = A1$$
(2) $B2(kBA) + C2(kCA) + E2(kEA) + F2(kFA)$
$$+ J2(kJA) + L2(kLA) = A2$$
. . . .
(6) $B6(kBA) + C6(kCA) + E6(kEA) + F6(kFA)$
$$+ J6(kJA) + L6(kLA) = A6$$

where:

$$
\left.
\begin{array}{l}
B1,B2,B3,B4,B5,B6 \;=\; \\
C1,C2,C3,C4,C5,C6 \;=\; \\
\ldots\ldots\ldots\ldots\ldots \\
L1,L2,L3,L4,L5,L6 \;=\;
\end{array}
\right\}
\begin{array}{l}
\textit{Actual total purchased costs} \\
\textit{of equipment categories for} \\
\textit{six different projects}
\end{array}
$$

$$
A1,A2,A3,A4,A5,A6 \;=\;
\left\{
\begin{array}{l}
\textit{Actual total purchased cost of} \\
\textit{bulk material Category A} \\
\textit{(Civil/Foundations) for six} \\
\textit{different projects}
\end{array}
\right.
$$

$$
BA,kCA,kEA,kFA,etc. \;=\;
\left\{
\begin{array}{l}
\textit{Bulk material factors for pur-} \\
\textit{chased cost of bulk material A} \\
\textit{(Civil/Foundations) associated} \\
\textit{with purchased cost of specific} \\
\textit{equipment category}
\end{array}
\right.
$$

The return costs from the six different projects should be adjusted and corrected so they are on a consistent and comparable basis. If the projects were completed in different years, then return costs should be escalated to a common year. Any known unusual or abnormal costs in an individual project should be adjusted to reflect what would have been a more normal cost.

Solutions. Theoretically, the solution of the prior equations may then be found by elimination, determinant or matrix methods. In practice this may not be so easy since the actual return costs from six projects will not fall neatly into six simultaneous equations yielding a unique solution for each factor. It becomes necessary to resort to methods of regression analysis or "best fit." Apart from the difficulty of obtaining a correlation, this method also has the disadvantage of becoming even more complex if the number of equipment categories is increased. If it is desired to develop factors for different types of equipment within one category, such as compressors/pumps, shell and tube exchangers/double pipe exchangers/air fin exchangers, different types of furnaces, etc., the number of simultaneous equations required and the complexity of solving these would become unmanageable.

If a relationship can be established between the factors in Eq. 1, then it is possible to calculate a single unique value for each bulk material factor from the return costs from a single project. The generalized Eq. 1 for bulk material category A will become:

Eq. 2: $B(kBA) + C(kCA) + E(kEA) + F(kFA)$
$$+ J(kJA) + L(kLA) = A$$
If a relationship is established between the factors, then
$$x_1(kBA) = x_2(kCA) = x_3(kEA) = x_4(kFA) = x_5(kJA) = x_6(kLA)$$
where x_1, x_2, x_3, etc. are numerical relationships between factors.

From the above:
$$(kCA) = (kBA)x_1/x_2, \ (kEA) = (kBA)x_1/x_3, \ etc.$$

Substituting for (kCA), (kEA), etc., Eq. 2 now becomes:
$$B(kBA) + C(kBA)x_1/x_2 + E(kBA)x_1/x_3 + F(kFA)x_1/x_4 \ etc. = A$$
Rearranging, this now becomes:

Eq. 3: $(kBA) = Ax_1/(B/x_1 + C/x_2 + E/x_3 + F/x_4 + J/x_5 + L/x_6)$
Values for kCA, kEA, etc. can then be calculated.

Factors calculated in this manner from the returns from a single project should not be considered representative. Factors should be calculated from the returns from a number of projects, making it possible to take an average or use a correlation to develop bulk material factors which can be used with some confidence when preparing new estimates.

The question now arises: "Is it possible to establish a relationship between the bulk material factors?"

Bulk material factor relationships. The ratio of the bulk material factors which relates the purchased cost of the individual equipment categories to the purchased cost of a bulk material category is derived from the composite of two components.

1. The purchased cost of bulk material generated by each piece of equipment.

2. The average unit cost for each equipment category.

The following is an example which illustrates the above:

Assume the average cost of a pump is $5,000 and the average pump contributes three instruments to the instrument category.

Assume the average exchanger costs $50,000 and contributes five instruments to the instrument category.

On an individual equipment basis, the ratio of the factors contributing to the instrument category would be three for pumps and five for exchangers.

On a cost basis, the ratio of factors will be considerably changed. $5,000 worth of pumps contributes three instruments (six per 10,000).

$50,000 worth of exchangers contributes five instruments (one per 10,000).

The ratio of factors adjusted on a cost basis is now six for pumps and one for exchangers. The quantities generated by each equipment item must be divided by the ratio of the average cost per equipment item, since the bulk material factors relate to purchased costs and not to individual equipment items.

Ratio guidelines. The following guidelines may be used to develop ratios of the purchased cost of bulk materials contributed by an individual item of equipment.

1. Foundations. The cost of foundation materials is in proportion to the equipment weight. If the weight of a shell and tube exchanger is 10 tons, and the weight of a process pump is 1 ton, the ratio of the factors relating the exchanger and the pump to the "foundations" bulk material category would be 10 to 1.

2. Piping. The contribution to piping per piece of equipment is in proportion to the number of piping line connections. This can be determined by taking a selection of typical piping and instrumentation diagrams and dividing each sheet into segments surrounding each individual equipment item. The number of pipe lines in each segment identifies the number of lines associated with that type of equipment. By repeating this exercise over a number of diagrams containing similar categories of equipment, a reasonable average number of piping lines can be obtained for each type of equipment.

3. Structures. There are three major types of structures:

- *Pipe bridges*—these will be in proportion to the ratios for piping.
- *Equipment structures*—these are more influenced by those equipment items which are normally supported off-grade by means of structures.
- *Cat ladders and platforms*—these are normally associated with towers and other similar types of equipment.

4. Instruments. These are in proportion to the number of instruments per item of equipment. This number can be determined from piping and instrumentation diagrams, in the same way as the assessment for piping.

5. Electrical. The electrical category is made up of three main con-
tributors:

- Electric power is proportional to the equipment items normally associated with electrical drivers such as pumps, compressors, blowers, air-
cooled exchangers, agitators and special equipment items.
- Electrical lighting is required by all equipment items in proportion to
their overall dimensions. Furnaces and towers require more lighting
than pumps.
- Electrical instruments. The electrical load associated with instrumentation and other utility/service items is in proportion to the instrument
factor ratios.

6. Insulation and protective coatings. There are two basic applications for insulation and protective coatings.

- Equipment insulation/coatings are in proportion to the average surface area of equipment.
- Piping insulation/coatings will follow the ratios of piping factors.

7. Buildings. The following are the more common types of buildings:

- Control room—The control room is dictated by the number of instruments and so will follow the ratio for instruments.
- Electrical buildings—These will be in proportion to electrical equipment loadings.
- Pump and compressor houses—When required for a specific project,
the pump and compressor categories will govern the cost of these types
of buildings.

8. Fireproofing. Fireproofing, where required, is normally only provided to structures supporting equipment and piping, to vessel skirts,
etc. The fireproofing ratios will, therefore, follow the ratios for structural steel, plus some added weight for vertical fireproofed vessels.

These guidelines are by no means complete, but they do suggest a
method whereby it is possible to develop the ratio of the contribution
that each equipment type makes to the bulk material categories.

Once the ratios per individual items of equipment have been determined, the next step is to adjust these to a cost base by dividing by the
average purchased cost for each category of equipment.

The average purchased cost of each category of equipment may be
determined by dividing the total purchased cost for the complete equip-

ITEM			EQUIPMENT CATEGORIES					
			B Furnaces	C Exchangers	E Towers	F Vessels	J Rotating Equipment	L Special Equipment
Ratio of Weights			62.6	2.8	18.8	1.8	9.0	5.0
Ratio of Costs			55.6	6.0	15.9	2.8	11.9	7.9
A Civil/Foundations	1		62.6	2.8	18.8	1.8	9.0	5.0
	2		23.4	9.8	24.5	13.6	15.6	13.2
H Structures	1		31.1	10.0	39.7	3.6	5.0	10.6
	2		7.2	21.5	32.0	16.9	5.4	17.1
M Piping	1		36.9	8.6	31.9	5.1	11.2	6.3
	2		8.7	18.8	26.2	23.7	12.2	10.4
N Electrical	1		17.4	8.1	11.8	2.1	45.8	14.7
	2		3.5	15.3	8.4	8.7	43.2	20.9
O Instruments	1		38.2	9.1	25.8	3.4	11.5	12.0
	2		9.1	20.2	21.6	16.0	12.9	20.1
P Insulation & Protective Coatings	1		17.6	6.4	45.4	5.4	13.6	11.5
	2		3.6	12.3	32.6	22.0	13.0	16.5

1 = Bulk Material Factor Ratios per Item of Equipment
2 = Bulk Material Factor Ratios per Purchased Cost of Equipment Category.

Figure 8—Worksheet for equipment/bulk material factor ratios.

ment category account by the number of equipment items in that category.

Fig. 8 illustrates a typical worksheet that has been used to establish the bulk material factor ratios. These values may then be inserted in Eq. 3 together with known return costs from a specific project, to give the actual bulk material factors for the project under consideration.

Evaluating labor and miscellaneous factors. Factors relating labor costs to equipment and bulk material purchased costs can be determined when return costs are available segregating labor hours and costs against each major equipment and material category. It is usually the practice of construction companies to charge labor hours against the equipment and bulk material accounts for purposes of productivity measurement and manhour control. In addition, labor manhour expenditures are also recorded by craft.

The labor factors relating labor costs to equipment and bulk material costs are obtained by dividing the appropriate return labor cost by the corresponding equipment or bulk material purchased cost.

If the same letters with the suffix (LAB) represent the labor cost of the equipment and bulk material categories, as follows:

Equipment categories

$B(LAB)$ = *Furnaces*
$C(LAB)$ = *Exchangers*
Etc.

Bulk material categories

$A(LAB)$ = *Civil foundations*
$H(LAB)$ = *Structures*
Etc.

then, the factors are calculated:

kBL = $B(LAB)/B$, *etc. where* kBL = *labor factor for*
                                          furnaces
kAL = $A(LAB)/A$, *etc.* kAL = *labor factor for*
                                          civil/foundations

In the estimating phase, the value of the labor account is determined by multiplying the purchased cost of the equipment or bulk material by the labor factor.

$B(LAB)$ = $B \times kBL$, *etc.*
$A(LAB)$ = $A \times kAL$, *etc.*

As in the case of bulk material factors, labor factors calculated from the return costs from a single project are not representative. The factors should be calculated from the returns of a number of projects to give a good representative average. The return labor costs should be adjusted for escalation and for varying labor productivities. An average labor productivity should be assumed when calculating factors, and all return costs adjusted to this average. At the time when the factors are used to prepare estimates a further adjustment must be made to reflect the actual labor productivity anticipated for the project being estimated.

Construction supervision and construction indirects which cover construction equipment, small tools and consumables are normally related to the total cost of labor. Once the labor costs for the individual equipment and bulk material categories have been determined, the sum of these gives the total direct labor cost. This cost may be expressed as direct wages or as direct wages plus benefits (payroll burden), whichever convention is used by the construction company. Wage benefits are a direct percentage of the base wage.

Averaging. Having determined the total labor cost, factors for the cost of construction supervision and construction indirects are determined by dividing these costs by the total labor costs. Again, the returns from a number of projects should be adjusted to a common basis to yield good average factors that can be used with confidence for estimating purposes.

The final major component in a project estimate is the cost of home office services (Engineering and Design). Traditionally, home office services are factored as a percentage of total installed cost (TIC). Again, this value is determined by expressing the actual home office costs on past projects as a percentage of the total installed cost.

It is interesting, as a secondary ratio, to relate the total home office cost as a percentage of the total purchased equipment costs, and also to check the ratio of field labor manhours to home office manhours.

Escalation. During periods of high or changing rates of inflation, escalation for a large project over an extended schedule can be significant to the point where it outweighs any other single account. For this reason, extra time and effort is justified to calculate escalation a little more precisely. Factored estimates provide a good basis for calculating escalation.

An approximate method that may be used for calculating escalation from factored types of estimates is described in the following paragraphs using the escalation calculation worksheet shown in Fig. 9.

With definitive estimates, escalation may be calculated more precisely by determining the commitment date for major categories of equipment and bulk materials.

ESCALATION FOR YEAR D = A(C/2 + 100 - B)/100 x $MM/100

PROJECT _ABC OIL Co_
JOB NO. _1234_
DATE _10/10/81_ REV. _0_

MAJOR ACCOUNT	% TIC $MM	ESCALATION METHOD		1	2 (YEAR)	3	4	TOTAL $MM
		*Compounded From Previous Years						
HOME OFFICE	10	Escalation Rate for Year % *	A	8	8.64	8.69	8.70	
	10	Cumulative Expenditure at Year End %	B	23	63	91	100	
		Amount Expended in Year %	C	23	40	28	9	
		Escalation for Year	D	0.708	0.492	0.200	0.039	1.439
EQUIPMENT	29	Escalation Rate for Year % *	A	9	8.72			
	29	Cumulative Expenditure at Year End %	B	51	100			
		Amount Expended in Year %	C	51	49			
		Escalation for Year	D	1.944	0.620	0	0	2.564
BULK MATERIALS	27	Escalation Rate for Year % *	A	10	8.8	8.7	8.7	
	27	Cumulative Expenditure at Year End %	B	10	50	78	100	
		Amount Expended in Year %	C	10	40	28	22	
		Escalation for Year	D	2.565	1.663	0.846	0.258	5.332
CONSTRUCTION DIRECT	25	Escalation Rate for Year % *	A	10	10.11	10.11	10.11	
	25	Cumulative Expenditure at Year End %	B	1	20	68	100	
		Amount Expended in Year %	C	1	19	48	32	
		Escalation for Year	D	2.488	2.461	1.554	0.444	6.947
CONSTRUCTION INDIRECT	9	Escalation Rate for Year % *	A	9	9.81	9.88	9.89	
	9	Cumulative Expenditure at Year End %	B	1	20	68	100	
		Amount Expended in Year %	C	1	19	48	32	
		Escalation for Year	D	0.806	0.790	0.498	0.142	2.236
START-UP EXPENSE		Escalation Rate for Year % *	A					
		Cumulative Expenditure at Year End %	B					
		Amount Expended in Year %	C					
		Escalation for Year	D					
OVERALL TOTALS	100	Escalation Rate for Year % *	A					
	100	Cumulative Expenditure at Year End %	B					
		Amount Expended in Year %	C					
		Escalation for Year ΣD	D	8.511	6.026	3.098	0.883	18.518

Figure 9—Escalation calculation worksheet.

Step 1—Determine the escalation rates over the project schedule.
The prediction of probable escalation rates over the next two to five
years is a matter of judgment. Reference should be made to business,
technical and estimating journals to obtain the average rate of inflation
forecast by economists and others. Frequently, purchasing organizations, large corporations and trade associations publish forecasts of cost
indexes for their range of services or materials. Different levels of inflation are forecast for home office wage rates, construction labor wage
rates, equipment and materials. If a project is being engineered, procured and constructed in different locations throughout the world, different escalation rates will apply. The agreed inflation rate for each year
of the project schedule should be entered into the escalation worksheet
under the appropriate year and type of cost.

Step 2—Allow for escalation compounding. Allowance must be
made for the fact that escalation compounds upon itself. In the calculation form a compounded escalation rate is developed for the second and
subsequent years. The escalation rate for each year must be multiplied
by the rates for all preceding years to give the compounded escalation
rate from the start of the project to the year in question. The compounded escalation rates are entered into the appropriate place in the
escalation calculation worksheet.

**Step 3—Establish the cumulative expenditure at year end and ex-
penditure in year.** The next step is to determine the cumulative percent
committed at each year end for home office, equipment, materials, construction, etc. The percent committed or expended may be taken directly from the detailed project schedule if this is available. If a detailed
schedule is not available, a good approximation can be obtained from
typical S-curves (Fig. 10). The cumulative expenditure for the year, expressed as a percentage, is entered in the appropriate column in the escalation calculation worksheet. The amount expended in the year is the
difference between the cumulative expenditure at year end, and the cumulative expenditure for the previous year.

Step 4—Calculate the escalation for each year. Escalation is calculated by multiplying the total amount yet to be expended at year end,
plus half the amount to be expended in the year by the compounded
escalation rate. It is assumed that expenditures in the current year will
occur evenly over the whole year so escalation can be approximated at
half the total amount. In cases where the expenditure starts or is completed part way through the year, as indicated by the barline on the calculation worksheet, then the year's escalation is prorated to match the
expenditure period.

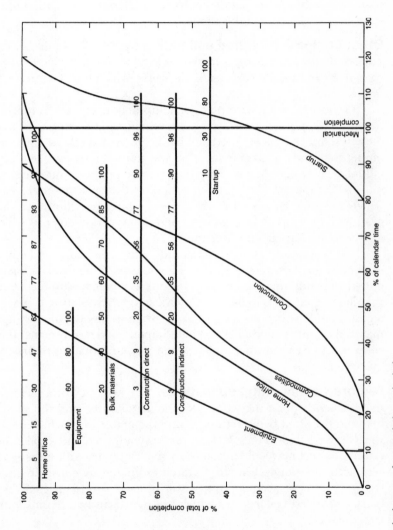

Figure 10—Typical curves for escalation calculation.

Step 5—Determine the overall escalation. The overall escalation is obtained by adding the horizontal and vertical columns. The escalation worksheet (Fig. 9) has been completed to illustrate the calculation steps. Greater accuracy can be obtained if time periods of three or six months are used in place of one year. Normally, yearly periods provide an estimate of escalation compatible with the judgmental estimation of escalation rates and schedule durations.

Other equipment-related estimating systems. A number of computerized cost estimating systems are available that derive total project costs from equipment costs using the same principle as factored estimating.

The concept is that each piece of equipment brings its complement of foundations, piping, structures, instruments and electrics. In many of these systems, a typical "module" has been created relating quantities of piping materials, instruments, electrics, foundations, etc. to each individual type of equipment. Specifics of the equipment item are entered into the computer. The program generates the bulk material quantities which can then be costed at the current unit rates. Similarly, the program will develop labor manhours and other associated costs which can also be costed at current unit rates.

These computer systems inherently have the same strengths and weaknesses as factored estimates. The quality of the final estimate generated depends upon how close the project being estimated is to the "module" contained in the computer. Factored estimating is based upon a cost module which can be just as accurate as any detailed equipment/material quantity module if it is based upon good cost returns. It is a lot simpler and easier to manipulate when quick estimating returns are required.

Factored estimating applications. The accuracy of a factored estimate depends upon the validity of the factors used and the similarities between the plant being estimated and the plants from which the factors were derived. Up-to-date factors, properly adjusted and applied, for the estimation of a new similar plant can give estimates within the ± 10 percent accuracy range. Usually factored estimates are considered to be in the ± 15 percent accuracy range with greater divergencies if the plant being estimated has features which are significantly different from previous plants.

There are so many intangible variables that affect project costs that estimate accuracy cannot be predicted within a finite range. The recommended approach is to analyze the cost components when the estimate has been completed and by means of statistical analysis predict the percent probability of cost overruns/underruns over selected cost ranges.

Other applications. Apart from the benefit of providing an early project cost estimate, factored estimates have a number of other useful applications.

- They allow for reconsideration of conceptual designs at an early date if total cost indications exceed economic payout guidelines.
- They develop component costs which can be used for budgetry, planning and intermediate control purposes before a definitive estimate is available.
- They provide a good basis for estimate adjustments for known differences in the project under consideration.
- They identify and direct attention to cost sensitive areas in overall project.
- They can be used to generate quantitative estimates for manhours and materials. The home office and labor costs or bulk material costs can be divided by average rates to generate typical manhours or material quantities.
- Factored estimates provide a quick and convenient method of checking estimates obtained by other methods.
- Factors can be used as a means of cost trending during project execution. The factors can be used during project execution to extrapolate the final costs of those accounts yet to be expended, and which are related accounts already committed or expended.
- A proper understanding of estimating factors ensures a proper understanding of cost relationships which, in turn, provides a good basis for project cost control.

Chapter 18
Contingency, Risk, and Sensitivity Analysis

SUBJECTS	1 PREAWARD	2 INITIATION	3 ENGINEERING	4 PROCUREMENT	5 CONSTRUCTION
A FINANCIAL/CONTRACTUAL					
B ORGANIZATION/EXECUTION PLANNING					
C MANAGING PEOPLE/COMMUNICATION					
D ESTIMATING/COST CONTROL	●	●	●	●	●
E RISK ANALYSIS	●	●	●	●	●
F SCHEDULING					
G TRACKING/TRENDING					
H PROGRESS/PRODUCTIVITY MEASUREMENT					
I MATERIAL MANAGEMENT					

A. E. Kerridge

The analysis of contingency, risk and sensitivity is an essential part of capital-cost estimation. An estimate, by definition, is an approximate computation of the probable cost. It would be unusual if the project's final cost exactly matched the estimate. Even if the overall final cost is close to the estimate, there will probably be wide variations between the estimate and the final cost at the detailed-component levels.

Those who are unfamiliar with estimating methods may expect more detail and more accuracy in an estimate than is achievable. There are so many variables and unknowns at the time an estimate is prepared that arriving at a reasonably close overall cost estimate is more art than science. Skill and judgment are needed to identify and predict the unknowns.

To help in this area, estimators and others have developed a variety of systems. To name a few:

- **The Monte Carlo simulation.** (Mathematics can predict the unpredictable.)
- **The random walk.** (Yesterday has nothing to do with tomorrow.)
- **Method of least squares.** (A straight line will pass through any set of points.)
- **Regression analysis.** (Any data can be made to fit an equation.)
- **Exponential function.** (Multiply it by itself a few times.)
- **Murphy's Law.** (The worst will happen.)

239

System needed. Some of these systems are highly technical and perhaps a little academic. Applying them to an estimate may be impracticable. The sophistication of the system may be out of tune with the coarseness of the raw data. Nevertheless, it is desirable to use a systemized approach to evaluate areas of risk, to determine relative sensitivities and to arrive at realistic contingencies.

Those unfamiliar with estimating methods are more likely to accept a contingency figure which can be supported by analysis than a number which appears to be someone's best guess. This article describes systems for the analysis of contingency, risk and sensitivity which are basically simple, and which can be applied readily to a wide range of estimates.

Definitions. The following are generally accepted definitions:

- **CONTINGENCY.** A provision for an occurrence dependent upon chance, accident or uncertain event.
- **RISK.** Exposure to mischance, danger, hazard, injury, damage, bad consequence or loss.
- **SENSITIVITY.** The quality of being keenly susceptible and responsive to external forces.
- **ANALYSIS.** A separating or breaking up of any whole into its parts so as to find out their nature, proportion, function and relationship.

These definitions are appropriate when applied to estimates. (So often words are jargonized and have different meanings when used by specialists.)

Types of project estimates. Contingency, risk and sensitivity analysis may be applied to any part of a project cost estimate, such as:

- Fixed capital
- Working capital
- Operating cost

Fixed capital refers to the material, labor and services required for the installation of the permanent plant covering equipment, buildings, process systems, utilities and ancillaries.

Working capital covers such things as inventories of feedstocks, intermediates, products and other consumables, funds for accounts payable and receivable, payroll, taxes, etc.

Operating cost covers feedstock materials, chemicals and catalysts, utilities, maintenance materials, operating supplies and consumables, labor, plant overheads, marketing costs, distribution costs, general overhead and administration expenses, financial costs.

Here, I will discuss the application of contingency, risk and sensitivity analysis to fixed capital cost estimates. The concepts can apply equally to working capital and operating cost estimates.

Fixed capital cost estimation. The first step in the preparation of a fixed capital cost estimate is to subdivide the project into its units or areas. A typical refining or petrochemical complex might be subdivided as shown in Fig. 1. This is not intended to be a complete list. It merely illustrates the first step in breaking down an overall complex into specific units, areas, or categories to facilitate cost estimation.

The next step is to take each one of these major subdivisions and apply a common code of accounts which will apply to all project subdivisions as shown in Fig. 2.

	PROJECT SUBDIVISIONS
00	PROCESS PLANTS
01	CRUDE UNIT
02	REFORMING UNIT
03	DESULFURIZING UNIT
10	UTILITIES AND SERVICES
11	WATER FACILITIES
12	STEAM FACILITIES
13	ELECTRICAL FACILITIES
14	FUEL FACILITIES
15	FLARE AND BLOWDOWN FACILITIES
16	WASTE DISPOSAL FACILITIES
20	STORAGE AND TRANSPORTATION
21	TANKAGE
22	DISTRIBUTION SYSTEMS
23	LOADING AND UNLOADING FACILITIES
24	MATERIALS HANDLING FACILITIES
25	DOCK AND WHARF FACILITIES
30	CIVIL WORKS
31	FENCES, ROADS, RAILROADS, DIKES
32	GENERAL ADMINISTRATION BUILDINGS
40	MISCELLANEOUS ACCOUNTS
41	SPARE PARTS
42	CATALYST, CHEMICALS AND CONSUMABLES
43	MAINTENANCE EQUIPMENT
44	MOBILE AND TRANSPORTATION EQUIPMENT
45	LABORATORY AND MACHINE SHOP EQUIPMENT
46	OFFICE FURNITURE AND EQUIPMENT

Figure 1—Subdivision of a typical refining or petrochemical complex.

```
┌─────────────────────────────────────────┐
│            CODE OF ACCOUNTS              │
├───┬─────────────────────────────────────┤
│ A │ EQUIPMENT                            │
│   │                                      │
│   │ A1   HEATERS                         │
│   │ A2   VESSELS AND TANKS               │
│   │ A3   HEAT TRANSFER EQUIPMENT         │
│   │ A4   ROTATING EQUIPMENT              │
├───┼─────────────────────────────────────┤
│ B │ BULK MATERIALS                       │
│   │                                      │
│   │ B1   CIVIL WORK                      │
│   │ B2   BUILDINGS                       │
│   │ B3   PIPING                          │
│   │ B4   ELECTRICS                       │
│   │ B5   INSTRUMENTATION                 │
│   │ B6   PROTECTIVE COATINGS             │
├───┼─────────────────────────────────────┤
│ C │ SERVICES                             │
│   │                                      │
│   │ C1   HOME OFFICE                     │
│   │ C2   CONSTRUCTION                    │
│   │ C3   MISCELLANEOUS                   │
└───┴─────────────────────────────────────┘
```

Figure 2—A code of accounts applies to all project subdivisions.

ACCT	DESCRIPTION	MATERIAL	LABOR	SUB-CONTRACT	TOTAL
A	EQUIPMENT				
A1	Heaters				
A2	Vessels and Tanks				
A3	Heat Transfer Equipment				
A4	Rotating Equipment				
	Sub-Total				
B	BULK MATERIALS				
B1	Civil Work				
B2	Buildings				
B3	Piping				
B4	Electrics				
B5	Instrumentation				
B6	Protective Coatings				
	Sub-Total				
C	SERVICES				
C1	Home-office				
C2	Construction				
C3	Miscellaneous				
	Sub-Total				
	Total				

Figure 3—Project code of accounts for each unit or area of the project.

A cost estimate summary is then made up for each unit or area of the overall project by code of accounts, covering material, labor and subcontracts, as shown in Fig. 3.

When each unit has been estimated in this way, then the estimate for the overall project complex is the sum of the unit estimates. This can be assembled in a matrix as shown in Fig. 4.

ACCT	DESCRIPTION	PROCESS PLANTS	UTILITIES & SERVICES	STORAGE	STORAGE & TRANSPORTATION	CIVIL WORKS	MISCELLANEOUS	TOTAL
		01 02 03 04	11 12 13 14	21 22 23 24		31 32 33	41 42 43 44	
A	EQUIPMENT							
A1	Heaters							
A2	Vessels and Tanks							
A3	Heat Transfer Equipment							
A4	Rotating Equipment							
	Sub-Total							
B	BULK MATERIALS							
B1	Civil Work							
B2	Buildings							
B3	Piping							
B4	Electrics							
B5	Instrumentation							
B6	Protective Coatings							
	Sub-Total							
C	SERVICES							
C1	Home-office							
C2	Construction							
C3	Miscellaneous							
	Sub-Total							
	TOTAL							

Figure 4—The overall project estimate matrix.

There is nothing new about this. It is the HPI's standard way of building up estimates. Standardized methods and techniques and the use of common codes of accounts assist with the buildup of cost statistics and the transfer of cost data and ratios from one project to another.

Estimate accuracy. Having prepared the unit and overall project estimates, the next question is "What is the accuracy?" A higher level of accuracy may be expected than is realistic. However, if the accuracy probability is assessed by a formal analytical procedure, then it will be more likely that a realistic contingency will be set.

The accuracy of an estimate is dependent upon the project definition and also upon the time and effort spent in its preparation. Fig. 5 indicates typically the probable accuracy of an estimate at each project definition stage. Moving from left to right, accuracy increases with project definition.

At stage 0, when the project is still in the initial conception phase, an order of magnitude estimate may have an accuracy of between ± 30 to 50 percent.

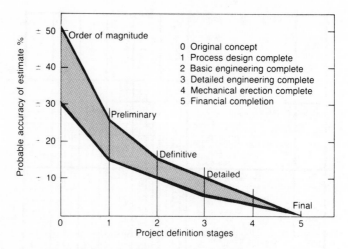

Figure 5—Accuracy of estimates relating to project definition.

At stage 1, when process design has been finalized, a preliminary or factored estimate from equipment costs may be prepared with an accuracy of between ± 15 to 25 percent.

At stage 2, when basic engineering is complete, i.e., piping and instrumentation diagrams, plot plans, arrangement studies, etc., have been completed, a definitive estimate can be prepared with an accuracy of between ± 10 to 15 percent.

At stage 3, on completion of engineering when final drawings and bills of materials have been completed and all material has been purchased, a detailed estimate can be prepared which may have an accuracy of between ± 5 to 10 percent.

Stage 4 corresponds to mechanical completion of erection, but even at this time the final actual cost of the project is still not known precisely.

The last stage, 5, at financial completion is when the final actual cost is known which is when all the bills have been settled. This may be several months after mechanical completion.

If the above ranges of accuracy are typical and have been proved by experience from many projects, then if one can define the stage of project definition, the likelihood is that the accuracy will fall somewhere in the shaded area indicated. It follows that an average contingency within this range should be allowed, depending upon the specific project.

Fig. 5 also indicates that accuracy is related to the proximity of the completion date. An estimate is more likely to be accurate if the time to completion is reduced. If there is a long schedule period, the probability of inaccuracy becomes much greater.

The need for a contingency. Regardless of the time and effort spent in the preparation of an estimate, there is always the possibility of errors due to:

- Engineering errors and omissions
- Cost and rate changes
- Construction problems
- Schedule slippages
- Miscellaneous unforeseens
- Estimating inaccuracies

During the preparation of the estimate, each item is costed by estimating the manhours or material content and applying a cost rate. At the preliminary estimate stage, the material content is not completely defined. An allowance is thus required which recognizes that the final material quantity will exceed the initial quantity. This is covered by a design allowance applied to the equipment and bulk material categories and is an integral part of the estimate. Design allowances are not part of the contingency.

The contingency is required to cover those events which could occur during the progress of any normal project. Complete coverage to cover the worst possibilities could require a significant contingency for each code of accounts. The sum of these contingencies would give a very large overall contingency for the total project.

The probability that things will go wrong on all accounts is unlikely. Therefore, the overall contingency does not need to be the sum of the maximum individual contingencies. It is an average contingency which should be adequate if it is assumed that not all things will go wrong and some things may go better than planned. The practice, therefore, is to determine an average contingency for each account. This is totalled and kept as a separate overall contingency, available to the project as a whole.

Method of determining contingency. The method of arriving at a reasonable contingency requires judgment. So, it is desirable that a consistent logical procedure be used in its development. The procedure should separate what may be termed the "average contingency" and the "maximum risk contingency," which would be the contingency required to cover the worst case.

Average contingency is determined by examining the project definition stage for each code of accounts and applying average estimating accuracy factors appropriate for the specific project. The maximum risk contingency (discussed later) is obtained by examining problem areas in each account code.

The average accuracy ranges are taken from the chart shown in Fig. 5 for each stage of definition. The probable accuracy selected for a specific project will be within the ranges shown in Fig. 5 for each stage. Whether the figure selected will be at the top or bottom end of the range will be determined by the variables and unknowns for the specific project.

For example, a Gulf Coast project for a conventional process unit would be at the lower end of the range, whereas a non-standard process unit in an overseas location would be at the upper limit of the range. Process unknowns, sources for engineering, procurement and construction, the schedule period, market and economic factors could all influ-

STAGE NUMBER	PROJECT DEFINITION	TYPICAL ACCURACY RANGE PLUS OR MINUS %	ACCURACY RANGE SELECTED FOR SPECIFIC PROJECT
0	Initial concept prior to finalization of process design.	25 to 50	30
1	Process design final with equipment defined but not quoted. Bulk materials factored but unpriced.	15 to 25	20
2	Completion of basic engineering, mechanical flow sheets, P&ID's, plot plans approved, equipment quoted and preliminary take-offs for bulk materials with quoted prices.	10 to 15	13
3	Engineering and design complete with final quantities taken off, firm orders placed for equipment and materials.	5 to 10	8
4	Mechanical erection complete.	0 to 5	4
5	Financial completion.	0	0

Figure 6—Basis for average contingency.

1	2	3	4	5	6	7	8	9	10	11	12
ACCOUNT NUMBER	DESCRIPTION	FORECAST VALUE $	% OF TOTAL COST	AT STAGE 0 o/o	AT STAGE 1 o/o	AT STAGE 2 o/o	AT STAGE 3 o/o	AT STAGE 4 o/o	AT STAGE 5 o/o	NORMAL CONTINGENCY o/o	NORMAL CONTINGENCY $

Figure 7—Contingency worksheet form.

ence the selection of the probable accuracy for the specific project. Following this evaluation, a chart as shown in Fig. 6 is drawn up for the specific project being evaluated.

To evaluate the average contingency, a standard worksheet form is used as shown in Fig. 7. *Columns 1 and 2* on the left hand side of the form list the equipment and bulk materials by code of accounts. The form may be subdivided under material, subcontracts and labor in a similar manner to the way in which the unit estimate is built up.

Column 3 shows the current estimate value or most recent forecast value in dollars.

Column 4 expresses the value in column 3 as a percentage of the estimate total. This is used for sensitivity analysis (discussed later).

Columns 5 through 10 indicate the percentage of column 3 that has been defined through to the stage indicated. For example, if the project is in the initial conceptual stage then it will show 100 percent under stage 0. If the account has passed through the definitive estimate stage and 50 percent has been purchased, then 50 percent would be at stage 2 and 50 percent at stage 3.

The object is to identify the degree of definition for the account by allocating the total 100 percent in the appropriate columns from stages 0 to 5. This allocation need not be too precise. It can be performed on an approximate judgment basis. It is of particular value if the project estimate is reviewed at periodic intervals and the contingency re-evaluated as the project definition improves. In such a case, the percentages will tend to move through from stage 0 finally through to stage 5.

Column 11, the average contingency percentage for the account, is evaluated using Fig. 6 which has established a probable accuracy and hence, an average contingency, for each project definition stage. The percent average contingency in column 11 for the account number is a simple calculation of multiplying the percentage in each stage by the average contingency for the stage.

$$\begin{array}{r} \text{percent Stage } 0 \times 0.30 \\ \text{plus percent Stage } 1 \times 0.20 \\ \text{plus percent Stage } 2 \times 0.13 \\ \text{plus percent Stage } 3 \times 0.08 \\ \underline{\text{plus percent Stage } 4 \times 0.04} \end{array}$$

Equals percent average contingency

Column 12 is obtained by multiplying the value in column 3 by the average percentage contingency evaluated under column 11 to give a dollar value. The overall average contingency required for the project is determined by totalling column 12 for all accounts.

RISK AREAS

● LABOR DISPUTES AND SHORTAGES	● EQUIPMENT FAILURES
● HIGH LABOR WAGE SETTLEMENTS	● POOR SUB-CONTRACTORS PERFORMANCE
● INCLEMENT WEATHER	● SUPPLIERS CLAIMS
● LOW PRODUCTIVITY	● DAMAGES AND LOSSES
● LATE DELIVERIES	● SCHEDULE COMPLETION PENALTIES
● MATERIAL SHORTAGES	● OPERATING PERFORMANCE PENALTIES

ITEM OF RISK	MAXIMUM EXTRA COST DUE TO RISK	% PROBABILITY OF RISK OCCURRING	NET RISK TO PROJECT

Figure 8—Risk areas.

Maximum risk contingency. After the evaluation of average contingency for each account, it is necessary to carry out a further evaluation to determine the maximum possible risk for each account and for the project overall. Each individual account should be considered for any specific unknowns or potential problems which might occur in this account. In this evaluation, the percentage schedule completion of the project should be considered. Particular areas of risk which might affect the account are shown in Fig. 8.

In each case the maximum risk contingency is evaluated by identifying and assessing the risk, firstly by each individual code of account and then overall. Again it is unlikely that all the risks, will occur for all accounts. The normal procedure is to identify the major items of risk and to assess the maximum cost impact of the risk. The next step is to attempt to assess the percentage probability that this risk will occur. The net risk then becomes the multiple of the maximum cost of the risk times the probability. The sum of all the net risks for each of the risk possibilities gives the total maximum risk contingency required. (See Fig. 8.)

Two separate analyses have now been performed. An average contingency evaluation and a maximum risk contingency evaluation. Again the overall contingency put into an estimate need not necessarily be the sum of these two. It requires judgment to assess which number is a reasonable contingency to apply against the estimate. It may be policy to include the two contingencies as separate items, i.e., including the average contingency as part of the estimate and maintain a maximum risk contingency as a separate fund to offset any major risk items which have been identified.

Other methods. There are many other methods for determining contingency and risk. Some of these are as follows:

First, build up an estimate by project subdivision and code of accounts as described previously.

Next, review each account in detail to determine the degree of definition, the accuracy of the data and the factors which could affect the final cost.

Following this review, a minimum cost, a most probable cost (which is normally the estimate) and a maximum cost is established. The information would be set out in a table as shown in Fig. 9.

If the above exercise has been performed rigorously, the probability is that the final cost will be above the minimum and below the maximum. The greatest probability is that it will fall at the estimated cost which can be called the "most probable cost." The next question is "What is the probability of the cost falling at any point between the minimum and the maximum, and what sort of distribution curve should be assumed?"

ACCT NUMBER	DESCRIPTION	MATERIAL			LABOR			SUB-CONTRACT			TOTAL		
		MIN	EST	MAX	MIN	EST	MAX	MIN	EST	MAX	MIN	EST	MAX

Figure 9—Evaluation of estimate minimums and maximums.

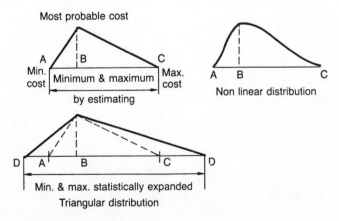

Figure 10—Probability distribution.

The simplest method is triangular distribution, a straight line between the minimum, the most probable and the maximum. Other more complex non-linear distribution patterns may be used. Statistical returns may show that the predicted absolute minimum and maximum may be exceeded, and that the mathematical probable distribution should allow for a minimum low and maximum high below and above the numbers predicted. Fig. 10 shows different types of probability distribution. The overall summation of the individual analyses can be presented in a probability curve as shown in Fig. 11. This curve gives the percentage probability of overrun for any cost between the absolute minimum and the absolute maximum. It then becomes a matter of discussion and agreement to decide what level of contingency is appropriate in relation to the probability of overrun.

These methods of analysis can become very complex, involving advanced mathematics. Because of the virtuosity of the systems, individuals may be misled into believing that the answers are more precise. In fact, the system is still only as good as the input data and the assumptions, which are based upon judgment.

Computer programs are available which generate a random value between the predicted minimum and maximum for each account code.

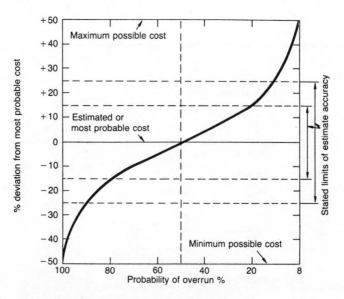

Figure 11—Typical probability curve for estimate over-run.

The sum of these values predicts a total cost. A large number of these simulations will generate a probability curve between the absolute minimum and absolute maximum as shown in Fig. 11.

Sensitivity. Having carried out the contingency and risk analysis, the last step is to perform a sensitivity analysis. The term may be interpreted in many ways. But in general, the requirement is to determine cost areas which could change significantly and which, in turn, would have the greatest impact upon the overall project cost. The overall project cost will be more sensitive to changes in some accounts than others. For example, if one account represents 1 percent of the total cost, then a 100 percent overrun in this account would only affect the total by a maximum of 1 percent. On the other hand, if another account represents 20 percent of the total cost, then a 10 percent overrun on this account could affect the total by 2 percent. Thus the total cost has greater sensitivity to this account than the first.

As the project proceeds, so sensitivities will change as certain of the accounts become firm and committed. Sensitive areas will be those accounts which still have the largest dollar values yet uncommitted and which require the largest contingency.

The analysis of average and maximum risk contingency provides an effective means of establishing sensitivity. A quick review of the required average contingency and maximum risk contingency against each of the account codes will indicate rapidly the potential areas with high sensitivity, i.e., the cost accounts which may have the maximum effect on the total cost forecast both in the areas of overruns and potential cost savings. It is, therefore, a valuable exercise to identify the highly sensitive areas. Following on from this, one may introduce some additional surveillance with checks and balances in these areas to attempt to minimize the potential overrun and maximize the potential for reducing the overall project total cost.

Having performed a review of each account for average and maximum contingency to identify potential areas for high sensitivity, the next step is to identify the impact of any specific cost changes. Examples: changes in labor productivity, changes in wage rates or extensions to the project schedule. For specific risks of this type, sensitivity curves can be constructed to show the impact of these cost changes.

Fig. 12 illustrates two types of such curves. The first shows the effect on labor cost of changing labor productivity combined with changes in the labor cost rate. As can be seen, the total labor cost is extremely sensitive to reduction in labor productivity, more so than increases in labor rate.

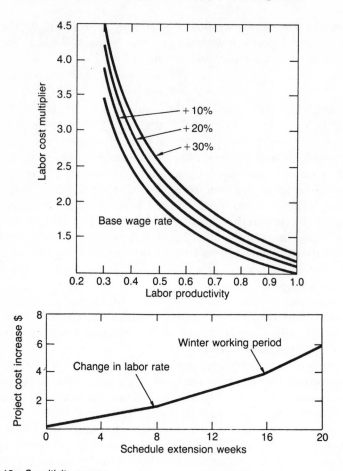

Figure 12—Sensitivity curves.

The second chart shows the potential effect of increased schedule time on project cost. It shows, for example, that the effect on project costs may be significantly increased due to possible changes in labor rates and possible changes in labor productivity rates due to running into winter working conditions, etc.

Judgment factor. The areas of contingency, risk and sensitivity analysis are interrelated. The subject provides a fertile area for mathematicians, statisticians and other analytical types with computers. At the same time, it is also apparent that no matter how refined a system is applied, both the basic input data and the final assessment depends heavily upon judgment.

Part 6:
Cost Control

Chapter 19

Control
the Cost of
New Plants

SUBJECTS	1 PREAWARD	2 INITIATION	3 ENGINEERING	4 PROCUREMENT	5 CONSTRUCTION
A FINANCIAL/CONTRACTUAL	●	●			
B ORGANIZATION/EXECUTION PLANNING	●	●			
C MANAGING PEOPLE/COMMUNICATION					
D ESTIMATING/COST CONTROL		●			
E RISK ANALYSIS					
F SCHEDULING		●			
G TRACKING/TRENDING					
H PROGRESS/PRODUCTIVITY MEASUREMENT					
I MATERIAL MANAGEMENT					

John H. Hanna

Escalation in the cost of materials and equipment for new plant construction has been rapid in recent months. These increases probably will continue, and labor increases may also grow. For this reason, I'll offer here some basic guidelines to minimize the threat of budget overruns on new plant construction. Overruns can be caused by escalation and other factors. So, the best cost control methods available are needed. These methods need to be based on carefully conceived execution plans, cost-conscious design and proven principles of cost control.

Execution plan. Project costs can be influenced considerably by the owner's choice of a basic execution plan. Broadly, the owner has three choices:

• Engineering and construction can be split between two separate organizations. Or, both can be the responsibility of one organization.
• A single entity can manage the whole project and both engineering and construction can be split among several organizations.
• Engineering and construction can be either on a cost-plus or lump-sum basis, or a combination of these.

Large potential differences in costs can result from different execution plans. For example, recent experiences are noteworthy.[1] On a recent, large, grass-roots project, the owner assigned engineering, procurement and construction to a single contractor. On previous large projects, the owner had parcelled out pieces and had done the managing itself. The project was completed within the budget and ahead of schedule. Conversely, at least one large earlier project handled differently was completed "much less favorably."

To be sure, other factors in the project execution plan also were important. But the fact remains—the owner's management made a choice in basic execution that they believe achieved better cost results.

The whole subject of choice of execution plans for design and construction work was treated by Joseph J. Jacobs in a recent article.[2] One very interesting proposition he made is that, with careful selection of a contractor by the owner, the single responsibility engineering-construction contract on a cost plus fixed-fee basis is the most economical.

Design philosophy. If plant costs are to be controlled, everyone contributing to the engineering design must be cost conscious. They must understand the direct relationship between cost and what may be called the operational characteristics of a plant.

Generally, increasing the operational factors of reliability, efficiency and flexibility costs money. The same is true for minimizing maintenance cost and minimizing future-expansion cost. Occasionally a technical breakthrough or an inspiration of ingenuity will allow operational factors to be increased without extra cost, or perhaps even at a reduction. But usually the plant which has near perfect operational factors is too expensive. A practical plant must be a compromise of reasonable operation factors and cost. Unless the team designing and constructing a plant keeps this in mind, cost control will be difficult.

Additionally, efforts must be made to seek out materials and equipment *available* in today's era of shortages. Designs must use reinforcing bar sizes, pipe wall thicknesses and material types that are not in very short supply, and hence only available at a premium cost.

Principles of cost control. The objective of cost control is to keep the project within budget. To do this, we need early warning of impending deviations, and the information to take corrective action before costs are out of control. Effective cost control depends on several basic principles:

- The owner's project team representatives must provide the lead to keep the job on cost target, without overemphasis on operational factors.
- The project schedule must be realistic and achievable with the personnel available to it, and the deliveries currently attainable. The schedule should be correlated to the over-all cost objective.

- All cost items should be compared to a budget prior to commitment, and as incurred.
- The effect on cost, of changes to project scope and design criteria, must be estimated and evaluated before final commitment.
- Cost data should be given to the various groups on the project team to stimulate an attitude of cost consciousness.
- There must be procedures for periodic reporting and evaluating of costs committed as well as incurred, and of estimating costs yet to be committed or incurred.
- Control is required both for quantities and unit costs.
- Project management should frequently review costs and commitments versus job progress. It should take corrective action wherever deviations occur from plans and budgets.

To implement these principles, a number of things are necessary: 1. preliminary estimate; 2. code of accounts; 3. cost trend estimates; 4. definitive estimate; 5. contingency; 6. management review; 7. cost and forecast report; 8. change orders; and 9. schedule monitoring. Let's look at these, one at a time.

1. Preliminary estimate. First, at the beginning of design, a preliminary estimate must be available (or made) and converted into a preliminary budget. Preferably, this should be good enough to generate confidence by the project team members. But *any* estimate and budget is better than *none* at this time.

Every proposed commitment or purchase must be compared to the appropriate item in this budget before finalizing. Any item found to cost over the budget should be reviewed carefully and efforts made to reduce the cost. Comparison and action process should be started at the beginning of the job when fairly large commitments for long delivery are often made.

2. Code of accounts. Second, a code of accounts should be prepared so that the cost of each item of equipment, material and labor cost can be estimated, charged, reported and forecast consistently for the specific project. The individual accounts codes should break costs down into many small pieces, but without creating excessive and confusing detail.

3. Cost trend estimates. Third, until design has progressed far enough to permit preparation of a detailed definitive estimate, frequent estimate summaries should be made of developing costs trends. These should include the amount that purchase commitments are over or under the budget, and the cost effect of changes in scope, quantities, design criteria and schedule.

This forecasting of cost trends provides the basis for intelligent management action as soon as significant trends develop. Forecasting also helps to avoid big surprises that require agonizing reappraisal when the definitive estimate is finished.

The estimates made for forecasting cost trends need not be highly accurate. Indeed, in the early part of the project developments often occur so rapidly that only order-of-magnitude estimates are possible. These estimates and the cost trends should be all reviewed with group leaders of the project team.

4. The definitive estimate. Fourth, a detailed definitive estimate should be made as soon as major equipment and other large items are committed (or the prices are known), and detail quantity take-offs can be made. This is usually possible before midpoint in design. By this time, the unit cost and quantities of equipment and materials are largely fixed. The principal uncertainties are construction direct and indirect labor costs, and the cost of completing design.

This estimate should contain the best assessment possible of the continuing effects of inflation until completion of construction. Today, *no one* knows what the future rate of inflation will be.

The longer the time frame of the job, the greater is the risk of under estimating the effects of inflation. This risk, together with other risks of omission and commission in estimating, should be assessed in setting the estimate contingency.

5. Contingency. There are many viewpoints as to the nature and use of a contingency. One view defines it as costs over and above the estimate that experience indicates will be spent in unpredictable categories, the amount of which must be established by judgment based on the risks involved for each specific project. This seems much more prudent than, for example, defining contingency as an amount in a request for appropriation approval as insurance against an overrun, but which will probably be spent later for other purposes.

The owner should also allow for the cost of changes that will probably occur between the time of the definitive estimate and project completion. Some changes are inevitable as new marketing data or other plant operating experience becomes available. Also important these days are environmental-requirement matters. These can change *during* a project.

6. Management review. Management should review the total definitive estimate, plus contingency, plus change allowance. If these are rational, then the estimate should be converted to a budget form. This budget controls all costs yet to be incurred. If this is not the case, then some reappraisal and changes will be necessary before the project can proceed much further. Recent experience in following the principles and procedures described shows that surprises usually will *not* occur at this time.

7. Cost and forecast report. Once the detailed control budget is available, the next step is taken. This is monthly preparation and review of a cost commitment and forecast report. A period of more than one month reduces the opportunity for timely control action. Trying for a period of less than monthly complicates the task of obtaining good cost accounting data. This report should be done in a manner to provide the means for *controlling* cost. Merely reporting and forecasting costs will not ensure against cost overruns.

The cost for each account code should be forecast by making the best assessment possible of the "to go" over the current cost and commitment reported for each account. Until some development occurs in an account after the definitive estimate, there may not be any basis for a "to go" assessment. But each month, more and more accounts can be forecast on a new assessment of "to go" as the project progresses and more actual costs are reported.

During the management review of each month's report, every account forecast over the budget should be checked to see if cost can be reduced. Those forecast under the budget should also be analyzed. Sometimes, an underrun forecast results from erroneously reporting costs in the wrong accounts. These figures will later show up as an overrun in another account.

8. Change orders. The eighth requirement relates to changes in scope or design criteria required after the definitive estimate. Such changes should be covered by written orders that describe and estimate the change in detail. These change orders should be reviewed and approved before implementation.

After approval, cost effects of the change order on each affected cost code should be added to the budget. With such cost data, meaningful comparisons can be made between the budget and cost incurred and commitments made.

9. Schedule monitoring. At the same time the monthly cost report is reviewed, the project schedule should be examined to compare actual versus planned progress. Activities significantly behind probably will cause increased cost, in time. Corrective action for such lags should always be considered. Extra expediting or premiums for corrective action often will more than save their own cost by avoiding more costly problems in construction.

The schedule is a tool to help achieve project objectives. It is *not* a straightjacket that cannot be changed. As the project goes on, developments may present opportunities for saving cost by changing activity sequences. These developments should be carefully and frequently examined for such opportunities.

Detail procedures. Forms and detail procedures must be developed for use with the nine steps I have described. Considerable variety can be tolerated to suit the general procedural approach and formats of different organizations. Regardless of variation of detail, the objective should be to provide the means to *control* cost during each phase—from the inception to completion of the project. Merely reporting and forecasting costs isn't enough.

LITERATURE CITED

[1] "How Carbide Got a New Plant that Works," *Business Week*, Aug. 11, 1973, Page 62J.

[2] "Construction Contracts," Joseph J. Jacobs, *Chemical Engineering*, Jan. 22, 1973, Page 109.

SUBJECT-PROJECT PHASE MATRIX

PROJECT PHASE

	SUBJECTS	1 PREAWARD	2 INITIATION	3 ENGINEERING	4 PROCUREMENT	5 CONSTRUCTION
A	FINANCIAL/CONTRACTUAL					
B	ORGANIZATION/EXECUTION PLANNING					
C	MANAGING PEOPLE/COMMUNICATION					
D	ESTIMATING/COST CONTROL		●	●	●	●
E	RISK ANALYSIS					
F	SCHEDULING					
G	TRACKING/TRENDING					
H	PROGRESS/PRODUCTIVITY MEASUREMENT					
I	MATERIAL MANAGEMENT					

Chapter 20

Control
Project Costs
Effectively

A. E. Kerridge

The first step in cost control is to prepare a good estimate. Cost cannot be controlled if there is an inadequate, incomplete, or unrealistic estimate. Fig. 1 illustrates the increasing probability of improved accuracy as estimates are made at progressive stages of project execution.

THE ESTIMATE

An **order of magnitude estimate** is derived from curves or return costs from previous projects and is prepared in the conceptual stage.

A **preliminary control estimate** is prepared when the process design is complete and equipment data and sizes are available.

A **definitive estimate** is prepared when basic engineering is complete and preliminary bulk material take-offs have been prepared.

A **detailed or check estimate** is prepared on completion of design engineering when production drawings, final material quantities and prices are known.

Variations. The last two stages shown in Fig. 1 illustrate that the final cost of a project is not known until financial completion, when all commitments and invoices have been paid. Prior to that time there is always the possibility of variation from an estimate no matter how detailed.

Normally, three levels of estimate are prepared during project execution.

261

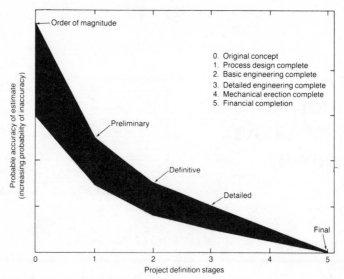

Figure 1—Project estimates and their accuracy improve as estimates are made at progressive stages of project execution.

- Order of Magnitude
- Preliminary Control
- Definitive

Cost control can only be applied at a level corresponding to the quality and detail of the estimate available.

Project cost control starts on the wrong base if there is a poor estimate. Estimates may be arbitrarily reduced or an estimating accuracy may be claimed which is not supported by the project scope definition available. Poor project execution may be blamed for cost overrun when an unrealistic or over optimistic project estimate is the problem.

Procedures. An essential requirement for the production of quality estimates is good estimating procedures. Detailed formalized procedures, consistency of method, feedback of previous cost data, and a standard code of accounts are the prime requisites for project estimating. Project costs must be reported under the same code of accounts to match the estimate to ensure good feedback for comparison.

Table 1 shows the major elements of capital cost in a project. Although cost control procedures should be applied to all areas of cost, a knowledge of the cost elements will allow additional vigilance to be applied to cost sensitive areas.

TABLE 1—Elements of capital cost in a project

	% of total		
	Low	Typical	High
Home office	8	10	12
Equipment	20	30	40
Commodities	25	31	40
Direct labor	15	20	25
Construction indirects	6	9	12
Total		100	

No matter how thorough the estimate, there may be errors, omissions, and unforeseen events. To allow for this, on completion of the estimate, a contingency and risk analysis should be performed. An appropriate contingency is included as an integral part of the estimate.

BASIC ENGINEERING

The intrinsic cost of a project is set in the basic engineering phase, during which the following major project definition documents are produced:

- Project Scope definition and coordination procedures
- Process design package
- General engineering specifications
- Equipment list and equipment data
- Piping and instrument diagrams (process and utility)
- Site and plot plans
- Single line electrical diagrams
- Construction plan
- Master project schedule.

Cost influence. Basic engineering fixes the quality and content of the project which in turn fixes the basic cost. Such things as the equipment, the material and design specifications, philosophies regarding reliability, spares, safety, environmental protection, automation and controls, extent of buildings and structures, etc., are fixed. After basic engineering has been fixed, the only opportunities for cost savings are by improved project execution efficiency and productivity in engineering and construction or by more competitive equipment and material purchasing.

Significant costs are saved only by reducing the scope of the project by removing equipment items or using less stringent design and material specifications.

Because the project costs are committed when basic engineering is approved, there should be a thorough cost review prior to approval. It should be a separate exercise from the technical review, to ensure that extra cost has not been built in unnecessarily.

EQUIPMENT

Equipment items are normally estimated with close accuracy provided the basic capacity, duty, materials, and type have been defined. Often there may be large price differences between bids. Careful commercial and technical analysis must be made to ensure that acceptable quality is selected at the lowest price to take advantage of specific market conditions.

A major problem controlling equipment costs is to stop price additions after the purchase order has been placed. Changes, such as nozzle sizes, ratings, orientations, attachments, instrument and electrical connections, etc., provide the vendor with an opportunity to increase his price unless fixed unit prices for additions have been established during the competitive bidding stage.

Control equipment costs. The following general rules should be part of the project procedures to control equipment costs:

- **Do not issue inquiries prematurely.** Wait until equipment definition is firm so that vendors can bid on information which will not change.
- **Obtain competitive bids** from at least three vendors. Search the market ahead of time to determine which vendor shops are hungry for work.
- **Obtain firm price quotations.** If escalation clauses are unavoidable, specify an escalation formula which can be monitored and relates to the required delivery.
- **If nozzles or other attachments may be added or changed,** obtain fixed unit prices for these additions prior to the placement of the purchase order.
- **If spares are required, obtain firm price quotations** with the bid or before placement of the purchase order.

COMMODITIES

Commodities or bulk materials include:

- Civil, structural and building materials
- Piping, valves, fittings, and associated materials
- Electrical equipment and materials
- Instruments and instrument materials
- Insulation, fireproofing, painting

The cost of commodities is set by quality and quantity. Quality is set by the specifications developed during basic engineering. Quantity is also set during basic engineering by the size, type, and number of pieces of equipment, the piping and instrument diagrams, the size of the plot plan, and the plant arrangement. When basic engineering is complete, the base cost for commodities has also been irreversibly established, even though at that point in the project execution the exact commodity quantities may not be known. Thereafter it is only possible to reduce excesses, wastage, or inefficiencies by good control during design engineering, procurement, and construction.

Document review. To reduce the base cost of commodities would require returning to basic engineering to reduce the quality of specifications, remove equipment items, or remove piping and instrumentation. This reinforces the importance of a specific cost review of the key basic engineering documents prior to the start of production design. Approval is a commitment for the quality and quantity of commodities required by the approved basic engineering documents.

Control commodity quantities. The following general rules should be observed to achieve effective control of commodity quantities:

- **Prepare a detailed commodity material estimate** and make this available to those responsible for final design drawings and bills of materials.
- **Estimate takeoff quantities must be referenced** to specific equipment items, P&ID's, pipeline numbers, plot plan area numbers, or other suitable identification so that it is possible to make comparisons during the progress of design engineering. The drawings used for takeoff should be retained.
- **Since the estimate takeoffs are based upon designs which are not final, appropriate allowances must be added** to the estimate takeoff

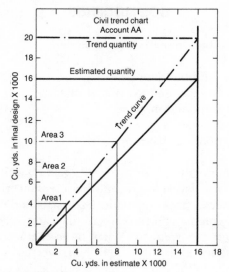

Figure 2—Commodity material trend curve.

to cover final design, construction and maintenance spares. Allowances must be identified. Unit prices used in the estimate must also be recorded.

As design proceeds, final takeoff quantities by area or system should be compared against the takeoff quantities for the same area or system in the estimate.

Figure 2 illustrates a typical trend curve which should be maintained for each major commodity material category.

Commodity price control. Commodity price control can be achieved by the following:

- **Obtain at least three competitive quotes.** Review the market ahead of time to determine which suppliers need work.
- **Do not issue inquiries** until specifications and quantities are firm so there is no chance for a bidder to change his price after the purchase order has been placed.
- **Attempt to obtain fixed price quotes** or fixed unit prices. Do not accept escalation clauses or other price adjustment clauses which cannot be easily monitored.
- **Do not place orders** which are open ended or where the fabricator can invoice according to his measurement. This particularly applies to pipe fabrication.

HOME OFFICE

Home office costs include the following:

• Salaries and benefits of home office personnel (engineering, procurement, and supporting services)
• Home office overheads for accommodation, facilities, and non chargeable support staff
• Home office expenses such as reproduction, communications, travel, business expenses, and computer time.

Of the above, the major cost is the salaries of the home office personnel. This cost can be controlled if the hours charged to the project can be controlled.

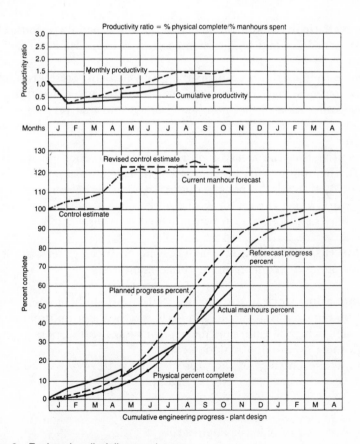

Figure 3—Engineering discipline trend curve.

The first step towards control is to prepare a man-hour estimate for each discipline. These man-hour estimates must identify the number of activities to be performed in terms of number of equipment items, requisitions, drawings, model tables, etc. The better the quality of the man-hour estimate, the better the opportunity for comparing physical progress and man-hours expended against the original plan and budget.

During project execution there should be continuous monitoring of man-hour expenditure, relating this to the progress achieved and the budget. A particular problem is the "90% syndrome" where progress and expenditure reports are favorable until 90% completion is reached, at which time the last 10% creates a considerable overrun in man-hours and schedule time.

Avoid 90% syndrome. The likelihood of the 90 percent syndrome occurring can be reduced by the following actions:

- **Use realistic man-hour budgets** and realistic schedule periods. Unrealistic schedules and budgets tend to create unrealistic and distorted reports.
- **Ensure that methods of measuring physical progress are factual.** This requires that the schedule activities are given weightings by proper allocation of the man-hour budget and that progress is measured against fixed yardsticks and does not reflect inexperience or optimism.
- **Recognize that the meeting of a schedule date does not mean that no further hours will be charged.** There is always followup work, removal of "holds," replies to queries, and other liaison and finalization work which carries on in engineering even though purchase orders may be placed and drawings issued for construction.

Reduce H.O. man-hours. The following are some general guidelines for controlling or reducing home office man-hours:

- **Do not allow work to start in the office** until all the necessary information required is available. An early start without information does not gain schedule time and merely consumes extra hours when the work must eventually be done again.
- **Complete each stage of the project work with reviews** and approvals before the next stage starts. Examples are:

> Process design
> Basic engineering
> Engineering design model

In each case subsequent activities should not be started until the preceding activity has been finalized, approved, and frozen.

- **Control review and approval procedures.** Do not submit documents for approval until they are complete and do not release them for further action until formal approval has been received. Do not accept comments or second thoughts after formal approval has been given. Do not submit documents for approval in a piecemeal manner and ensure that approvals are complete or that approvals with qualifications are clear.
- **Make every effort to minimize the products of engineering (specifications, requisitions, and drawings).** Do not do more than is needed by the Procurement and Construction organizations. Every item eliminated is a reduction in man-hours. Use standard drawings and drawing forms to the maximum extent.
- **Do not do work out of sequence and avoid recycle.** Aggressively oppose project changes which are matters of opinion or improvements which are only marginal.
- **Maintain individual trend curves** as illustrated in Figure 4 for each of the major disciplines showing man-hour expenditure and progress achieved against the plan.
- **When work within discipline has been completed, close the job out** for that discipline. Consider the formation of a small general purpose task force to finish off the project.

In addition to home office man-hour costs there are non payroll costs such as computer charges, travel, communication, and reproduction. Continual vigilance is required to cut unnecessary expenditures in these areas.

CONSTRUCTION

Construction costs include the following:

- Wages and benefits of the direct hire construction labor
- Salaries, benefits, and expenses of construction supervisors
- Rental, purchase and maintenance of construction tools and equipment
- Provision of temporary construction facilities, buildings, utilities, construction supplies, and protection materials.

Of the above, the major cost is the wages of the construction labor which can be controlled if the labor hours can be controlled.

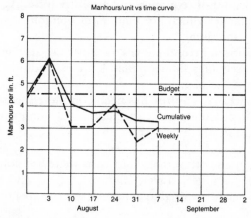

Weekly piping costs - manhours per lin. ft.

Client	XYZ Oil Company					Job No. 1234	
Location	Southwest Tx					Account HE03	
Description	CI B & S U.G pipe					Period Sep 7	

Period Ending	Lineal feet installed		Manhours expended		Manhours per lin. ft.	
	This week	To date	This week	To date	This week	To date
Aug 3	100	100	600	600	6.0	6.0
Aug 10	200	300	600	1200	3.0	4.0
Aug 17	200	500	600	1800	3.0	3.6
Aug 24	150	650	600	2400	4.0	3.7
Aug 31	250	900	600	3000	2.4	3.3
Sep 7	100	1000	300	3300	3.0	3.3
Sep 14						
Sep 21						
Sep 28						
Oct 2						

Figure 4—Construction trade trend curve.

Detailed estimate. As with engineering, the first step towards control is to prepare detailed labor man-hour estimates for each trade. These man-hour estimates must identify specific activities to be performed by code of accounts such as equipment items to be erected, cubic yards of concrete to be placed, feet of pipe to be laid, etc. The better the quality of the labor man-hour estimate, the better the opportunity for comparing physical progress and man-hours expended against the original plan and budget.

Normally, the initial field labor man-hour estimate is prepared in "standard" labor man-hours and then converted to the project labor man-hours by dividing by the anticipated productivity factor. For example, if the "standard" man-hour estimate is 100 and the productivity factor is 0.8, then the project man-hour estimate becomes 100 divided by

0.8 equalling 125 man-hours or an increase of 25%. Because labor productivity is a reciprocal factor, a relatively small drop in the factor creates a large percentage increase in the man-hours. This increase is exponential as the productivity drops. Therefore, the assessment and subsequent control of labor productivity is of overriding importance to achieve control of construction costs.

Control field man-hours. The following are some general guidelines for controlling or reducing field labor man-hours:

- **Ensure that the construction management team is strong** with experienced construction planners, estimators, and cost engineers. It is important that the detailed construction planning is performed at the jobsite and is responsive to the day-to-day needs.
- **Do not allow work to start in the field** until all the necessary information and materials are available. An early start which cannot be sustained will only waste labor man-hours.
- **Pay proper attention to material** receipt, identification, storage, and protection. Ensure that material is controlled and used for the intended application only. Maintain material usage trend curves against design quantities to give early warning of potential shortages.
- **Plan the logistics of man and material movement.** Many man-hours can be wasted moving men and materials around the jobsite.
- **Ensure that methods of measuring physical progress are factual.** Weight construction activities by proper allocation of the labor man-hour estimate and measure progress by means of predetermined physical units or yardsticks.
- **Maintain individual trend curves** as illustrated in Figure 4 for each of the major trades showing productivity, man-hour expenditure, and progress achieved.
- **Do not work out of sequence.** Plan the work from the ground up and the inside out. Maintain a clean and tidy site with clear and well maintained access roads and drainage ditches.
- **Provide optimum working conditions** for labor. Consider early erection of plant buildings to provide prefabrication and assembly areas under cover.

Construction supervision is scaled to the size of the project and the estimated number of labor man-hours. A low labor productivity requiring a larger labor force will require a greater number of supervisors. The quality of the supervision is important for the control of labor productivity which in turn has the major influence on field costs. Review periodically to ensure that there is the proper level of supervision.

Adequate construction equipment, tools, and supporting facilities will help improve labor productivity. However, excessive construction equipment which is available but not used, is merely an added expense to the job. When construction work is approaching completion, it is sometimes difficult to run down and reduce supervisory staff and labor. A formal construction closeout plan is required which is implemented towards the final phases of construction. Any field purchases of commodities and construction consumables should be controlled in the same way as for commodities purchased by the home office.

FIELD SUBCONTRACTS

The organization and planning of subcontracts must occur during the engineering and purchasing phase prior to start of work in the field. The following are some general guidelines for controlling or reducing subcontract costs:

- **Preselect subcontractors** to whom inquiries will be issued on the basis of their past performance, work experience, and capability.
- **Do not issue subcontract inquiries prematurely.** Be sure that the inquiry documents are complete and final, cover the scope of work, and fully define the subcontractor's responsibilities.
- **Check that the inquiry puts the responsibility on the subcontractor** to familiarize himself with site conditions and for movement and removal of materials and labor.
- **Do not impose schedule start and completion dates** on the subcontractor which are dependent upon completion of work by others without provision for adjustment prior to the start of work without cost penalty.
- **Attempt to obtain lump sum quotations** when the scope definition is firm. Do not attempt to obtain lump sum quotations with an inadequate definition or if the work may be changed. In either case, obtain a full scale of unit rates to allow for additions and extensions.
- **After bids have been received, meet with the recommended subcontractor** and review with him the total scope of the work to be sure he understands and accepts it before the contract is awarded.
- **Do not allow the subcontractor to start in the field** until such time as his work can proceed without interruption.
- **If changes are required, ensure there is a proper definition** and that the subcontractor provides a fixed price quotation before work is started.

- **On reimbursable type contracts require the subcontractor** to provide work schedules, progress measurement and performance reports in a manner which can be monitored. Require that the subcontractor's method of costing and invoicing is subject to audit.

SCHEDULE

There is an optimum project schedule which is the most efficient and which will yield the lowest cost. Below this optimum period cost may increase due to the following:

- Equipment and materials purchased for shortest delivery and not lowest price.
- Extra men applied in engineering and/or construction to reduce time at the expense of efficiency.
- Overtime hours worked requiring overtime premium.
- Arbitrary decisions made in the interest of speed without proper analysis of the cost impact on engineering or construction.

Although a reduction in the project schedule below the optimum may increase the capital cost, it may not increase the total cost to the owner. The increase in cost to reduce the construction period may be more than recovered by the reduced interest on capital and the earlier earnings generated.

An increase in the project schedule over the optimum also adds to the project cost due to the following:

- All costs related to calendar time are extended such as:
  Supervision in the home office and the field.
  Use of facilities, rental equipment, and tools.
- The impact of escalation may be significant. Escalation, like interest, compounds upon itself so that its effect is increased when the project schedule is extended.
- An overextended schedule tends to allow more man-hours to be spent unproductively with consequential loss of efficiency.
- Interest costs and other financial charges are extended.

Optimize schedule. The above establishes the importance of developing an optimum schedule period at the start of project execution and thereafter making every effort to hold to this schedule. Every member of the project team is jointly responsible for keeping to schedule for the activities within his control. This responsibility is better appreciated if all members of the project team have an awareness of the impact that schedule delays have upon project costs.

PROJECT CHANGES

Project changes are the chief cause of late schedules and cost overruns. There is an appropriate time in the project schedule allocated for review and approval when minor comments and changes can be accommodated. Changes introduced after approval become extremely costly.

Changes must be controlled by a formalized procedure which requires that all changes be recorded with an estimate of the effect on schedule and cost.

The cost estimate should take full account of the disruption and rework. In most cases there is inadequate allowance for the cost of schedule slippage, the cost of rework, and the potential for increased error. The project management should resist changes at all times and only allow them if . . .

- It can be proved that the project will not work without the change
- The change has been fully recorded and has been authorized by the owner who has accepted the impact upon cost and schedule.

This resistance to change must be applied equally firmly by all members of the project team.

Use the basics. Project costs can be controlled if there is proper cost control and cost reporting supported by a cost conscious project team applying the basic rules of cost control. Every project has its unforeseens for which there must be the contingency.

Part 7:
Tracking
and Trending

SUBJECTS	PREAWARD 1	INITIATION 2	ENGINEERING 3	PROCUREMENT 4	CONSTRUCTION 5
A FINANCIAL/CONTRACTUAL					
B ORGANIZATION/EXECUTION PLANNING					
C MANAGING PEOPLE/COMMUNICATION					
D ESTIMATING/COST CONTROL					
E RISK ANALYSIS					
F SCHEDULING					
G TRACKING/TRENDING			●	●	●
H PROGRESS/PRODUCTIVITY MEASUREMENT			●	●	●
I MATERIAL MANAGEMENT					

Chapter 21

Check Project Progress with Bell and "S" Curves

A. E. Kerridge

"S" and Bell curves can't replace present means for planning and controlling projects. Nor can they identify critical paths or specific trouble spots. Nevertheless, the fact that they are *quantitative* rather than qualitative can be an asset.

After all, many planning and scheduling problems are quantitative. For example, 8,000 isometrics must be produced in five months, or 50,000 tons of fabricated piping must be erected over the same period. In these cases, it doesn't really matter which isometrics or which pieces of pipe are erected by a specific date. The important thing is to know whether the job is being handled volumetrically at a rate appropriate for the time span. This is where "S" and Bell curves can be valuable adjuncts to the more complex systems. They can be developed rapidly and have great flexbility in their application.

Visual impact. The visual impact of "S" and Bell curves may be influenced by changing the horizontal or vertical scales. Most of the figures in this article have equal vertical and horizontal scales. A larger horizontal scale will flatten or elongate the curves. A larger vertical scale will increase the slope and the peaks and valleys, which may be desirable for dramatic effect.

A basic "S" curve (Fig. 1) is drawn on a grid with a horizontal axis showing percentage calendar time from 0 to 100 percent and a vertical axis showing percentage completion from 0 to 100 percent. Any single

277

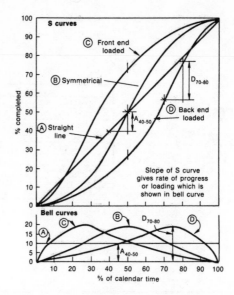

Figure 1—These examples show basic Bell and S curve shapes.

activity, group of activities, or overall project expressed in the form of an "S" curve must start at 0,0 in the bottom left hand corner and to be complete must reach the top right-hand corner at 100,100. The shape of the curve between 0 percent and 100 percent can be an indicator of comparative performance and efficiency.

Simplicity. The simplest "S" curve is a straight line as shown in Fig. 1, curve A. An "S" curve shows cumulative values from 0 to 100, and its shape shows the rate of progress or loading at each point in time. In reality, it is rarely feasible to apply full loading instantly and to maintain a constant load throughout the time span. Usually, there must be an initial lead-in period for mobilization before peak effort can be applied and a tail-off period towards the end. Fig. 1, curve B, shows a typical symmetrical "S" curve which has an equal buildup and tail-off.

The Bell curve is derived from the "S" curve and shows the amount of vertical movement of the "S" curve (the rate of progress or loading) for a finite interval of time. In the case of the straight line "S" curve, the slope or loading is constant indicating a constant effort throughout the total period. Thus the derived Bell curve is also a straight line. This shape of curve is normally the most efficient and hence the most desirable when related to manpower loading. It may not necessarily be so for dollar expenditures where it may be more desirable to defer expenditures to the latest possible date.

The loading curve developed from a symmetrical "S" curve shows the conventional Bell shape with a symmetrical peak considerably higher than the average. This indicates a lower rate at the beginning and end with the maximum rate during the central period.

Symmetry. "S" curves are not usually symmetrical. They may be front end loaded or back end loaded as illustrated in curves C and D in Fig. 1. An actual "S" curve might follow any shape within the grid but will probably fall between the extremes of the two "S" curves shown. The closer the "S" curve is to the 45° straight line, the greater is the degree of resource leveling that has been achieved and the greater the theoretical efficiency.

"S" CURVE APPLICATIONS

- Engineering by manhours or by physical completion
- Drawings by number or weighted value
- Requisitions by number or dollar value
- Purchase orders by number or dollar value
- Construction by manhours, by units of work activity, or by physical completion
- Expenditures or cash flows in dollars.

"S" curves can be applied equally effectively to a variety of miscellaneous activities or items such as:

- Material take-off quantities
- Isometrics drawn and checked
- Cubic yards of earth excavated
- Cubic yards of concrete placed
- Feet of pipe placed
- Feet of cable installed.

The most common "S" curves used for overall project review are for Engineering, Procurement, Material Delivery and Construction.

Engineering curves. Fig. 2 contains a tabular spread sheet distributing engineering planned progress and manhour expenditures by discipline from project start to mechanical completion. The figures show the percent manhours expended and progress achieved in each period and cumulatively. Superimposed on the spread sheet is the same information expressed in the form of "S" and Bell curves. Notice how much greater

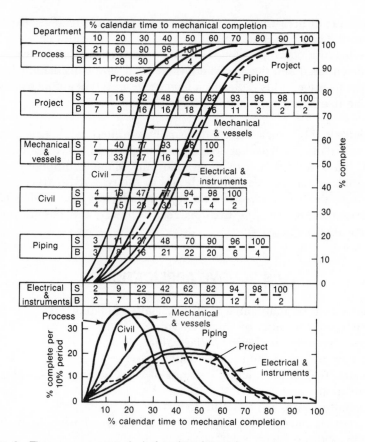

Figure 2—These curves are typical of engineering work.

is the visual impact and information given by the curves than by the figures.

In a normal project, the work flows through Process, Equipment Groups (Vessel and Mechanical), Civil and Structural, Plant Design, and finally, Instruments and Electrical. This typical relationship between the "S" curves for the various engineering disciplines holds for most projects. If the progress for any one discipline runs late, then all succeeding disciplines must be affected and will also be forced to run late.

If planned manhour and progress curves are prepared at the start of a project and actual manhour expenditure and progress recorded at each reporting date, any deviation from plan is very visible. Even more important, schedule slippage in one area can be easily trended to evaluate the potential impact upon the schedule of other areas.

Individual discipline curves. Fig. 3 shows individual discipline curves plotted over the scheduled completion time for the discipline. In these curves, 100 percent completion refers to completion of schedulable activities within the scheduled completion time for the discipline. For engineering disciplines, this is normally at a point when 90 to 95 percent of the manhours have been expended. The final 5 to 10 percent of the manhours are required for engineering closeout and follow-up of vendor and field queries.

Basically, three typical curve shapes cover all engineering disciplines. Fig. 3, curve 1 shows a fast buildup, early peak which applies for Process, Mechanical, Vessels and Equipment disciplines. Fig. 3, curve 2 shows a normal buildup with a long even peak which applies for Project and Support Engineering disciplines. Fig. 3, curve 3 shows a slow buildup and late peak which applies for the major Drafting disciplines.

Generally speaking, a planned "S" curve for any engineering or drafting discipline will fall somewhere within this envelope. For preliminary planning purposes, this typical shape of "S" curve can be assumed for manhour, manpower and progress planning. Note that the normal

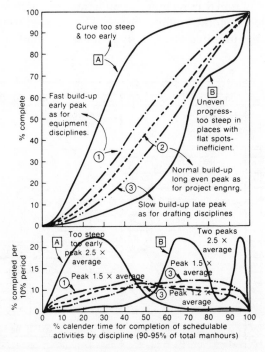

Figure 3—Note the contrast in these normal and unacceptable engineering curve shapes.

"S" curves produce corresponding Bell curves where the peak is about 1.5 times the average.

Unsuitable curves. Also shown in Fig. 3 are curve shapes unacceptable for engineering disciplines. Fig. 3, curve A is too steep and too early. It shows an unrealistic peak of 2.5 times the average with a long slow tail-off. Fig. 3, curve B shows two steep portions with a central flat area. The derived Bell curve shows two short term peaks with low progress achievement over the central portion of the project. These curve shapes show inefficient manpower loading. If they were produced either as planned or actual, there is something seriously wrong with project planning or performance.

Plan, measure, report. Fig. 4 illustrates the method of preparing a planned, weighted progress "S" curve for an engineering discipline for comparison against physical achievement and manhour expenditure. First list the activities and estimate the manhours for these activities. The "weight" of an activity is the ratio of the activity manhours to the total discipline manhours expressed as a percentage.

Next prepare a bar chart schedule showing the planned periods for the activities. The planned percentage completion for each activity at each reporting period is marked above the bar. The planned weighted percent completion is the multiple of the activity percent complete times the ac-

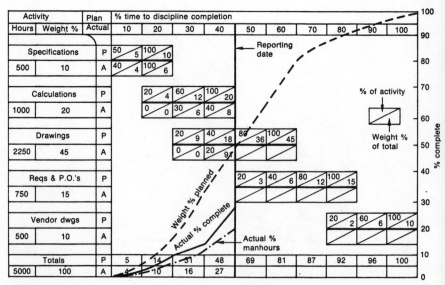

Figure 4—Curves can be used to prepare a weighted progress report.

tivity weighting. The vertical totals for each reporting period generate a weight percent planned progress "S" curve as illustrated.

At the time when the planned "S" curve is prepared, the Bell curve generated should also be examined. This will show the planned manhour and manpower expenditure for each reporting period. Any excessive peaks or fluctuations should be corrected by adjusting the bar chart schedule to achieve more even loading.

Periodic recording. At each reporting period, physical completion for each activity is recorded. This physical percent completion is multiplied by the activity weighting. The sum of these multiples gives the total physical percentage completion for the over-all discipline. Physical completion and manhour expenditures are plotted on the same form with the planned progress curve. A comparison between the planned percent complete, the physical percent complete, and the percent manhour expenditure will quickly show the productivity and performance trend. It is then possible to forecast over-all completion and over-all manhour expenditure.

This method of developing planned progress "S" curve is a basic method. Many variations can be done manually or by computer with networks and/or bar charts.

Manpower forecasting. Fig. 5 shows how curves can be used to forecast manpower requirements. Normally the planned progress curve is

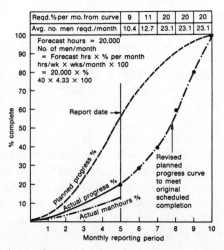

Figure 5—Manpower forecasting can be done from curves.

prepared after the manpower requirements have been determined and leveled to even out peaks. However, sometimes during the progress of a job, when the end date has been fixed, and progress and manhour expenditures have varied from the initial plan, it is necessary to redetermine the manpower requirements to meet the original schedule. The steps are as follows:

1. The current position is the end of the actual progress curve, assuming the method of measuring physical percent completion is realistic.

2. From this point extend a revised planned progress curve approximating to the shape of the previous planned "S" curve and meeting the required completion point.

3. Note the cumulative percent completion required at the end of each month on the revised planned progress curve.

4. Tabulate for each monthly reporting period the required percent to be completed per month which is the difference between the cumulative numbers noted under 3.

5. To predict the number of men required per month, take the total forecast hours based upon productivity and performance to date. Multiply the total hours by the percent to be completed per month and divide it by the hours worked per month. This will give the number of men required per month.

6. Review the number of men required thus calculated and even out the numbers if there are large differences on a month-to-month basis.

7. Confirm that the number of men indicated can be realistically applied to the job. If the number indicated is greater than can be obtained or realistically applied to the job, then the schedule will have to be extended. Alternatively, if more men are available and can be applied to the job than is required, it may be possible to reduce the schedule.

Master project schedule. Fig. 6 shows a typical bar chart master project schedule. Start/complete dates and relationships between the various major activities are expressed as a percentage of calendar time to mechanical completion.

Superimposed on the bar chart are "S" curves for Procurement, Engineering, Material Delivery, and Construction, which are normally considered the key progress measurement curves for an overall project. The relationship between the "S" curves matches the relationship between the corresponding activities in the bar chart. Whereas the bar chart shows specific start and finish dates for activities, the "S" curves show required rates of progress and cumulative completions at various stages of the project.

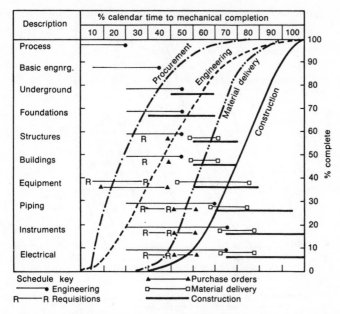

Figure 6—These are typical master project schedule and curves.

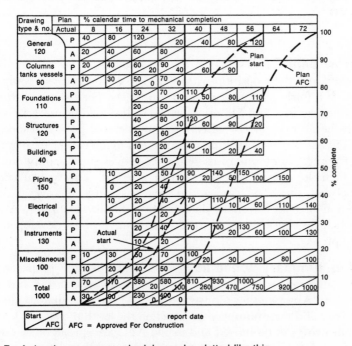

Figure 7—A drawing summary schedule can be plotted like this.

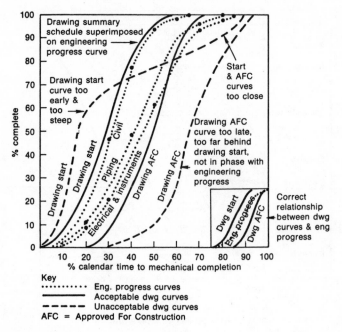

Figure 8—These curves show the relationship between drawing start/AFC and engineering progress.

A narrow band. The shape of the "S" curves, their relationship to each other, and their position with regard to overall project completion fall within a fairly narrow band for all projects. For example, Procurement, Engineering, and Material Delivery all should be essentially complete at the 50 percent, 70 percent and 80 percent points, respectively. Little is to be gained by starting construction much earlier than at the 30 percent point. If any one of these curves moves significantly out of its place, then the overall schedule will be affected. The typical relationships between these "S" curves and their position in the overall project completion provide excellent data for preliminary planning. Also the curves help to check the realism of any detailed plans developed for a specific project.

Drawing summary schedule. Fig. 7 illustrates the preparation of drawing summary schedule curves showing drawings started and drawings issued "Approved for Construction" (AFC). The major categories of drawings and their numbers are listed on the left-hand side. The numbers of drawings to be started and issued AFC are spread out across the form corresponding to the activity periods established in the project schedule. The column totals are the total numbers to be started and issued AFC in each period. From these, the "S" curves can be generated as illustrated.

As the project proceeds, the actual number of starts and AFC issues can be entered and compared against the plan. This simple but effective method helps assure that overall drawing progress is maintained to meet the requirements of the project schedule. Fig. 8 shows the drawing summary schedules (in heavy solid line) superimposed on the engineering curves for the drafting disciplines (reference Fig. 2). Note that the engineering discipline progress curves fall right between the drawing start and drawing AFC "S" curves. This is where they should be.

Unacceptable curves. Fig. 8 also shows unacceptable drawing curves (in heavy dotted line) in relation to the drafting discipline progress curves. The following points are unacceptable:

1. The drawing start curve is too optimistic. Drawing starts should not be made too early and too fast. Progress cannot be maintained since it runs well ahead of the engineering development.

2. The drawing AFC curve is too late. This is running too far behind the planned progress.

3. There is too wide a gap between the drawing start and the drawing AFC curve in the early phases. This means the drawings are started and left incomplete for too long. This usually reflects inefficient operation.

4. The end portions of the curves are too close showing an unrealistic expectation. Drawings cannot be started and issued AFC without adequate time in between for the actual drawing, checking, review and finalizing before issue.

5. The average slope of the drawing curves from start to completion is offset from the required engineering discipline progress curves. In general, the rate of progress of the drawing production has to be equal to or greater than the overall engineering progress curves.

The correct relationship between an engineering discipline progress curve and its drawing start and drawing AFC curves is illustrated in the insert. Entirely similar types of curves can be generated for equipment requisitions, purchase orders, and deliveries. Again, the requisition and purchase order curves must have a fixed relationship, one to the other and also to the progress of the engineering disciplines.

Construction curves. Fig. 9 shows typical Construction Craft "S" and Bell curves. The actual shape of Construction "S" and Bell curves differs from those of the engineering disciplines. Nevertheless, the over-

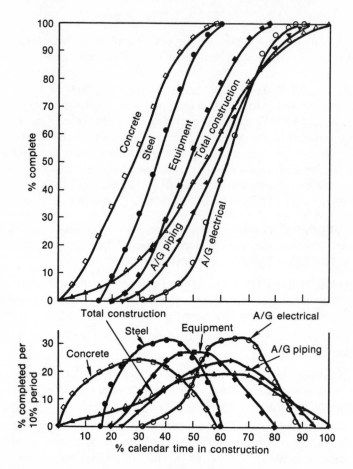

Figure 9—Construction craft curves may look like this.

all concept for their preparation and application is entirely similar. In a normal project, construction work flows through concrete, steel, equipment, piping and electrical as shown.

This typical relationship between the "S" curves for the various Construction Crafts holds for most projects. If progress for any one craft runs late, then all succeeding crafts will be affected and will also be forced to run late. Planned manhour and progress curves may be prepared at the start of the project against which actual manhour expenditure and progress achieved can be recorded for schedule control and forecasting.

Plan and track. Fig. 10 shows use of "S" curves for construction planning and tracking. In just the same way as there is a relationship be-

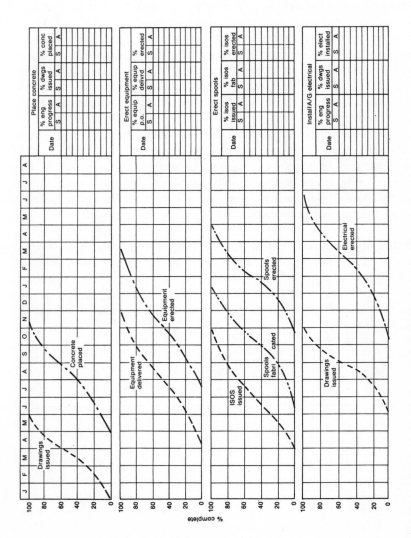

Figure 10—Progress is seen at a glance with use of planning and tracking curves.

tween the equipment and drawing curves and engineering progress curves, there is a similar relationship between the construction progress curves. Construction cannot proceed until AFC drawings and materials are received.

A good way of planning and monitoring construction progress is to plot the AFC drawing release and equipment delivery "S" curves with the corresponding construction craft curve. Good planning allows an adequate lead time between receipt of AFC drawings and material and planned construction progress. Thereafter, if a record is maintained of the actual AFC drawing releases and actual material deliveries, it is possible to determine ahead of time whether or not construction progress can be maintained.

Fig. 10 illustrates a selection of only four out of the many construction crafts and activities. But it is an exceptionally effective and easily followed method of tracking construction progress. A full set of these curves set out on one wall of a field planning office can be updated frequently. Any deviation from plan immediately shows up the potential impact upon subsequent activities.

Simple but useful. The difficulties of plant construction today demand that the most appropriate of the available comprehensive specialized control systems be used. However, do not scorn the simple approach. "S" and Bell curves can be applied in conjuction with any system. Their message is understood from top management to junior supervision.

Chapter 22

Predict Project Results with Trending Methods

SUBJECT-PROJECT PHASE MATRIX		PREAWARD 1	INITIATION 2	ENGINEERING 3	PROCUREMENT 4	CONSTRUCTION 5
	SUBJECTS					
A	FINANCIAL/CONTRACTUAL					
B	ORGANIZATION/EXECUTION PLANNING					
C	MANAGING PEOPLE/COMMUNICATION					
D	ESTIMATING/COST CONTROL					
E	RISK ANALYSIS					
F	SCHEDULING				●	● ●
G	TRACKING/TRENDING				●	● ●
H	PROGRESS/PRODUCTIVITY MEASUREMENT				●	● ●
I	MATERIAL MANAGEMENT				●	● ●

A. E. Kerridge

Project trending provides an early indication of what may be expected when an activity or project is completed. Effective project trending techniques require 1. a logical and systematic means of identifying at each reporting period the deviation between the actual performance and the plan or budget for the activity under consideration, and 2. a method to extrapolate these deviations from the reporting date to the activity completion date.

Applications. Project trending methods can be applied to specific work activities or areas within a project in addition to the overall project. The most common use is for schedule and cost trending. Other typical applications are:

- **In engineering**
  Manhour expenditure v. budget
  Productivity/performance v. target
  Drawing production rate v. plan
  Final material take-off v. estimate
- **In procurement**
  Inquiry/purchase order cycle time v. plan
  Purchase commitment rate v. target
  Actual vendor delivery time v. promise
- **In construction**
  Labor manhour expenditure v. budget
  Labor productivity/performance v. target
  Equipment/material erection rate v. plan
  Material quantities used v. material quantities estimated

The above are merely a few examples of areas where trending techniques may be appropriate. Although trends may be displayed by means of a variety of forms or charts, they all use the same basic methods to determine and project the deviations.

Limitations. Trending techniques may range from "scientific" to what might be called "gross free hand." Before a trend projection technique is selected, the objective should be kept in mind. Over-sophistication and excess precision is not appropriate and could lead to a false sense of accuracy in the prediction. Trending techniques do not provide definitive answers. They are just as dependent as any other technique upon accurate input and data at each reporting stage.

Many individuals decry the concept of trending because they try to make it do more than it can realistically accomplish. Trend projection is only an approximation. Trending charts cannot predict the date by which a project will be complete, nor can they tell the cost or total manhours at completion. Realistically, they can provide projections which may be closer to the completion dates, closer to the completion costs and closer to the manhours required than might otherwise be reported. If they are used with this expectation, and reviewed in conjunction with other conventional project reports, then managers will not be disappointed with the indication they provide.

Only an inexperienced manager would use the results of trend projections as project forecasts. Equally, it would be an unwise manager who fails to take into account persistent trend indications when making forecasts. If, at each reporting period, the trends consistently indicate a cost overrun or schedule delay, it would be naive to predict completion within budget and to schedule, without at least carrying out a detailed analysis of the reason for the trend report, and developing an action plan to reverse the trend indication. Once a trend becomes established, it acquires a lot of inertia. It requires effort and a positive action plan to reverse a trend.

Benefits. The major benefit of project trending is that it can give project and senior management an early indication of any changes in the project which could cause serious deviations from the project objectives at completion. In particular, senior management do not wish to become victims of the 90% syndrome, when project reports indicate satisfactory performance to the 90% completion point, after which costs and schedules start to exceed budgets and targets which previously had been considered achievable.

Frequently, conventional project status and forecasting methods merely reflect the balance of the budget to completion. A constant no-change forecast at each reporting period provides a false sense of security until the 90% point is reached. Then it is too late to start corrective action. Trending techniques should not only forestall the occurrence of the 90% syndrome, but should also prevent unrealistic turnaround projections by project managers. Indications from trend display charts can warn top management to discount unrealistically optimistic predictions by a project manager when they obviously run counter to indicated trends. Project completions in contradiction to persistent trends are not usually attainable. It is for these reasons that higher levels of management are usually more in favor of the use of trending techniques than those at the working levels.

Projected deviations. The first step in trending is to determine the deviation at each reporting period from the plan or budget, and to project this deviation to completion. At this point, trending methods are just as dependent upon accurate and current project status reports as conventional project monitoring and reporting systems. Fig. 1 shows a typical table of data which would be generated at a reporting period. This information would be generated for conventional reporting, not specifically for trending.

Columns A and B identify project activities which could be major group activities or detailed activities in engineering, procurement or construction.

Column C is the budget hours for each activity.

A	B	C	D	E	F	G	H	I
Activity number	Activity description	Budget hours	Physical % complete	Earned hours C × D/100	Actual hours expended	% budget expended F × 100/C	Budget less earned hours C-E	% Deviation F × 100/E or G × 100/D
1	Activity AA	200	80	160	150	75.0	40	93.8
2	Activity BB	150	100	150	140	93.3	0	93.3
3	Activity CC	250	70	175	210	84.0	75	120.0
4	Activity DD	300	50	150	160	53.3	150	106.7
5	Activity EE	150	30	45	60	40.0	105	133.3
6	Activity FF	400	20	80	120	30.0	320	150.0
7	Activity GG	350	10	35	70	20.0	315	200.0
8	Activity HH	200	5	10	20	10.0	190	200.0
		ΣC	ΣE × 100/ΣC	ΣE	ΣF	ΣF × 100/ΣC	ΣH	ΣF × 100/ΣE
	TOTAL	2,000	40.3	805	930	46.5	1,195	115.5

Figure 1—Typical data for a single reporting period.

Column D is the percentage that each activity is physically complete. Physical percent completion should not be taken from a percentage of the calendar time expended. Physical percent completion should be an independent appraisal or measurement of the work done.

Column E, the earned hours, represents the percentage of the budget corresponding to the physical percent complete.

Column F, the actual hours expended, is obtained from manhour bookings and time sheets.

Column G is the percent of the budget expended which is the actual hours expressed as a percentage of the budget hours.

Column H shows the budget hours less the earned hours, which, in effect, is the budget hours corresponding to the physical work remaining.

Column I, the percent deviation, is the percentage ratio of the actual hours over the earned hours or the percent budget expended over the percent physical complete.

Fig. 1 is a table of typical data which could apply to a wide range of project activities at both the summary and detail level. Trending techniques require that a deviation is projected for each activity, and for the combined activities overall. There are a number of methods to arrive at the projected deviations. Four of the most common methods follow.

- **Trend method 1.** This method assumes that the work yet to be performed will be performed in accordance with the original budget regardless of the actual performance to date. The overall projection is, therefore, the actual expenditure to date, plus that portion of the original budget for the amount of work yet to be completed. The application of *Trend Method 1* to the data in Fig. 1 is illustrated in Fig. 2. This method is reasonable when the deviation is minor and the activity is below 50% complete. There is then a reasonable prospect that the balance of the work can be performed according to the original budget allocated for the remaining work. The method is not appropriate when the activity is over 50% complete, and there has been a wide deviation between actual performance and the budget. Here it would be unreasonable to expect that the remaining work can still be performed in accordance with the rate set in the original budget.

- **Trend method 2.** This method assumes that the balance of the work to be completed will be performed in accordance with the performance achieved to date. The projected manhours (cost) at completion will be the manhours (cost) to date extrapolated to 100 percent. This method is reasonable when the percentage completion exceeds 50 percent, by which time the performance to date will give a realistic indication of the performance expected to completion. The method is less reason-

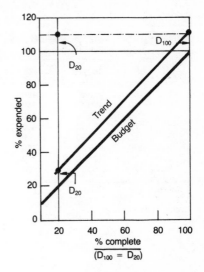

Trend =	Actual performance to date plus balance of unearned budget		
Activity number	F	+ H =	T_1
1	150	+ 40 =	190
2	140	+ 0 =	140
3	210	+ 70 =	285
4	160	+ 150 =	310
5	60	+ 105 =	165
6	120	+ 320 =	440
7	70	+ 315 =	385
8	20	+ 190 =	210
Totals	930	+ 1,195 =	2,125

Overall % deviation $= \dfrac{2,125 \times 100}{2,000} = 106.3\%$

Figure 2—Trend method 1.

able when there is a wide deviation at a low percentage point and there is a large "leverage" on the extrapolation, even though the deviation itself could be relatively small. Fig. 3 shows the application of *Trend Method 2* to the data in Fig. 1. Fig. 3 shows very clearly that the trend deviations vary widely from the budget in those cases where the extrapolations are for activities with low physical percentage completions.

• **Trend method 3.** This method is a combination of *Trend Methods 1* and *2. Trend Method 3* uses *Trend Method 1* when the physical percentage completion is less than 50 percent, and *Trend Method 2* when the physical percentage completion is 50 percent or greater. *Trend Method 3*, therefore, eliminates the weaknesses of *Trend Methods 1* and *2*, and uses the trending methods where they are most viable. (See Fig. 4.)

• **Trend method 4.** This method uses a slightly different approach. Here the deviation for each activity is tabulated separately. However, the overall deviation for the group of activities is a weighted value which has a greater contribution from those activities which have a higher percentage completion. The application of this method is shown in Fig. 4. The overall weighted deviation is obtained by multiplying each individual deviation by the physical percent complete for that activity, and then dividing the sum of the multiples by the sum of the physical percent completions.

Trend = Ratio of performance to date extrapolated to 100%				
Activity number	F	×	100/D	=	T_2
1	150	×	100/80	=	188
2	140	×	100/100	=	140
3	210	×	100/70	=	300
4	160	×	100/50	=	320
5	60	×	100/30	=	200
6	120	×	100/20	=	600
7	70	×	100/10	=	700
8	20	×	100/5	=	400
Totals	930	×	100/32.7	=	2,848

Overall % deviation $= \dfrac{2{,}848 \times 100}{2{,}000} = 142.4\%$

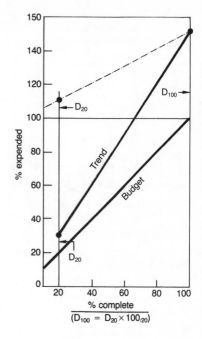

Figure 3—Trend method 2.

Trend = Trend Method 1 Physical % < 50% Trend Method 2 Physical % > 50%			
Activity number	Physical %	Method	T_3
1	80	2	188
2	100	2	140
3	70	2	300
4	50	2	320
5	30	1	165
6	20	1	440
7	10	1	385
8	5	1	210
Totals	–	–	2,148

Overall % deviation $= \dfrac{2{,}148 \times 100}{2{,}000} = 107.4\%$

Trend = % deviation × % complete/sum of Physical % complete				
Activity number	I	×	D	=	W
1	93.8	×	80	=	7,504
2	93.3	×	100	=	9,330
3	120.0	×	70	=	8,400
4	106.7	×	50	=	5,335
5	133.3	×	30	=	3,999
6	150.0	×	20	=	3,000
7	200.0	×	10	=	2,000
8	200.0	×	5	=	1,000
Totals	111.1	×	365	=	40,568

Overall % deviation = 40,568/365 = 111.1%

Figure 4—Trend method 3 (upper boxed portion) and trend method 4 (lower boxed portion) showing weighted deviation.

• **Analysis of four methods.** The deviation derived from the four trending methods for the data in Fig. 1 is as follows:
Trend Method 1 = 106.3%
Trend Method 2 = 142.4%
Trend Method 3 = 107.4%
Trend Method 4 = 111.1%

Of the four methods described, *Trend Method 3* is probably the most practical and realistic. The 50% breakpoint between *Trend Methods 1* and *2* is an arbitrary choice. It could be 60/40 or 70/30 or vice versa, depending upon the activities and application under consideration. It should be remembered, however, that trending is an approximation. Over-sophistication and precision in the method is not warranted, and might give a false sense of exactness.

Trend projection. Having established the projected deviation for an activity or group of activities at each reporting period, the next step is to project trends from the reporting periods through to completion on a trend report form or trend display chart. The three most common trend projection techniques are:
• Straight line projection
• Best and worst line projection
• Least squares method of projection

Fig. 5 illustrates these projection techniques.
Straight line projection is simply drawing a line by eye which appears to be a best fit for the points on the chart. In most cases, the best fit line will be readily apparent if there is a smooth trend in the monthly project deviations.
The best and worst line projection technique draws the projection through the highest and lowest points. This then allows for a best and worst case trend to be reported.
The least squares method of projection is the scientific method of providing a line which best fits a set of points. For the usual trending application, the accuracy given by this method is not required. However, there may be occasions when the deviations are so scattered that this is the only way to arrive at the projection.
The trend projection techniques may be applied to the whole range of projected deviations, the last five, or last three. The choice is a matter of judgement. It will be influenced by the project status and factors which have influenced deviations over the past few months. It may be that factors which have caused deviations in the early phases of the project no longer apply. Hence it is justifiable to ignore earlier projected deviations.

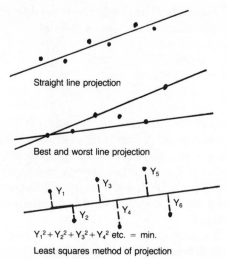

Figure 5—Trend projection techniques.

Performance trending. Performance is measured by comparing the hours actually spent with the hours that should have been spent for a given piece of work. The hours that should have been spent are the estimated hours derived from "standard hours." Standard hours are the average hours required for the piece of work as determined from the returns for a number of past projects. The deviations from this average, or standard, is a measure of performance.

- **Productivity.** Another term for performance is productivity, which can be calculated by either 1. Productivity ratio = standard hours/ actual hours, or 2. Productivity ratio = percent physical complete/ percent manhours spent.

  Both methods will give the same answer if the work is initially estimated and "weighted" in terms of standard hours, and the completed work is measured by physical methods, independently from the actual manhours expended. The total work is equal to the standard hours in the estimate. The work achieved to date is equal to the standard hours allocated for this amount of work. The physical percent complete is the standard hours for the amount of work achieved expressed as a percentage of the total standard hours in the estimate. A productivity ratio greater than 1 indicates a performance better than budget.
- **Performance monitoring.** There are two main reasons why monitoring performance is an important part of project control: 1. Deviation

from the performance plan can have a significant impact upon costs. The direct manhour budget will be exceeded if performance is below standard with possible unfavorable consequences upon the supervisory and indirect manhour budgets, and 2. An increase in the manhour forecast may also necessitate an increase in the level of resource application or manpower loading. If the budget is exceeded, the only way to maintain the schedule is to work more hours in the available time. This can be achieved by the use of overtime (at extra cost) or by applying more manpower. (If manpower is available, it can be applied economically, and is not limited by work breakdown or space restrictions.)

Since performance has a direct and major effect upon cost, schedule and resource, performance trending techniques can provide an early indication of potential problems and, in turn, allow for early corrective action.

- **Typical progress report.** Fig. 6 shows a typical engineering monthly progress report which may be used for individual engineering disciplines or for the overall engineering effort. The bottom part of the report shows three S-curves plotted on a monthly calendar scale.

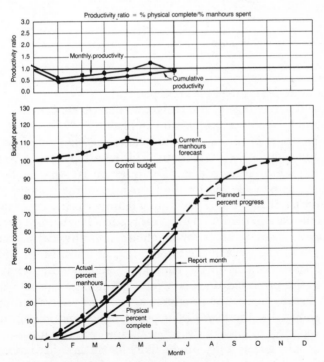

Figure 6—Typical engineering monthly progress report.

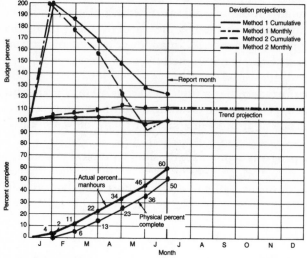

Figure 7—Manhour performance trending.

• The monthly percentage progress planned.
• The actual percentage of the budget manhours expended.
• The monthly percentage physical completion.

The upper part of the report form shows the manhour forecast, the monthly and cumulative productivity. This report gives a very clear picture of the performance to date. The question is, what is the performance that can be expected for the remainder of the project?

• **Manhour trending.** Fig. 7 shows manhour performance trending applied to the data in the Fig. 6 progress report. The bottom part of Fig. 7 replots the actual values for manhours and physical percent complete curves. The table at the top of Fig. 7 is a worksheet which uses *Trend Methods 1* and *2* on the cumulative and monthly deviations to calculate the projected deviation for each month. These values are plotted directly above the progress curves. The analysis of the trend curves shows that there was poor performance and low productivity during the early months of the project. However, this has steadily improved to give a near unity productivity for the last three months. On the basis of this display, a trend projection of the *Method 2* cumulative calculation appears reasonable which indicates the trend is 110% of budget. Had the projected deviations continued to be divergent a very different trend projection would have resulted.

This format for progress reporting and trending may be used for both engineering and construction manhours. Construction reports often use manhours for the vertical scale in place of percent complete. In this case, the actual manhours used are plotted and the physical completion curve is plotted in standard manhours. The productivity ratio is the standard manhours divided by actual manhours. In all other respects, the curves, and trending techniques are similar.

• **Unit rate trending.** Fig. 8 illustrates a different method of performance trending which may be more appropriate for construction. Fig.

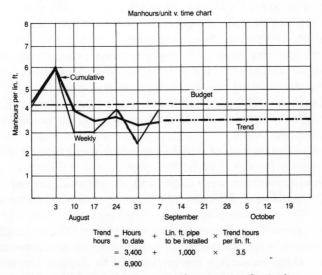

Weekly piping costs – Manhours per lin. ft.

Item   6″ CI U.G. pipe
Total amount   2,000 ft.
Budget rate   4.5 Hrs/lin. ft.
Budget hours   9,000

Job no.   1234
Account   M101
Period   Sept. 7

Period	Lineal feet installed		Manhours expended		Manhours per lin. ft.	
	This week	To date	This week	To date	This week	To date
Aug 3	100	100	600	600	6.0	6.0
Aug 10	200	300	600	1,200	3.0	4.0
Aug 17	200	500	600	1,800	3.0	3.6
Aug 24	150	650	600	2,400	4.0	3.7
Aug 31	250	900	600	3,000	2.4	3.3
Sept 7	100	1,000	400	3,400	4.0	3.4
Sept 21						

Manhours/unit v. time chart

$$\begin{aligned}
\text{Trend hours} &= \frac{\text{Hours}}{\text{to date}} + \frac{\text{Lin. ft. pipe}}{\text{to be installed}} \times \frac{\text{Trend hours}}{\text{per lin. ft.}} \\
&= 3,400 + 1,000 \times 3.5 \\
&= 6,900
\end{aligned}$$

Figure 8—Typical progress and trending report for a construction trade.

8 monitors the activity of installing 2,000 feet of underground pipe for which the estimate is 4.5 hours per lineal foot installed, giving a total budget of 9,000 hours. Actual performance in terms of lineal feet installed, and manhours expended is tracked weekly. The actual manhours per lineal feet, both weekly and cumulatively, are plotted on the chart. The cumulative plot is extrapolated to give a trend projection of 3.5 manhours per lineal foot. From this trend projection, the trend hours can be calculated using *Trend Method 1,* as shown in the box below the chart. The ratio of the budget rate at 4.5 hours per lineal feet over the trend rate of 3.5 hours per lineal feet gives the trend productivity of 1.29.

This same information could have been depicted by plotting the standard hours corresponding to the feet of pipe installed with the actual hours for each reporting period, together with the weekly and cumulative productivity obtained by dividing the standard hours by the actual hours. An extrapolation of the cumulative productivity line would give a productivity trend projection of 1.29, which corresponds to 3.5 manhours per lineal foot. Fig. 8 is an alternative way of tracking and reporting productivity which may be convenient for activities which are measured in terms of standard hours per unit of work.

Schedule trending. Trending techniques used for schedule performance are in general more subjective than those used in other applications. The reason is that it is difficult to quantify the impact of schedule deviations for difference activities. A schedule report may show that an activity is a number of days late. But unless this activity is on the critical path it is difficult to assess the effect this will have upon the overall project schedule. In spite of these limitations schedule trending can have value if the trending techniques apply to overall rates of progress or to milestone, or critical activities. A common method of schedule trending is to assess the physical percent completion that must be achieved each month if the scheduled completion date is to be met. Measured monthly deviations from the required rate of physical progress can be used to develop a schedule trend.

Fig. 9 shows a method of schedule trending applied to the data in the Fig. 6 Progress Report. The bottom part of Fig. 9 plots the values for the planned percent progress curve and the physical percent complete curve. The horizontal difference between the curves shows the schedule deviation. The cumulative and monthly schedule deviation is plotted on a schedule trend chart above the progress curves. The extrapolation of the cumulative schedule deviation projections gives a schedule trend projection which shows that the project will be 30 days late at completion. Analysis of the trend curves shows poor schedule performance dur-

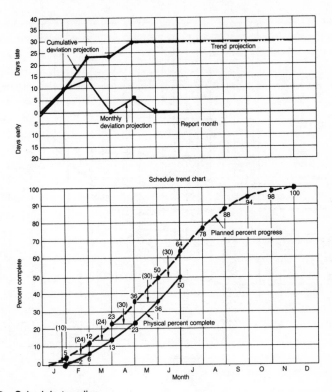

Figure 9—Schedule trending.

ing the early months of the project which has steadily improved to give progress rates close to the plan for the last three months, although initial lost time has not been regained.

Fig. 10 shows a different approach to schedule trending. Key milestone schedule dates are entered on the schedule display chart. At each reporting period the milestone schedule dates are reforecast. As the early milestones are completed the actual completion dates are entered showing the schedule deviations which have occurred. This type of schedule trend display chart clearly illustrates that negative schedule trends for early project schedule milestones must also impact subsequent milestones. It would be unreasonable to predict overall completion to schedule if the schedule display chart shows major schedule deviations for the intermediate milestones.

Cost trending. Most of the techniques described for performance trending can be applied equally effectively for cost trending. Manhours and cost are synonymous.

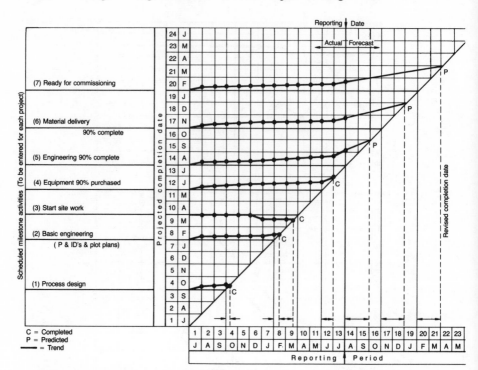

Figure 10—Schedule trend display chart.

Figs. 7 and 8 can be expressed as a percentage of total cost or in dollars in place of manhours. Trending charts similar to Fig. 8 may be drawn up which express cost ratios or ratios of cost to manhours. Examples of this are:

- Computer cost per engineering manhour
- Non chargeable staff cost to chargeable staff cost
- Cost of supplies per unit of work produced
- Bulk material cost as a ratio of equipment cost
- Cost of construction consumables per labor hour expended
- Cost of equipment maintenance per hour of equipment utilization
- Material to labor cost

The above are merely a few examples of cost ratios that may be tracked and monitored during project execution. All the above can be set up on trend charts to give a cost trend projection.

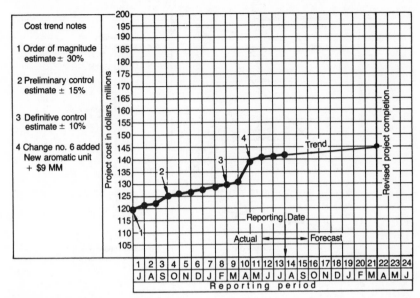

Figure 11—Cost trend display chart.

Fig. 11 is a display chart for trending total project or major unit costs. This report which shows the predicted cost at each reporting period, can be a very effective trend indicator, in spite of its simplicity. If there is continuing change in the projected cost at each reporting period a trend chart of this type graphically illustrates the potential problem.

• **Combining cost and schedule trend.** When projecting cost and resource trends, a mistake often made is to project them to the original planned completion date. The projection of cost and resource trends should be carried out to the completion date that is projected by the schedule trend.

Fig. 12 shows the effect of combining cost and schedule trends. Many project costs are directly affected if the schedule is extended. Such things as supervisory staff, indirect costs, equipment and space rentals are all proportional to calendar time. Schedule trending should be performed prior to the cost trending exercise so that the schedule trend can be taken into account in the cost trend display charts.

Material trending. Trending techniques can also be used effectively to monitor material quantity usage during the design and construction of a project. Equipment items which normally carry their own tag number are usually tracked individually. Bulk materials in the civil, structural, piping, instrumentation and electrical areas are more difficult to track.

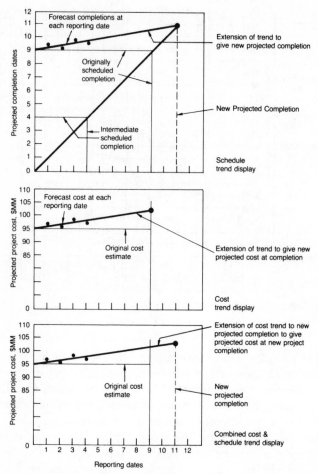

Figure 12—Combining cost and schedule trends.

There are two main areas of concern: 1. That the quantities generated by the final design drawings and bills of materials will differ from the quantities contained in the estimate take off from preliminary drawings, and 2. That the final quantities actually installed by the construction forces will differ from the quantities set forth in the final design drawings and bills of materials.

Significant deviations in either of these areas can have a major effect on the overall project cost and schedule. Excess quantities will provide a material surplus problem at project completion and will incur unnecessary project costs. Late ordered material to make up for shortages will cause schedule delays.

A difficulty common to all the bulk material categories is that there are blank periods in the flow of material quantity information. Quantities taken off for estimating and early bulk ordering purposes cannot be finally checked until the last bill of material or the last isometric has been processed. Similarly, the total quantities required by the field are not known definitively until the last drawing has been installed.

Material monitoring and trending methods can help to provide indicative information during these blank periods so that corrective action can be initiated in good time. Material trending is no different from other forms of trending in that it requires measurement and comparison of actual achievement against budget or plan.

- **Material identification.** For material trending to be effective the material quantities in the base control should be coded and subdivided in a way which corresponds to the way in which the final material quantities will be identified.

Frequently, bulk material quantities are generated at an early stage in the project for cost and estimation purposes by means of factors or ratios. These methods may be quite effective for generating global quantities and costs, but they do not provide sufficient definitive quantity information for detailed material monitoring and trending. The material groups and subtotals in the initial control documents should be the same as those taken off from the completed design drawings, and finally installed in the field. The following are some of the ways by which bulk materials can be identified for monitoring and trending purposes.

- Unit and plot plan area designation
- Material specification
- Pipeline or circuit number reference
- System or application
- Key plan or drawing number reference

Bulk materials which have been identified initially can be tracked by the same identification in the final drawings and bills of material as they are produced, and ultimately by the field forces as the material is installed.

- **Common bulk materials.** Fig. 13 illustrates a method of bulk material trending which can be used in a wide variety of applications. In this case, the cubic yards of concrete generated in the design drawings are compared against the cubic yards in the estimate, and from this a trend is projected. The top part of the figure shows the projected deviation worksheet. The total cubic yards in the estimate are allocated to individual areas or drawings. The percentage of the design that is complete is noted against each area or drawing, together with the quantity that has been taken off to the point that the design has been

Sample report no. 3—Deviation projection worksheet

A Area drawing structure or equipment reference	B Total estimate quantity Cu yds	C % of design complete	D Estimate quantity for % design complete B × C cu yds	E Actual design quantity required Cu yds	F Actual design % of estimate E × 100/B	G Projected total quantity B × E/D Cu yds	H Projected deviation % G × 100/B	I Trend method
A	300	100	300	350	117	350	117	2
B	250	65	165	200	80	303	121	2
C	400	80	320	320	80	400	100	2
D	200	45	90	130	65	240	120	1
E	500	40	200	250	50	550	110	1
F	350	36	125	150	43	375	107	1
Total	2,000	60 ΣD×100/ΣB	1200	1400	70 ΣE × 100/ΣB	2218	111 ΣG × 100/ΣB	3

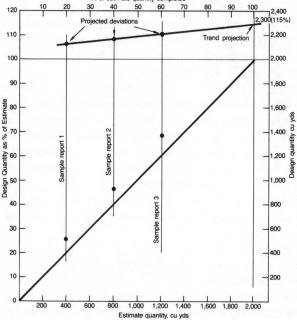

Figure 13—Bulk material trending.

completed. The comparison between the actual design quantities and the estimate quantities provides a projected deviation and overall trend projection.

• **Sample trending.** Material trending need not be performed at fixed project progress reporting periods. It should be performed at selected points during the design progress to give a representative sampling of the work achieved to date. In the example shown, Sample Report 3 has been taken at about 60 percent through the work. Prior sample reports were taken at about 20 percent and 40 percent points. In each case, the projected deviations are displayed on the lower part of Fig. 13. The trend projection is the extrapolation of the projected deviations from the sample reports prepared during the progress of detail design. This type of report form can equally well apply to the construction work to compare actual quantity of concrete poured against quantities called for in the drawings. This will trend the accuracy of the final take off quantities in the drawings, and also the amount of construction over-pour.

- **Piping materials.** Piping materials are difficult to trend because of the large number of different sizes, material specifications and components that make up the total piping material account. A trending method for piping must select some part of the whole and then apply the trending techniques to this part, assuming that it will give an indication for the whole. A method frequently used is to take off piping materials by flow sheet line number, and then compare final quantities against the preliminary take off on this basis. Other methods are to identify materials by area or by system. Fig. 14 shows a method of trending piping material. In this instance, the trending is done by

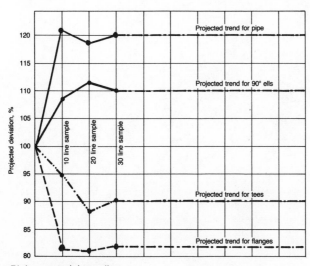

Piping component worksheet—Range 3 in.–24 in.–30 line sample

Piping component	Unit	Total quantity in estimate	Estimate quantity for 30 lines	Design quantity for 30 lines	Projected total quantity	Projected deviation %	Projected deviation quantity
Pipe	Ft.	10,000	3,000	3,600	12,000	120	+ 2,000
90° Ells	No	600	180	198	660	110	+ 60
tees	No	100	30	27	90	90	− 10
flanges	No	80	24	20	67	83	− 13

Figure 14—Piping material trending.

sampling a number of lines from the total. The actual material taken off for the sample lines is compared against the material in the estimate for these same lines. The projected deviations from the sample reports provide a basis for trending actual quantities against estimated quantities for the major components. Fig. 14 is an example which trends pipe, elbows and flanges for a combined range of pipe sizes. It is preferable to trend each pipe size and each pipe material, but this would be too time consuming and laborious if done manually. The trending of piping materials is best performed if the piping quantities are taken off by computer so that the comparison and trending exercise can also be done by computer. Manual systems can be used effectively on selected materials and size ranges, and may also be used for piping material cost trending.

Simplicity. Project trending is not a substitute or replacement for normal project monitoring and reporting methods. A variety of trend report formats can be applied to a wide range of project variables. Trending is most effective when simple approximations are used with flexible techniques. Excessive precision and refinement are not appropriate. A project manager who uses project trending selectively and who is also aware of the benefits and limitations will find that project trending can be a very useful additional weapon in his armory of project controls.

Part 8: Procurement

	SUBJECTS	1 PREAWARD	2 INITIATION	3 ENGINEERING	4 PROCUREMENT	5 CONSTRUCTION
A	FINANCIAL/CONTRACTUAL					
B	ORGANIZATION/EXECUTION PLANNING					
C	MANAGING PEOPLE/COMMUNICATION					
D	ESTIMATING/COST CONTROL					
E	RISK ANALYSIS					
F	SCHEDULING					
G	TRACKING/TRENDING					
H	PROGRESS/PRODUCTIVITY MEASUREMENT					
I	MATERIAL MANAGEMENT				●	●

Chapter 23

How to Evaluate Bids for Major Equipment

A. E. Kerridge

The analysis of the investment and return on a major piece of equipment has the same ingredients as the analysis of a complete process plant. It is only a matter of scale. To do his job properly, an engineer must be able to do more than check out the bids technically. He must perform a combined technical and commercial evaluation and take many non-technical factors into consideration.

Eleven phases. There are 11 phases to the major-equipment bid-evaluation process: 1. Pre-select vendors, 2. Prepare inquiry, 3. Receive bids, 4. Make preliminary evaluation, 5. Make technical evaluation, 6. Make commercial evaluation, 7. Conduct pre-award meeting, 8. Condition bids, 9. Select vendors, 10. Conduct pre-commitment meeting, and 11. Award order. Let's consider these one by one.

1. Pre-select vendors. Before inquiries are issued, potential bidders should be pre-selected from ones who have the experience and who have performed satisfactorily in the recent past. Before sending an inquiry to a new vendor, pre-qualify him by asking for a presentation of his qualifications, his prior and similar experience and a list of references. Follow up the references. Visit his manufacturing plant, look at his organization, meet some of the key people and test their caliber. Look at the equipment and facilities. Generally get a feel for the competence and capability available.

Another point to look for is current shop workload. A manufacturer that is too busy may cause late delivery. On the other hand, a manufacturer whose workload is too light may be in difficulty. He may go out of business before he can complete your work. Don't select a vendor who is too hungry. The management may be spending more time worrying about keeping the company solvent than attending to your project.

Don't let anyone bid just because they ask. If the vendor is persistent, let him give you a pre-qualification presentation. If he doesn't meet your criteria, tell him why. You may think it costs you nothing to let him bid if he wants to, but it will waste your time to review bids which are not acceptable.

Don't ask a vendor to bid just to get an extra quote to keep your favorite vendor competitive. And don't send an inquiry to a vendor if you are not prepared to give him the order should his bid be technically and commercially acceptable. Apart from wasting your own time, it is unfair to ask a vendor to prepare a bid if you have no intention of placing an order. Whenever you ask anyone to bid, he must have a reasonable expectation of getting an order.

Finally, don't send out too many inquiries. Four to five bidders are enough to get a competitive price. Six is normally the maximum number of bidders to whom inquiries should be sent so as not to use up too much of your time and also the time of a large number of vendors.

2. Prepare inquiry. Provide the vendor with all the information he needs to make a specific bid. Tell him exactly what you want. To help the vendor, give him a set of documents, with an index, assembled in a logical order. Make it easy for him to find the important requirements. It doesn't help you or the vendor if critical points are hidden away in some obscure part of the documentation. If the vendor fails to allow for these in his quotation and you subsequently insist upon them being supplied, it merely creates ill feeling and friction. There may be claims for extras which could hurt the overall quality of the job. In general, the inquiry document should be divided into clear-cut sub-sections as follows:

- **Technical**—1. Process duty specifications, 2. Materials of construction, 3. Special design features, 4. Overdesign/redundancy requirements, 6. Ancillary equipment required, 7. Evaluation criteria (pay out period, value of feedstock, utilities, consumables, etc.), 8. Electrical & utility data, 9. General design data, 10. Applicable design codes, standards, etc., and 11. Related specifications.
- **Documents**—1. Drawing/document approvals, 2. Number of reproducibles/prints required, 3. Quality of drawings/data sheets, 4. Definition of drawing needs (foundation, arrangement, terminal connection, cross-sectional and parts), 5. Number and content of

operating/maintenance manuals, 6. Spare parts list and recommendations for specified period, and 7. Performance curves, test certificates
and reports.
• **Commercial**—1. Commercial terms, 2. Required delivery date and
location, 3. Expediting and progress reporting, 4. Inspection requirements, 5. Painting, finishing and packing, 6. Invoicing and payment
terms, 7. Names and addresses of contacts, 8. Warranties and guarantees, 9. Bid due date, 10. Sealed bid instructions (if applicable), 11.
Service representatives at site, and 12. Unit rates and extensions.

On major projects it is desirable to use the sealed bid procedure. Vendors are required to submit their quotations in sealed envelopes provided by the inquirer. This ensures confidentiality until all bids have
been received. Bidders should be asked to separate the commercial and
technical portions of their quotations so these can be processed independently.

A common fault is to issue an inquiry with a complete volume of the
project job specifications appended. This leaves it up to the vendor to
find out for himself to what extent the specifications apply to the equipment under consideration.

You may think this practice provides you with cover, saves your time
and puts the onus on the bidder. But this is not the case. In due course,
you will have to review the bidder's specifications and drawings to check
that the requirements of the specifications have been met. You have a
much better chance of getting a bid which meets the specification requirements if you extract relevant parts of the specifications and include
these in the specific inquiry documents.

An inquiry should be as specific as possible to ensure that all bidders
respond on a common basis. But inquiry documents should not be so
restrictive that they exclude alternative proposals. The inquiry document should instruct the vendor to provide his base bid exactly in accordance with the inquiry specifications. However, he should be permitted
to offer alternative designs which will meet the requirements so long as
deviations or alternates to the base specification are clearly defined. In
this way you allow the vendors to show their initiative and to introduce
new designs or concepts. It also helps you to keep up to date with the
market place.

A final point. Before the inquiries are issued, check with each vendor
to ensure that he is interested in receiving the inquiry and will provide
you with a bid by the due date. It can be frustrating to issue inquiries
and then receive decline to bid letters just prior to the due date. This will
mean lost time if a second round of inquiries has to be initiated with new
vendors.

3. Receive bids. As soon as the inquiries have been issued, phone the vendor to check that he has received the bid documents. Midway through the bidding period, make another call to check that the vendor is working on the bid and intends to submit a bid by the required date. Finally, a week prior to the bid due date, remind the vendor that bids are due on the date specified. This continual contact during the bidding period is well worthwhile for major equipment. It lets you know how active and responsive the individual vendors are to your inquiry. And you get early warning if a vendor is going to decline to bid or be late with his submission.

If a vendor is going to be late, he should advise you sometime before the bid due date to request an extension. You can then check with the other vendors to find out whether they also need an extension. If so, you might agree that an extension would be worthwhile overall to get more complete and better quality bids. If, however, one vendor alone asks for an extension or fails to ask for an extension and submits a bid late (whereas all other vendors have met the bid due date) then his bid should be disqualified. The fact that he cannot get a bid in on time shows he may be equally late with his drawing and material deliveries.

During the bidding period, all vendors should be given an equal opportunity to bid and have equal access to any information available to help them prepare their bids. Clarifications or answers to questions raised by one vendor should be disseminated to the other vendors.

If the sealed bid procedure is being used, any bids received prior to the bid due date should be kept sealed until the official opening on the bid due date. Vendors should submit their bids in the envelopes provided and the envelopes should be properly sealed according to instructions. Sealed bids should be opened in the presence of two or more nominated persons who will witness that at the time of opening the seals were intact. The individuals attending the opening of the sealed bids will sign both the envelopes and the cover sheet of each bid to witness the fact that the bids were sealed until the time noted. If the sealed bid procedure is used, any bids received after the bid due date should be disqualified and returned to the late bidder unopened.

If bidders have been asked to submit separate commercial and technical bids, this will allow a wider distribution of the technical portion and a more restricted distribution of the confidential commercial information. If the sealed bid procedure is not used, then it is still good practice to hold all bids in a secure place until the bid due date and open them simultaneously. This ensures that there is not early access to confidential pricing information, leading to the possibility of unethical disclosure.

4. Preliminary evaluation. Once the bids have been received and opened, simply check that the bids are complete. Have the bidders responded fully? Do you have all you need to make a proper evaluation?

For the preliminary evaluation, prepare a checklist of the known components required, the drawings, data sheets and the documents that should have been provided, and the key points in the commercial terms. A simple check is entered against each item under a column for each bidder. At the bottom of the preliminary evaluation enter the quoted cost plus any extras or adjustments which may apply for items omitted. Also note the promised delivery date for the equipment and for the drawings.

At this point, a meeting may be desirable to list the acceptable bidders in ascending price order to eliminate bidders whose quotations appear to be unacceptable. The purpose of the preliminary evaluation is to focus attention quickly on a short list of vendors whose bids appear to be acceptable and whose prices are competitive. Time need not be spent evaluating bids where the price is obviously high, the bid is incomplete, or the delivery or other aspects are unacceptable.

Another benefit of the preliminary evaluation is that it brings to light areas where required information is missing or bid data needs clarification. In these cases, the vendors can be immediately contacted to provide the additional information needed.

5. Technical evaluation. Once the bids have been initially checked out for completeness, perform a complete technical evaluation from the short list of the most promising bids.

Refer to bid tabulation forms for similar equipment used on past projects. For a major complex equipment item, it is unlikely that a standard form will exist which covers all the components and requirements. Normally, it is necessary to make up a bid tabulation form for the specific equipment item under consideration using past bid tabulation forms as a checklist. You can save time if you prepare your bid tabulation form at the time when you are preparing the inquiry documents. This has the double advantage, 1. it ensures that you include all the information you require from the vendor in the inquiry document, and 2. it allows you to proceed with the technical evaluation immediately.

Fig. 1 is a typical technical bid tabulation form which provides a checklist of general points to be considered during the technical evaluation. If the inquiry documents have been assembled consistently and logically, the same format may be used for the bid tabulation form. Once you have made the basic check that the equipment is technically acceptable and meets the inquiry specification, then you should look for additional benefits. Examples: efficiency, utility consumptions, superior quality of materials, redundant/spare capacity, and other design benefits which are specific to the bidder.

Look for hidden additional costs or cost savings. A smaller, lighter piece of equipment will require smaller foundations, smaller structures and less permanently installed handling and maintenance equipment. A

TECHNICAL

CLIENT: ABC CO — MULTI-UNIT
PROJECT: ANY TOWN
LOCATION: TYPICAL
ITEM DESCRIPTION:

BY AEK   CHECKED VG

TECHNICAL BID TABULATION

CLIENT: ABC CO — MULTI-UNIT
PROJECT: ANY TOWN
LOCATION: TYPICAL
ITEM DESCRIPTION:

DATE: 1 AUG 83
JOB NO.: 1234
REQ. NO.: 001
ITEM NO.: T-1
SHEET NO.: 5
REV. NO.: 0

BY AEK   CHECKED VGA   APPROVED MBC

ITEM	VENDOR A	VENDOR B	VENDOR C	VENDOR D
GENERAL				
VENDOR				
QUOTATION REFERENCE				
QUOTATION DATE				
VALIDITY EXPIRY DATE				
EQUIPMENT DELIVERY DATE				
MAJOR COMPONENTS (list below)				
ROTATING EQUIPMENT				
TYPE				
MFCTR/MODEL NO.				
FLUID				
FLOW DESIGN/OPERATING				
SUCTION PSIG DESIGN/OPERATING				
DISCHARGE PSIG DESIGN/OPERATING				
DIFFERENTIAL PSI DESIGN/OPERATING				
SUCTION °F DESIGN/OPERATING				
DISCHARGE °F DESIGN/OPERATING				
ROTOR/IMPELLER DIA REQD/MAX				
SPEED RPM				
PERFORMANCE DATA				
CAPACITY				
FLOW				
YIELD				
H.P. REQUIRED				
MATERIALS CASING				
ROTOR/IMPELLER				
COUPLING MFCTR/TYPE/MODEL				
LUBRICATION				
OVERALL DIMENSIONS L/W/H				
OVERALL WEIGHT				
ACCESSORIES				
DOCUMENTATION				
ARRANGEMENT DRAWINGS				
DATA SHEETS				
PARTS LISTS				
RECOMMENDED SPARES				
TEST CERTIFICATES/CURVES				
OPERATING/MAINTENANCE MANUALS				
DRAWING DELIVERY PROMISE				
DRIVER				
TYPE				
MFCTR/MODEL NO.				
H.P./SPEED/S.F.				
VOLTAGE				
EFFICIENCY FL/3/4L/1/2L				
ENCLOSURE				
CLASSIFICATION				
BEARINGS				
STEAM PSIG IN/OUT				
LBS/HR				
MATERIALS				

ITEM	VENDOR A	VENDOR B	VENDOR C	VENDOR D
INSTRUMENTS				
FLOW NO/TYPE				
TEMPERATURES NO/TYPE				
PRESSURE NO/TYPE				
LEVEL NO/TYPE				
ANALYZER NO/TYPE				
RELIEF/SAFETY NO/TYPE				
ALARMS NO/TYPE				
OTHER NO/TYPE				
PIPING				
INTERCONNECTING PIPE				
PIPE SCHEDULE/FLANGE RATING				
PIPE DESIGN CODE				
INTERNAL CLEAN PICKLE/BLAST				
VALVES TYPE				
NO OF TERMINAL CONNECTIONS				
PIPE SUPPORTS/SPRING HANGERS				
ELECTRICAL				
SWITCHGEAR				
TRANSFORMER				
POWER VOLTAGE				
INTERCONNECTING CABLES				
LIGHTING				
STRUCTURAL				
PLATFORMS				
LADDERS				
STAIRWAYS				
LIFTING/HANDLING EQUIPMENT				
PROTECTIVE COATINGS				
INSULATION THERMAL				
PERSONNEL				
PAINT				

ITEM	VENDOR A	VENDOR B	VENDOR C	VENDOR D
EXCHANGERS				
TYPE				
OVERALL DUTY BTU/HR				
FLUID SHELL/TUBE				
DESIGN FLOW SHELL/TUBE				
OPERATING FLOW SHELL/TUBE				
DESIGN PSIG SHELL/TUBE				
OPERATING PSIG SHELL/TUBE				
DIFFERENTIAL PSI SHELL/TUBE				
DESIGN °F IN SHELL/TUBE				
OPERATING °F IN SHELL/TUBE				
DESIGN °F OUT SHELL/TUBE				
OPERATING °F OUT SHELL/TUBE				
SURFACE AREA SQ FT				
SHELL DIA/LENGTH				
TUBES NO/O.D./THKNSS/LENGTH				
NO. OF PASSES				
BAFFLES NO/TYPE				
HEAD TYPE				
MATERIALS TUBES/TUBE SHEETS				
SHELL/HEAD				
DESIGN CODE				
OVERALL WEIGHT				

ITEM	VENDOR A	VENDOR B	VENDOR C	VENDOR D
VESSELS				
TYPE				
DIA/LENGTH				
SHELL THICKNESS				
HEAD TYPE				
HEAD THICKNESS				
SUPPORTS/TYPE				
PRESSURE PSIG DESIGN/OPERATING				
TEMPERATURE °F DESIGN/OPERATING				
INTERNALS				
TRAYS NO/TYPE				
COLLECTORS NO/TYPE				
DISTRIBUTORS NO/TYPE				
PACKING SUPPORTS NO/TYPE				
BAFFLES NO/TYPE				
PACKING MATERIALS				
DEMISTERS				
CATALYST				
DESSICANT				
RINGS				
MANHOLES NO/SIZE/RTG				
CONNECTIONS				
MATERIALS SHELL				
HEAD				
INTERNALS				
DESIGN CODE				
OVERALL WEIGHT				

ITEM	VENDOR A	VENDOR B	VENDOR C	VENDOR D
TESTING				
HYDROSTATIC				
RADIOGRAPHIC/ULTRASONIC				
OPERATING				
MATERIAL				
OTHER				
OPERATING DATA				
HOURS/YEAR ON STREAM				
UTILITIES PER HOUR				
STEAM				
ELECTRICITY				
WATER				
AIR				
OTHER				
FEEDSTOCK				
PRODUCTS				
CATALYSTS				
LUBRICATION				
NOISE LEVELS				
OPERATORS HRS/YR				
MAINTENANCE HRS/YR				
SPARES				
ITEMS REQUIRED/PERIOD				

Figure 1—Typical technical bid evaluation form.

well laid out modular piece of equipment may require fewer piping connections and better access for installation and maintenance. A simpler, more positive design may require less external instrumentation and control for operation.

Look also at the availability of vendor support. Does he have local representation and service facilities? What is the quality of the drawings and documentation provided with the bid? When does he promise final certified drawings? What warranties and guarantees does he provide?

Evaluate the operating cost over the required payout period. Typical items to be considered for operating costs are:

- Feedstocks required and products produced
- Utilities, catalyst and chemicals consumed
- Spare parts cost and replacement period
- Maintenance/service frequency and manpower
- Operating manpower levels.

To evaluate operating costs, establish a present-day unit rate for labor and utilities together with a compounded escalation index for these unit rates for the future years to be evaluated. With these factors, the expenditures for utilities, maintenance, etc., can be determined in future years as illustrated in *Fig. 2*.

6. Commercial evaluation. A preliminary commercial evaluation is performed when the bid is received. The main purpose is to establish the short list of bidders requiring serious consideration. The detailed commercial evaluation should be performed after the technical evaluation is complete.

The first thing to check is that everything required in the specification has been included in the quoted price. Some things to look for are: drawings, documents, maintenance and operating manuals, test facilities and test certificates, painting and insulation, shop assembly, packing and crating, field service representatives, freight to specified delivery point, and insurance cover until ownership transfer.

Having checked out the basic items which could affect the cost, examine the commercial terms. Is a down payment required with intermediate progress payments? What warranties and guarantees are offered? What delivery date is promised?

Check that unit rates or per diem rates have been quoted for possible additions or extensions of service personnel. If the price is not fixed, but subject to escalation, check that the escalation formula clearly defines the material, labor and other components and the national indices used.

Annual operating costs are calculated from equation:

$$C = H \times U \times R \times E$$

Where
C = Annual Operating Cost for Year in Question ($)
H = Operating Hours Per Year (Hrs)
U = Units Consumed Per Hour (Lbs, No., Mhrs, Etc.)
R = Todays Unit Rate ($/Unit)
E = Compounded Escalation Factor from Today to Year in Question
The above can be applied to:
UTILITIES, CONSUMABLES, FEEDSTOCK, SPARE PARTS, OPERATING LABOR, MAINTENANCE LABOR, ETC.
If annual escalation percent (p) is constant then:

$$E = (1 + p/100)^n$$

Where n = Future Year No. in Question
If annual escalation percent (p) is variable then:

$$E = (1 + p1/100) \times (1 + p2/100) \times (1 + pn/100)$$

Figure 2—Evaluating operating costs.

Fig. 3 shows a typical commercial bid evaluation form which enumerates the above points.

Once the base prices have been checked, the next step is to apply adjustments and corrections. Add allowances for differential freight costs, import costs, currency exchange, agents and any other additional services which may be required.

Take into account the cost of money. The simplest method is to adjust all costs to a present-day value. Allow a discount equal to the prevailing interest rate for money which will be paid in the future.

This will penalize vendors requiring a high down payment and large interim progress payments and favor those vendors who do not require payment until job completion. If you can defer payment of money, you have the benefit of "float" interest the money can earn while in your possession. Paradoxically, this approach may penalize a vendor offering a delivery date much earlier than is required. Too early a delivery date will cost you money. It may also invalidate warranties if the equipment is not put into service for some months after it has been received.

The best plan is to insist upon a delivery date which meets your field erection schedule. The conversion of quoted cost to present-day values

COMMERCIAL BID TAB

CLIENT   ABC CO
PROJECT   MULTI-UNIT
LOCATION   ANY TOWN
ITEM DESCRIPTION   TYPICAL

BY   AEK   CHECKED   AAA

ITEM	VEN.
GENERAL	
VENDOR	
QUOTATION REFERENCE	
QUOTATION DATE	
VALIDITY EXPIRY DATE	
CONTACT NAME	
VENDOR SHOP LOCATION	
LOCAL REPRESENTATIVE	
DELIVERY	
MATERIAL START/COMPLETE	
DRAWINGS START/COMPLETE	
DELIVERY POINT	
COMPONENTS (LIST BELOW)	
FINANCIAL	
MATERIAL BASE PRICE	
ESCALATION TERMS	
UNIT RATE EXTENSIONS	
SERVICE REPRESENTATIVE RATES	
1st PAYMENT AMT/DATE	
2nd PAYMENT AMT/DATE	
3rd PAYMENT AMT/DATE	

Figure 3—Typical commercial bid evaluation form.

COMMERCIAL BID TABULATION

CLIENT   ABC CO   DATE: 8 AUG 83
PROJECT   MULTI-UNIT   JOB NO.:   1234
LOCATION   ANY TOWN   REQ. NO.:   001
ITEM DESCRIPTION   TYPICAL   ITEM NO.:   T-1
                                              SHEET NO.:   2
                                              REV. NO.:   0

BY   AEK   CHECKED   AAA   APPROVED   BBC

ITEM	VENDOR A	VENDOR B	VENDOR C	VENDOR D
MISCELLANEOUS				
RECOMMENDED SPARE PARTS				
MANDATORY SPARE PARTS				
NAMEPLATES & PERMANENT TAGS				
SHOP ASSEMBLY				
SHOP PAINTING				
SHOP TESTING				
PACKING & CRATING				
CATALYST/CHEMICALS				
LUBRICANTS				
DRAWINGS/MANUALS				
ENGINEERING SERVICE				
WARRANTIES/GUARANTEES				
INSURANCE				
TEST CERTIFICATES				
IMPORT DUTIES				
AGENT FEES				
CURRENCY EXCHANGE				
INSPECTION FEES				
* COST ADJUSTMENTS				
ADJUSTED BASE COST				
EXTRA ENGINEER/EXPEDITE/INSPECT COST				
FREIGHT COST ESTIMATE				
OPERATING COST ESTIMATE				
FIELD SERVICE ESTIMATE				
ALLOWANCE FOR ESTIMATED EXTRAS				
* SEE WORKSHEETS FOR BACK-UP				
TOTAL ESTIMATED PRESENT COST				

Present worth of a single future payment

$$P = S/(1 + i)^n$$

where
- P = present worth
- S = future payment/cost
- i = interest rate per period
- n = number of periods

The above can be applied to:

PROGRESS PAYMENTS, FUTURE PAYMENTS FOR SPARES, SERVICE, ETC.

Present worth of a future uniform series of payments

$$P = A[(1 + i)^n - 1]/i(1 + i)^n$$

where
- P = present worth
- A = uniform future payments/ costs at each period
- i = interest rate per period
- n = number of periods

For a uniform series of payments for n2 years starting n1 years in the future.

$$P = P1/(1 + i)^{n1}$$

where $P1 = A[(1 + i)^{n2} - 1]/ i(1 + i)^{n2}$

The above can be applied to:

FIXED ANNUAL COSTS IN FUTURE YEARS

Present worth of a future non-uniform series of payments

$$P = A1/(1 + i)^{n1} + A2/(1 + i)^{n2} + \text{etc.}$$

where
- $A1, A2$ = non-uniform future payments/costs at each period
- i = interest rate per period
- $n1, n2$ = future year

The above can be applied to:

VARIABLE ANNUAL COSTS IN FUTURE YEARS

(as may be affected by variable escalation predictions)

Figure 4—Converting future costs to present day costs.

applies to down payments, progress payments, final payments, operating costs, escalation costs, field services costs, and other costs.

Fig. 4 shows methods of converting future costs to present-day costs.

7. Pre-award meetings. Pre-award meetings should be held with the short listed vendors prior to selection. At the pre-award meeting, review any questions which have arisen during the technical and commercial evaluations. Give the vendor a final chance to confirm or clarify points contained in his bid.

Prior to the meeting, prepare an agenda. List all your questions and points of concern. Request that the vendor come to the meeting prepared to answer all items on the agenda. Following the meeting, the vendor should be given a short time to confirm in writing any additions, changes or clarifications to his technical specification and any adjustments to his price. The pre-award meeting should not allow vendors to modify their base bids—merely amplify and clarify bids already submitted.

8. Conditioning of the bids. After the complete technical and commercial review, the next step is to "condition" the bids. The conditioning process allows you to take into account intangible and other factors which might influence the vendor selection. A low bid may not necessarily be the cheapest bid. One vendor may require more engineering follow-up, another may require more extensive expediting and inspection.

Consider these points when conditioning bids: Additional engineering review required, late receipt of engineering drawings, additional expediting/inspection required, learning curve for new vendor, retraining of operators for new equipment model, interchangeability of spare parts with existing equipment, support local/national vendors, future service availability, ease of maintenance and suitability for incorporation into plant layout.

9. Vendor selection. Having gone through all the above steps, you are now ready to come to select a vendor. Normally, this is not done by one person alone. The technical and commercial evaluations will be signed off by the technical management, the commercial management and possibly the client. If you have prepared your case properly, support and approval may simply be a matter of circulating the forms for signature. On the other hand, it may be necessary to call a meeting and make a walk-through presentation of the pros and cons of the bidders and justify the basis for your recommendation.

10. Pre-commitment meeting. Once agreement and approval have been reached about the vendor, call the vendor in for a pre-commitment meeting. This meeting is to let him know that he is close to getting an order. But before you actually place the order, be sure that all points are fully understood and confirmed.

The agenda for the pre-commitment meeting would be to thoroughly review the inquiry document and specifications, all the points arising from the pre-award meeting and any subsequent correspondence and in general, to be sure that the vendor has a complete understanding of the requirements and that there are no ambiguities in the scope of his supply or his pricing arrangements. If the pre-commitment meeting is complete with no outstanding points, then the vendor may be verbally advised that he has received the order. If, however, as a result of the pre-commitment meeting there are still some points to be clarified or confirmed by the vendor, then the vendor should be required to put these in writing before he officially receives the order.

11. Awarding the order. The last step is to formally award the order. A telex or letter of commitment may be adequate initially. But this should be followed up as quickly as possible with a formal purchase order. Attach all the updated specifications, data sheets and documents originally included in the inquiry document.

Do not allow too much time to elapse between the letter or telex of commitment and the formal purchase order. In the final analysis, the formal purchase order is the contract document, binding on the vendor.

If you have done your job thoroughly, you can now sit back and feel confident. You have elected the most competent vendor on all accounts.

Chapter 24

Procurement
in Developing
Countries

	SUBJECTS	1 PREAWARD	2 INITIATION	3 ENGINEERING	4 PROCUREMENT	5 CONSTRUCTION
A	FINANCIAL/CONTRACTUAL					
B	ORGANIZATION/EXECUTION PLANNING					
C	MANAGING PEOPLE/COMMUNICATION					
D	ESTIMATING/COST CONTROL					
E	RISK ANALYSIS					
F	SCHEDULING					
G	TRACKING/TRENDING					
H	PROGRESS/PRODUCTIVITY MEASUREMENT					
I	MATERIAL MANAGEMENT		●	●	●	

W. Shillitoe

With capital expenditures increasing as they have in third-world countries (Fig. 1), procurement costs have gone up proportionally.

In the last decade we have seen a very significant escalation in the construction of major projects within the Third World developing countries for crude oil, natural gas, pipelines, oil refineries and chemical processes.

In fact, some may argue that due to the increase in volume of materials and equipment purchased, total procurement costs have escalated much *more*. Consequently, it has become even more necessary for the owner's project management team to closely control procurement. They must ensure that provision is made for the differences, in cost and in time, needed to procure material for developed and less-developed countries.

What is procurement? A definition can have many connotations. It depends upon the environment in which the word is being used. Procurement can be viewed as one of the oldest trading professions in the world, or as the modern business of buying equipment and materials for a project. Small wonder, then, that the extent of the procurement activity is not always fully appreciated in some of the world's developing areas. This often results in the owner's management team not being aware of the risks of project overruns, both in cost and time, due to inadequate procurement.

It has become accepted, in the world's developed areas, that procurement activities include the functions of 1. purchasing, 2. expediting, 3.

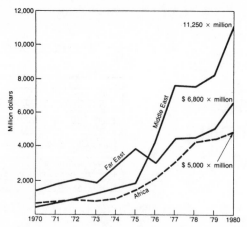

Figure 1—Estimated project capital expenditures for Africa, Far East and Middle East, 1970 to 1980. (Not adjusted for inflation.)

inspection and 4. transport. There are variations on this grouping, such as the matter of inspection. However, I will discuss inspection more fully later.

Procurement's responsibilities start with the selection of qualified and competitive vendors to supply a commodity or service. It ends with the timely delivery of that commodity, manufactured to specifications.

Relative costs. The overall costs of procurement, relative to the other principal activities of engineering design and construction, form most of the project investment. Fig. 2 shows they can run 50 to 60 percent of the total project cost depending on the progress and degree of vendor shop fabrication. However, the engineering costs are likely to be as low as 8 percent, rising to perhaps 12 percent. And construction costs will range from 28 percent to 43 percent.

Contained within these procurement costs are 1. actual material and equipment costs, 2. freight and 3. the cost of providing the procurement service.

This very broad split of project costs is not peculiar to underdeveloped areas. But, the absolute values will be somewhat different for such areas. This is due largely to both the geographic disposition of the project being developed compared to supply areas and possible political restraints. Many engineering contractors (E/Cs) have found that the procurement functions will be considerably more costly (Table 1).

All of these activities can be divided into two parts, pre-commitment and post-commitment. Here I will identify some significant differences

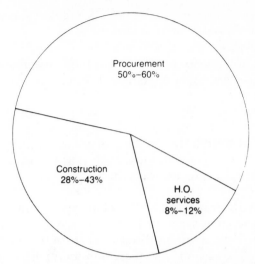

Figure 2—Procurement costs are a big slice of the project-expenditure pie.

TABLE 1—Cost of procurement geographically

Function	Typical average percentages of project material cost	
	Developed area	Developing third world
Purchasing	0.9	1.2
Expediting	1.2	1.6
Inspection	0.8	1.4
Freight	12.0	24.0
Export preparation	1.5	5.0

between procurement for developed and less-developed areas, that contribute to higher costs.

First I will discuss the pre-commitment phase, dealing primarily with the purchasing function. I will then discuss the post-commitment phase, consisting of the expediting, inspection and transport activities.

THE PRE-COMMITMENT PHASE

Purchasing. The objective of Purchasing is to buy materials and equipment at a realistic, economical price, in accordance with the design specifications, for delivery compatible with project requirements. However, these objectives are often influenced by political and statutory considerations. These need to be provided for in the

* Qualification of suppliers and the preparation of a project vendors list
* Preparation and issuing of invitations to bid
* Bid evaluation
* Commitment.

Qualification of suppliers. In the highly industrialized areas of the world, a project list of qualified suppliers is much easier to get than in a developing country. There are two principal reasons:

* There are usually available a wealth of historical data relative to vendors (e.g., production range and capacity, and past performance).
* There are available more localized market sources or trading communities (e.g., European Economic Community). This minimizes imported commodities.

However, the owner in the less-developed area is not always so well placed. So in addition to making the usual technical and production assessments of potential suppliers, he needs to take into account *where* the materials and equipment items are to be *delivered.* In the course of developing the vendors list, which results from the qualification of suppliers, the owner must answer the following questions:

* **Politics.** Is the potential supplier located in an area politically acceptable to the country where the material is to be imported? Purchase order commitments have been made with manufacturers included in a boycott list prohibiting them from trading with the country within which the purchase orders originated.

Perhaps an even greater risk is the possibility of the vendor becoming an unacceptable supplier to the country of the purchase-order originator during manufacture. For major and critical items of equipment this can result in costly remedies. An alternative source of supply may be hard to find. This can have a disastrous effect on the project schedule. Also, remember that similar restraints equally apply to sub-suppliers.

* **Logistics.** Is the location of the supplier such that extraordinary arrangements have to be made to get the materials or equipment to the proper site?

Where there are competitive alternatives, do not make purchase commitments with suppliers located in areas not serviced regularly by carriers to the country in which the project is being constructed. Where such regular transport facilities are not available (the more obvious form is by sea) deliveries to the project site are delayed. One must wait for a suitable carrier. It can even be necessary to pay freight inducement for *normal* cargo.

- **Finance.** Are locations of vendors dictated by the terms and conditions of financial aid? Some projects are supported with financial aid by one of the world's lending agencies or by other foreign governmental support. Qualification of vendors must be carried out in accordance with conditions determined by the agency controlling the credit, and within the location defined in the loan-agreement conditions.

Invitations to bid. The quality of bid proposals, and the product received, will only be as good as the quality of the enquiry packages sent to bidders. This applies to projects in *any* part of the world. But it is never more true than for projects being constructed in the less-developed areas.

Both the material or equipment specifications and quantities required will at least be adequately determined in most invitations to bid. However, many owners or E/Cs have suffered big cost overruns because of their failure to provide definite instructions to bidders. They may fail to allow for environmental conditions or project requirements peculiar to a project being constructed in a developed area. Or for that matter how many vendors have failed to complete their commitments, or even gotten themselves into serious financial difficulties, simply because of their failure to appreciate the total extent of their responsibilities? Such a situation often arises because of their failure to understand or seek clarification of the poorly written enquiry documents. It is, of course, no satisfaction to any Owner to have a Vendor who fails to complete his purchase order commitments. At the very least such a circumstance results in additional costs and at the worst can lead to an extension of the construction schedule.

Conditions. What are some of these conditions to which vendors need to give more than usual attention, and where the owner needs to define specific requirements?

To enable project commodities to be bought and delivered, the volume of paper necessary to satisfy governmental authorities and financing agencies is usually in proportion to the degree of sophistication a developing country has reached. The less developed a country is, the greater the volume of documents. These may include bid bonds, advance payment bonds, performance bonds, invoices, certificates of origin, acceptance certificates and documents necessary for transport. This is a realistic comment rather than a cynical one. Failure to recognize the realities can result in inadequate documents being prepared, failure to recognize the importing country's requirements and the need to allow for language barriers. Why, for example, should one assume that an Arab port worker in an Arabian Gulf Port can read English? I can almost hear those readers who have suffered, asking "How many port workers can read?"

All documents required to support the supply and transport of commodities for a project must be identified in the "invitations to bid" by the owner or E/C. Clearly, such definition places responsibility on the bidders to include the costs of preparing, processing and legalizing documents. These can form a significant element of bid prices.

It is a sobering thought that the processing and cost for a package of documents required to support a complete purchase order can be the same for $10,000 worth of piping as for a compressor costing $500,000. The cost of the documentation for the $10,000 purchase order is obviously disproportionate to the value of the commodity ordered.

Protection of materials. The failure of the buyer to determine the minimum package and protection requirements is, unfortunately, blatantly obvious. One can see the evidence on many construction sites. Materials and equipment are seen deteriorating in storage facilities that are often very basic and usually of only a temporary nature.

Materials are frequently shipped to a project site with inadequate protection against the climate or the sometimes indifferent handling at ports. How often have we seen the nebulous words "packed for export" without any reference to given standards of packing and protection or minimal requirements for the prevailing storage and climatic conditions?

Such lack of definition leads to the vendors trying to have a competitive bid. They may minimize their protection of materials. In extreme cases, this can result in replacement material bought at the buyer's expense.

Many commodities, particularly the lower-value items, are often purchased from relatively small suppliers, who are seldom internationally oriented and are ignorant of conditions in the country in which they are selling.

Spare parts. There are varied opinions of the levels of spare parts stock which need to be maintained to operate a plant in a less-developed location. This is understandable. Owners must develop their spare parts policies relative to the geographical location, taking into account:

- Delivery lead times
- Standardization
- Local manufacturing facilities

It is not unreasonable to expect the spare parts stock levels for an operating plant in a developing area to be about 40 percent above those normally carried in the industrialized area.

It is a little surprising that even some of the major manufacturers of equipment in the world fail to recognize the importance of having the correct spare parts at the right time in a location thousands of miles away from the place of manufacture. What can the buyer do about this?

Bidders should be instructed to provide their recommendations for spare parts, taking into account the local conditions and maintenance policy for:

- Commissioning the plant
- Operating the plant
- Vital insurance of capital spare parts

Receipt of these recommendations enables the owner to make evaluations. He can take into account spare parts policy, delivery lead times quoted, and make commitments linked with purchase-order penalty conditions for late deliveries.

The bid evaluation. Assume that the invitation-to-bid documents include clear, definitive specifications. The technical evaluations for equipment or materials to be installed in a less developed area are no more onerous than they are for similar commodities destined to an industrialized location.

However, the commercial evaluation has to take into account the indirect costs that the owner or E/C has to bear over and above the bidder's quoted prices. These can be more significant and far reaching factors. The more obvious ones are:

- Freight
- Currency
- Servicing

- **Freight.** The cost of freight is an important consideration with any bid evaluation. But the location of many projects within the developing world often limits the carriers available from certain countries. The consequences are:
- Long delivery time from the point of manufacture to the project site

- Limited ability to negotiate competitive freight rates
- Necessity for equipment to be delivered in more than one piece or even in a "knock down" condition. Result: greater construction costs.
- **Currency.** The policy of the owner determining the currency in which bidders are required to make their offer is normally decided by the finance source. Usually, however, bids will be called for against a common currency such as the U.S. dollar or in the national currency of the country in which the bidder is located. In the latter case, the risk of it being necessary to adjust the committed purchase order values as a result of countries revaluing or devaluing the currency is obviated. Where bids are called for in a common currency, however, the fluctuations between the established common currency and the vendor's own national currency become a risk factor. It has to be assessed and provided for in the evaluation.
- **Servicing.** For certain major items of equipment, the vendor's servicemen are often required for both the supervision of installation and commissioning. This can be costly enough to influence the selection of a vendor. The differential in total costs for servicemen from countries "A" and "B" can be in excess of 100 percent, excluding the indirect costs of living accommodations.

The commitment. The validity period of bids from vendors tends to be much more critical for projects in developing areas. This is because of the numerous parties interested in any financial commitments being made, particularly where a lending agency is associated with financing the project. The result can be too long a lead time from bid to commitment.

Twelve weeks for evaluation of bids and authorization to commit is about "par for the course." Bear in mind that the average maximum bid validity periods vendors will offer is 90 days. The risk of bidders opting to revise their prices and deliveries is thus high indeed.

In keeping with normal commercial practice, the purchase order defines all the usual data such as prices, deliveries, terms and conditions, etc. However, for a project in a developing area the formal issue of signed purchase orders often becomes protracted. This naturally results in a high volume of letters or telexes of intent.

The owner or E/C should issue, and the vendor receive, a letter of intent. It should be definitive relative to the agreed pricing structures, performance schedules, documentation and bonding arrangements. It is important to recognize that "letters of intent" are not legally binding in many countries. They therefore become only a document for reserving vendors' production capacity.

POST-COMMITMENT PHASE

Expediting. Sadly, suppliers don't always make their deliveries in accordance with the dates agreed to and established in the purchase order. The role of expediting, albeit costly, is thus an important one. It is an important function within procurement for all projects, regardless of where they are being constructed. But for projects in the developing countries there are several special facets of expediting worthy of comment.

Perhaps the functions most critical to a project located in such countries, apart from that of ensuring the vendors perform in accordance with their purchase order commitments, are:

- Shipping documents
- Transportation time
- Rectification of materials received at the project site damaged or incorrect in quantity or specification.

- **Shipping documents.** Most project managers responsible for major projects in the developing world have suffered from the frustration of having their project material "frozen" in the importing port. Sometimes this is within sight of the job-site. Usual reason: authorities won't clear it against unsatisfactory documentation. Often delays are for weeks or even months. With this comes the cost of demurrage, storage, uneconomic construction, possible material deterioration and late completion.

  The need to identify early the documentation required to support the delivery of materials and equipment has been dealt with earlier. The gathering of such documents can be a time-consuming task. This is particularly so when it is necessary to process certain documents (e.g., certificates of origin) through chambers of commerce for verification and through embassies for legalization.

  It is not uncommon for embassies to be located several hundred miles away from vendors. Their "turnaround time" for legalizing can be two weeks or more. So, the following up and checking for accuracy for all shipping documents is clearly an important expediting function. If not carried out, it will result in loss of all the advantages of having negotiated good material deliveries from the vendors.

- **Transportation time.** The transporting time of materials and equipment from the point of manufacture to the importing port or job-site is a very significant factor. A common error is to believe the total transport time from country "A" to country "B" is the time cargo is actually being transported. This is not the case. When determining realistic overall transportation times, take into account:

- The processing of shipping documentation
- Ancillary carriage of cargo
- Port handling limitations.

These functions can often result in the transport time of, say, three weeks, escalating to 12 weeks or more. Therefore, to accurately predict when cargo will arrive at the job site, expeditors should allow for *each* of the component activities of overall transportation time.

- **Rectification of materials.** Some material will be received in error, as a result of damage, incorrect specification where inspection was waived or incorrect quantities. Also, in many less developed areas, the risks of pilferage or deterioration due to poor storage are high. Some E/Cs are known to apply a risk factor of 2.5 over the average losses of total bulk material in a developed area to cover these hazards.

Here again the role of expediting is clear. It must ensure that material exceptions are corrected quickly. Take into account the time problems due to geographical factors, satisfying financial controls and insurance requirements.

Inspection of materials. Historically, the quality control of materials and equipment has been administered by the E/C's or owner's procurement organization. The policy being "let the people buying the commodity stand up and be counted with the end product."

In recent years this philosophy has started to change within the developed countries. This is a direct result of the emphasis now being given to statutory health and safety requirements. The Occupation Safety and Health Administration (OSHA) in the United States and the Health and Safety Act of the UK are both examples. This has resulted, to achieve unbiased quality control, in a tendency by owners and E/Cs to separate their quality control operations independently from other principal disciplines such as engineering design or procurement. However, many developing countries don't have such far-reaching laws on health and safety. Therefore, the need for autonomous quality control operation is not usually a prime consideration. Nevertheless, quality control is as important for projects in the developed areas and perhaps even more so. This is because of the inherent problem of geographical remoteness often compounded by the lack of owner engineering standards and minimal statutory requirements.

The employment of a "third party" inspection authority is usually necessary to satisfy specific design code or insurance requirements. Additionally, owners in less-developed areas, due to limited availability of trained personnel, will tend to employ "third party" organizations to supplement their own monitoring function.

Transport. The most expensive single factor, after *buying* the commodity, is the cost of freight. Freight cost within the developed world runs about 12 to 15 percent of the material value for a major project. But it is more realistic to expect freight costs of at least 18 percent rising, depending on the geographical location of the project, to 24 percent of the material value (see Fig. 3). For $50 million worth of material, the freight account can reach $10 million. This very significant project cost sometimes comes as a shock to project managers.

Transporting commodities from the point of manufacture to the site is naturally at the end of the procurement chain. Psychologically, this can and often does encourage insufficient detailed planning of project logistics early in the overall project schedule.

Owners and E/Cs will usually plan transport at the onset of a project. But often this is limited to considering the estimated total volume of cargo to be moved and determining how the largest piece of equipment can be carried to the job-site. However, it is unusual for that large heavy reactor or stripper tower to develop into a very real transport problem. After all, there are many "heavy lift" transport organizations to provide expertise. But how many projects have been delayed because of inade-

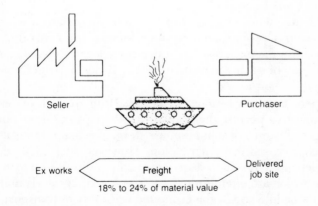

Figure 3—Typical freight costs for a process plant.

quate attention to transporting that mundane and much less newsworthy box of pipe fittings?

Poor logistical planning and administration will lead to even greater freight costs than those in Fig. 3. It is thus essential that owners and E/Cs develop a transport policy, at the onset of a project, which will achieve the most economical results compatible with the scheduled requirements.

Key questions. In developing a policy, the following questions must be asked to arrive at an economical plan.

- **Which vendor delivery terms (e.g., FOB, CIF, etc.) should be called for?** This will depend on whether a freight agreement for the total project cargo is to be developed with a single carrier or group of carriers (e.g., conference line agreement that will enable the owner to benefit from preferential freight rates in exchange for guaranteeing all cargo to the conference-named carriers. The value of the discounted rates naturally varies according to the estimated total tonnage. The greater the volume, the greater the discount). Where a project freight agreement is developed it is unlikely that there will be any economic advantage in the vendor being responsible for arranging the freight. He can offer only limited volume of cargo to the carriers.
- **What limitations are there in transporting to the project site heavy abnormally sized pieces of equipment?** An early survey of the geographical limitations as well as the transporting and handling equipment available is necessary to influence 1. the degree of manufacturer's shop fabrication versus field fabrication and 2. the engineering design (Is it necessary to have two small pressure vessels or can we transport one large one?).
- **Should the owner or E/C ship by direct negotiation with carriers or develop a project door-to-door forwarding contract?** To make this decision the owner or E/C must consider the advantages and disadvantages of each alternative. Table 2 demonstrates some of the points to be considered.
- **Are there any advantages in marshalling project materials and equipment to permit the transport?** Perhaps the most obvious advantages of cargo consolidation are those of economics resulting from ships charter and containerization. However, such methods of shipment depend to no small degree on 1. the project's importing port facilities, which are often limited and congested, 2. the flexibility of the project schedule and 3. the economic feasibility of transporting materials from numerous geographical manufacturing locations to a convenient marshalling area.

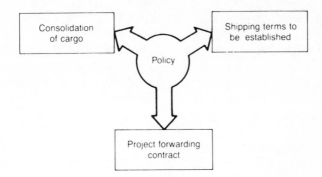

Figure 4—These shipping-policy decisions must be made before a purchase-order commitment.

TABLE 2—Shipping alternatives

Direct freight negotation	Project forwarding
Owner can negotiate cargo for multi-projects	Fixed consolidated freight rates
More favorable freight discounts	Reduces owners activities
Greater flexibility in transport arrangements	Places responsibility for all related non-sea transport on forwarder
Avoid carrier's payment of commission to agents	Takes responsibility for cargo clearance

Overall project procurement costs can be a formidable 60 percent of the total project costs. It is thus a sobering thought for both owner and E/C project managers that the quality of procurement activities determines either directly or indirectly

- The overall project schedule
- When construction work can economically commence
- The date commercial operation of the plant will commence
- The reliability of the plant.

Chapter 25

Investigate Suppliers to Maintain Quality Control

SUBJECTS	PREAWARD 1	INITIATION 2	ENGINEERING 3	PROCUREMENT 4	CONSTRUCTION 5
PROJECT PHASE					
A FINANCIAL/CONTRACTUAL					
B ORGANIZATION/EXECUTION PLANNING					
C MANAGING PEOPLE/COMMUNICATION					
D ESTIMATING/COST CONTROL					
E RISK ANALYSIS					
F SCHEDULING					
G TRACKING/TRENDING					
H PROGRESS/PRODUCTIVITY MEASUREMENT					
I MATERIAL MANAGEMENT				●	

Richard L. Clark

Astute purchasing groups within the hydrocarbon processing industry (HPI) face increasingly international competition among businesses who furnish products and services. This makes their task of selecting and qualifying suppliers more imposing than before. Buyers must choose those who can meet the requirements of quality, delivery and price from a crowded field of competitors, and eliminate those who cannot qualify.

The selection and qualification of suppliers who can consistently perform in accordance with the stated requirements of a purchase order or contract is the most difficult aspect of the purchasing function. This holds equally true whether the purchased item is a service, such as engineering; a manufactured product, such as a valve or compressor; or a fabricated item, such as a pressure vessel or piping.

Appearances. Unfortunately, suppliers are not always what they seem. Sometimes those who appear as pictures of efficiency during the sales phase of obtaining a purchase order prove to be less than competent when it comes to fulfilling the requirements. The chagrined purchasing agent may find the purchased item not acceptable to the specification, will not be delivered when it is needed or cannot be furnished for the agreed-upon price.

Many options are available to buyers when dealing with poor supplier performance. But when the troublesome purchased item just happens to be on the critical path and is adversely impacting the schedule of an entire project, the buyer has much less latitude in which to maneuver out of trouble. Project managers take a dim view of anyone or anything that threatens the continuity of the project. Buyers have to live with their decisions, but bad suppliers tend to make them live longer with those decisions which have proven to be unwise.

The 'track record.' The key to successful purchasing operations is good suppliers. However, a "good" supplier is one with a proven history of acceptable performances. Before a supplier becomes "good" he must be approved. To be approved he must be able to demonstrate capability through some form of qualification.

The qualification of suppliers is accomplished by a variety of methods as diverse as the businesses who engage in the practice. Many of the larger companies such as the engineering contractors maintain teams of specially trained and qualified auditors. These auditors evaluate vendors through surveys and audits as part of their quality assurance systems. Some companies hire contract inspection groups who have skilled professionals to conduct vendor evaluation surveys. Other companies, less technically sophisticated, consider a slick brochure and a half-hour tour capped off with a martini lunch and a lot of glad-handing as adequate qualification of a supplier.

At the other extreme is a giant engineering contractor. The E/C can be a disruptive influence by descending upon hapless suppliers with too many people for too many days, ostensibly to survey or to reaffirm (audit) that supplier's capability. Then there are the companies who never visit the supplier's facility. Instead, they accomplish their qualification objectives through the mail. They simply send the supplier a questionnaire to fill out and qualify or disqualify on that basis.

THE QUALIFICATION PROCESS

Whatever method of supplier qualification is used, the objective—to determine a supplier's suitability—remains the same. The sequence of actions in the qualification process flow, from the gathering and classification of data, through the evaluation of that data, to the determination of the supplier's suitability.

The process works something like this:

1. The supplier's sales organization asks to be considered for pending or future purchases or contracts by the buyer's company. The supplier submits to the buyer's qualification process.

2. The buyer provides the supplier with a *Supplier Data Form* (SDF) to fill out and return. The buyer's organization then makes a preliminary evaluation of the data to determine if the supplier should be disqualified,

or surveyed to verify accuracy of the data and to gain first-hand knowledge of the supplier's capabilities.

As a common alternative, the qualification process has the buyer's surveyor or survey team member record all data on the SDFs during the supplier evaluation survey. In such cases the suppliers provide information, but do not write on the forms.

3. The evaluation phase consists of comparing significant aspects of the supplier's data, first with pre-established standards of comparison, then with identical types of information taken from other competitors. The pre-established standards might be formally defined creations of company procurement procedures' national standards, codes, even federal specifications or combinations of each. In some cases, the only standard of comparison will be someone's unjustifiable and probably preconceived notion.

The supplier is qualified (approved), disqualified (disapproved) or qualified conditionally. To be qualified conditionally usually means the supplier is qualified pending the completion of some mutually agreed-upon corrective measures or the supplier has a restricted qualification to furnish only certain specified items or services.

Supplier data form. The Supplier Data Form (SDF) is at the very center of the qualification function. That hard-working document is termed supplier evaluation report, vendor survey form, supplier evaluation report, vendor information survey and others.

Two different types of SDFs are in use. At least this is true in the HPI, where variations of such forms have proven to be immensely useful to supplier-qualification efforts and are used in connection with surveys, in place of them or both.

The first and most common is the *general* type. It is designed to seek broad-ranged, routine information about the prospective supplier's operations. The intent of the general form is to provide a framework for collection of information that touches lightly upon all the more common aspects of the supplier's company. The objective of this form is to demonstrate potential and capability by describing a supplier's personnel, facilities, equipment, workload, etc. A list of the type of information in such a form is in Table 1.

The 'big picture.' The general form is usually popular with purchasing people because it conveys a concise, overall picture in terms that can be quickly understood and compared without lengthy analysis or discussion. It provides a ready reference to a supplier's capabilities. If a purchasing specialist wishes to know if "Company A" has the capability of fabricating a 180-foot-length pressure vessel, he can refer to the SDF

TABLE 1—Supplier data form information

1. Name of firm.
2. Location of firm.
3. Name of parent company (if subsidiary or division).
4. Name and location of subsidiaries or other major divisions.
5. Date organized.
6. Type of organization (corporation, partnership or proprietorship).
7. Name and title of officers, partners or owners.
8. D & B Rating.
9. Name of bank used.
10. Public accounting firm employed.
11. Description of shopload (heavy-average-light).
12. Projected six month shopload (heavy-average-light).
13. Percentage of operating capacity which is committed.
14. Percentage of orders delivered on time.
15. Backlog of unfilled orders as of _____ value is $ _____.
    date   amount
16. Principal products designed, manufactured or fabricated.
17. Current major customers or clients available for reference.
18. Percentage of business with largest customers.
19. Plant location (if different from firm location #2).
20. Plant area (sq/ft).
21. Production area (sq/ft).
22. Number of bays and dimensions.
23. Number of cranes and capacities.
24. Indoor storage area (sq/ft).
25. Outdoor storage area (sq/ft).
26. Describe facilities and equipment for nondestructive testing.
27. Describe facilities and equipment for heat treatment.
28. Describe facilities and equipment for laboratory.
29. Describe facilities and equipment for metal finishing.
30. Describe facilities and equipment for cleaning.
31. Describe facilities and equipment for welding.
32. List modes of transportation available and describe percentage of usage for each (truck, air carrier, rail, water).
33. Personnel employed by company (total number).
34. Engineering personnel.
35. Graduate engineers.
36. Registered professional engineers.
37. Drafting personnel.
38. Production personnel.
39. Production managers and supervisors.
40. Production breakdown of skills (machinists, welders, fitters assembly).
41. Quality control personnel.
42. Quality engineers.
43. Quality managers and supervisors.
44. Ratio of Production personnel to Quality personnel.
45. Nondestructive testing technicians.
46. Type of quality system (code, specification or standard).
47. Name of authorized inspection agency (if applicable).
48. Describe quantity and type of major production or fabrication equipment (attach list).
49. Describe packaging and shipping facility.
50. Name of labor union (if applicable).
51. Date for contract renewal (if applicable)
52. Date for vacation shutdown (if applicable)
53. Describe product liability suits.
54. Describe licensing agreements to produce parts or all of your product in foreign countries.
55. List government agencies or prime contractors with which your company presently has or has had contracts (within the last three years).
56. Percentage of your company's product manufactured outside of the U.S. and where.
57. List services which are subcontracted.
58. Name companies who perform source inspection at your company's facility.
59. Describe training programs.
60. Name and title of person supplying information for this form.

and check bay dimensions and crane capacities, etc. He can also find out if the supplier has heat treatment facilities, access to rail transport and many other useful pieces of information.

Specialized forms can and should be developed to meet special needs.

Quality system form. Another type of form which has proven as useful as the general form is the Quality System Form (QSF), which deals exclusively with the quality system of the potential supplier. It differs fundamentally from the first form in two respects. First, it is specific rather than general, and secondly, it probes more deeply into the supplier's organization for its information. Typical questions asked on a QSF appear in Table 2.

Actually, QSFs accomplish more than listing a supplier's capabilities. Their more ambitious role is aimed at projecting or predicting a supplier's probable performance in terms of the quality (conformance to specification) of the product. The data they seek are used to measure the supplier quality assurance/quality control/inspection system effectiveness or competence. The results of such measurements are sometimes referred to as the *Supplier Quality Profile.* Some purchasing people concede a direct correlation between a highly-rated quality system and a high-quality product; others do not.

The purchaser must be able to accurately estimate the number of man-hours required to inspect a specific product at the facility of a particular supplier. Ability to secure contracts and to execute them profitably depends upon it.

Source inspection. When estimating the time required to perform source inspection assignments, several factors must be considered. First, there is the relative efficiency of the inspector. Next, comes the extent or scope of inspection required, then the quantity and nature (complexity) of the item(s) to be inspected and, finally, the quality competence of the supplier.

The first three factors present no obstacle to making an estimate because the information would, in each case, be at hand. For instance, the performance level of the inspector involved would surely be known. The extent of inspection required, together with the quantity and relative complexity of the item to be inspected, can be determined from drawings, specifications, standards, purchase orders and orally specified requirements. Only the quality competence of the supplier stands in the way of a reasonably accurate estimate of the time required to complete an inspection assignment.

The quality (conformance to specification) of a finished product is roughly proportional to the effectiveness of the QA/QC-Inspection sys-

TABLE 2—Quality system

1. Indicate the specification from which your quality system was derived or to which it most nearly conforms. (List specific ones).
2. Is your company's quality system described in a manual?
3. Will you provide a copy of the manual to us?
4. Are written procedures available to control the performance of the following activities? (List the activity, cite the procedure and state person or authority who approved it).
5. Is there a report form on which to record nonconformities?
6. Does that form provide space to report information on Discrepant characteristics, Cause of discrepancy, Applicable standards, Corrective action, Drawing number, Part number, Item number, Shop order, Purchase order, Names of cognizant persons, Signatures of decision makers, Significant dates, Sequentially numbered and Corrective action statement?
7. Write the name and title of the person who developed the written quality system manual and the name of the person who is responsible for revising manual now.
8. Indicate date when quality system was initially established.
9. Indicate date when quality system manual was last revised.
10. Indicate the names of companies who have surveyed and approved your quality system.
11. Indicate the name and company title of the person who directs the quality system. (For the purposes of this survey form, we shall refer to the person heading the quality system as the (QSD) quality system director.)
12. Does the quality system director hold other titles and have duties and responsibilities in addition to those pertaining to the quality related functions?
13. Should the answer to No. 12 be affirmative, please list the titles, duties and responsibilities.
14. How long has the quality system director been in charge of the quality system? Date?
15. What position did this person hold prior to assignment as quality system director? Indicate title of position.
16. Is the quality system director qualified for the present position by experience? If answer is affirmative, list the type and extent of qualifying experience.
17. Is the quality system director qualified for the present position by means of special training? If answer is affirmative, list type and extent of qualifying training.
18. Indicate the Professional Technical Societies of which the QSD is a member.
19. Indicate the volumes, codes or standards presently available in the Quality System Department area. (List each, specifically).
20. Indicate name and title of person to whom the QSD reports.
21. Indicate name and title of person who signs QSD's paycheck.
22. Based upon the information contained in No. 13, does the QSD have sufficient authority and organization freedom to successfully resist the pressures of production when making quality related judgments?
23 Does the Quality Department have the authority and responsibility to review and approve all drawings, shop orders, procedures and instructions for inclusion of quality requirements?
24. Are sign-off spaces provided on the above mentioned documents for Quality Department verifications?
25. Are all purchase orders for code materials reviewed and approved by the Quality Department prior to release to vendors? Is a sign-off required?
26. Are all code materials inspected by Q.C. upon receipt, and are material test reports compared to the material specifications in ASME section II prior to release of materials from receiving inspection? Is a sign-off provided?
27. Are nonconforming materials or items clearly identified? or segregated?
28. If the answer to No. 27 is affirmative, how are the nonconforming materials and items identified or segregated?
29. Are reports prepared to indicate the results of inspections ____, tests ____, NDT ____ and heat treatments ____?
30. Are all welders and procedures qualified in accordance with ASME BVP code section IX?
31. Indicate the name and title of the person who is responsible for maintenance of PQR's, WPS's and WQR's.
32. What types of NDT are performed?
33. Indicate the number of qualified SNT-TC-1A levels Is, IIs and IIIs employed by your organization for liquid penetrant, magnetic particle, ultrasonic, radiography, eddy current, leak testing, and other.
34. What is the name of the person who performs the level III function for your organization?
35. Is this person qualified to level III by virtue of ASNT examination?
36. Does your company have a written procedure for the training and qualification of NDT personnel?
37. Who in your organization has the responsibility for writing heat treatment procedures and surveillance of HT activities?

tem of the manufacturer or fabricator. We find that good products usually come from good quality systems and the reverse is equally true.

Nonconformance. It is less expensive to inspect good items because nonconforming items require substantially more time to deal with than do conforming ones. This is because the rejection process usually triggers reactions that cause the involvement of additional client and supplier personnel. They must spend time and energy to investigate, communicate, discuss, conclude and, hopefully, solve the problem created by the rejection of the nonconforming item(s).

Communications from such activities are usually channeled through the inspector during the time-consuming moves toward a solution. For these, and other reasons, products which conform to the specification require less supplier surveillance effort than do the products of ineffectively controlled systems. *Product quality is a direct reflection of the quality system effectiveness.*

There are various ways to get a reading on the quality competence of the supplier. Though the HPI does not subscribe to the use of a data bank system such as CASE (aerospace-nuclear), SPEAR (automobile industry GM) or IDEP (U.S. government) for collection of supplier data, there is a surprising amount of free exchange of information between inspectors of various organizations.

Camaraderie. There seems to exist among some inspectors a tacit obligation to warn their opposite number (even competitors) about suppliers who practice poor or deceitful quality practices. Suppliers who are unaware of this would do well to become so, because reputations for quality are quickly lost, but slowly regained. The information exchanged between inspectors is usually succinct, informal oral comments about the strong points or the shortcomings of a supplier's quality system. Such commentaries seldom contain enough detailed information to use without additional support information.

When it is not practical to conduct a survey, and when all other sources for obtaining information have been exhausted, there is still an alternative action that can sometimes yield sufficient data to develop a supplier quality profile. This is, of course, the *Quality System Form.*

Quality system. A fabricator or manufacturer quality system consists of four parts:

First, there is the system's manual or written description which usually outlines the framework and sets the tone for the rest of the parts.

Next, is the system's people—those who try to translate the system's written directives into controlled actions.

Third, there is the paperwork generated as a byproduct of the system in the form of working documents and objective evidence.

The fourth part of the system is the physical facilities and equipment which support the system.

Each part of the quality system has to be dealt with in the QSF, if the form is to provide a clear supplier-quality profile.

QS QUESTIONS

The first question we would ask a company is what kind of quality system they have. Quality systems are usually characterized by the code, standard or specification from which they are derived, or to which they most nearly conform. A variety of systems are in use that span a wide range of technological effort. There is, for example the MIL-I-45208A which establishes the criteria for a relatively uncomplicated inspection system. Then there is the ANSI/ASME Boiler and Pressure Vessel Code which, through its various sections, defines quality system requirements for the makers of power boilers, valves, pressure vessels and nuclear power plant components. Many other such codes, standards and recommended practices apply as well.

Quality systems range from the less to the more complicated. A complex quality system such as one of aerospace or nuclear orientation presupposes a formal adequately documented, well budgeted and equipped program administered by quality professionals.

Less complex systems are much more common. They extend from the very good to those which lack real substance. Then there are the facades. These are to give an *impression* of competence by exhibiting the external trappings of a QA/QC-Inspection system. The latter creates serious problems for purchasers.

Written documentation? Next, we would wish to know if the quality system is described in a written form. The manual or procedure can be valuable for various reasons. It states the policy, explains the system, diagrams the areas of personnel responsibility and describes the functions used to control quality of the finished product and to provide objective evidence of that control.

Conversely, systems not reduced to writing, are subject to individual interpretation. This creates variations that cannot be understood in the same way by all participants. Therefore, they cannot be adequately verified by a surveyor.

Quality systems accustomed to evaluation by outside sources use written procedures and/or manuals to aid *understanding*. A copy of the manual can be obtained and critiqued prior to visiting the supplier to verify implementation. This makes a shorter visit with less disruption of the supplier's routine.

We always seek a copy of the system's manual or other documentation. However, some company policies prevent this. In such instances, the document's parentage may be questionable. Some other companies have policies which prevent them from approving the quality systems of suppliers which refuse to provide them with copies of manuals.

Quality procedures can be highly revealing indicators of quality system effectiveness. They serve as extensions of the quality system description (manual) by refining and augmenting its directives into working documents. These documents have sufficient detail and definition to prescribe with technical accuracy the step-by-step instructions used to control quality. Clear and precise procedures are among the more evident byproducts of a vital, effective quality system.

Various types of quality related procedures are used in the manufacturing and fabrication of HPI equipment. Some of these follow:

1. Inspection
2. Dimensional measurement
3. Testing (functional, pressure, metallurgical)
4. Welding
5. Nondestructive testing
6. Heat treatment
7. Coating
8. Cleaning
9. Packaging
10. Painting

Any document or form used to record nonconformities is important. Because the control of quality is essentially the control of conditions adverse to quality, the most critical functions of the system are those dealing with nonconformities. All other quality activities by comparison are ancillary to those which detect, report, correct and prevent recurrence of conditions adverse to quality.

Nonconformity documents are known by titles such as Discrepancy Reports, Rejection Reports, Nonconformance Reports and Material Review Actions.

Such a form should address every significant aspect of the nonconformity such as description, area of violation (drawing, specification, standard, code, etc.), cause and sphere of responsibility. Then, there should be adequate space to describe the disposition or corrective action as well as signature blanks for the decision makers who agree to the final course of action.

Naturally, such a form would include spaces for all significant dates and identification data such as drawing number, part number, item number, shop order, purchase order number and the names of persons. It should be sequentially serialized as well.

The degree of skill with which nonconformance reports are employed in a quality system directly reflects not only the system efficacy, but also is quite indicative of its integrity.

Reports. The results of certain critical activities should be documented in the form of reports of certificates. Report formats vary widely. Usually they describe the results, the method by which they were achieved, the date when they were accomplished, the signature(s) of the certifier(s) and, if required, witnesses as well. Examples of some quality related activities for which reports or certifications should be prepared in support of are:

1. Manufacturer's data
2. Certificate of compliance
3. Material test
4. Nondestructive test
5. Pressure and/or functional test
6. Heat treatment
7. Calibration
8. Inspection

We include a section on reports and certifications. The readiness of and organization to certify the results of its efforts often mirrors the amount of pride and confidence the organization has in its work, and therefore in its technical competence.

Customer input. Insight into a company's quality system competence can sometimes be provided by their customers. It is usually fair to assume that a company who sells to customers of a high order of technical sophistication probably has previously been qualified by surveys and audits to the approved supplier list of the customers.

The abilities of the person who directs the Quality System, plus the comparative strength of that position in relation to the rest of the supplier's organization, is a key factor in the performance of the Quality System. Accordingly, the form should inquire about the person's qualifications and the relative power of the position.

Supplier survey forms are a simple, inexpensive mechanism to inform us about potential suppliers by providing information about their capabilities and probable level of performance.

SUBJECT-PROJECT PHASE MATRIX

SUBJECTS	1 PREAWARD	2 INITIATION	3 ENGINEERING	4 PROCUREMENT	5 CONSTRUCTION
A FINANCIAL/CONTRACTUAL					
B ORGANIZATION/EXECUTION PLANNING					
C MANAGING PEOPLE/COMMUNICATION					
D ESTIMATING/COST CONTROL					
E RISK ANALYSIS					
F SCHEDULING					
G TRACKING/TRENDING					
H PROGRESS/PRODUCTIVITY MEASUREMENT					
I MATERIAL MANAGEMENT				●	

Chapter 26

How to Prepare Inspection Reports

Richard L. Clark

Purchasers of equipment and materials for the hydrocarbon processing industry can realize a greater value for their source inspection dollars by improving the preparation and use of inspection reports.

Source inspection is a common part of the purchasing process, especially where expensive or critical items are involved. Companies which require the source inspection of purchased equipment or materials employ their own inspectors or contract the work to third party inspection services. In either case, inspection reports are prepared.

A description. An inspection report is a description of conditions observed, and in some cases formally witnessed, during the performance of inspections, examinations, tests and various quality related activities conducted in accordance with the specifications and requirements of the purchase order. Inspection reports are prepared by inspectors during the course of, and at the conclusion of, inspection assignments.

The inspection report is the essence of an inspection assignment. It survives as a record long after the assignment has been completed. It remains as tangible evidence of all that transpired during the course of the inspection visit. It is capable of serving many useful purposes if it is properly prepared and used.

Inspection assignments are usually conducted at the location of manufacture or at some other site where the purchaser's inspector can compare the seller's product against the requirements of the procurement documents. His goal is to determine if the product is suitable to the purchaser's needs.

351

The inspector. The prime function of a source inspector is to decide, by comparing product with specification, if the product will meet the end use requirements of the purchaser he serves. To effectively make this judgement, he must be competent in a range of specialties relating to the purchased product. Competent mechanical inspectors can often demonstrate expertise from a diverse spectrum of disciplines such as metallurgy, mechanics, welding, metrology, physics, engineering and non-destructive testing.

Specialized knowledge and experience is vital to an inspector. His conclusions and decisions are sometimes so controversial that he assumes an adversary role and must explain his conclusions and defend his decisions. Obviously, since the decisions on whether to accept or reject a product can result in far reaching consequences, it is only natural to assume that his report reflects a degree of care and detail worthy of a professional involved in critical work.

Unfortunately, this is not always the case. Some inspection reports are neither prepared nor used to best advantage. Their potential value is often unrecognized and is, therefore, underused.

Report criteria varied. Companies who employ or contract the services of inspectors have taken various approaches to the task of inspection report preparation. The type and quality of inspection reports are as varied as the individuals who write them because there is no standard available to compare them with.

Some contract inspection services edit and rewrite their inspectors' reports. They do this to project an image of professionalism to their clients. They also aim to accomplish continuity and standardization. This practice relies heavily upon the exact translation of sufficient and accurate information. It is somewhat inefficient and, depending upon the degree of editorial enhancement involved, subject to dangerous inaccuracies.

Printed forms. Many companies use a basic printed form designed to simplify the report writing process by eliminating descriptive options. The forms usually consist of series of blanks, boxes and squares to be filled in and checked off by the inspector. These provide a standardized document which can be easily prepared and interpreted. Such forms are widely used and are popular due to their simplicity.

Understandably, the brevity and compact format which characterizes the prepared forms are the very factors which limit their effectiveness. They restrict the amount of information and discourage both narrative and graphic support elements of the report.

ELEMENTS OF A GOOD REPORT

Certain basic elements of information are essential to the make-up of a good inspection report. Critiques of substandard reports usually reveal omission of one or more of those elements. Poor inspection reports are quite often characterized by a *lack* of the following:

1. Sufficient information
2. Adequate organization
3. Clarity of expression
4. Legibility
5. Photographs
6. Sketches

Lack of sufficient information, photographs and sketches probably is the most common failing of otherwise good reports. The importance of the latter two elements cannot be over-emphasized.

Photographs convey more information in less space than either drawn or written material. Neither words nor sketches can adequately communicate certain types of information as well as photographs. For this reason photos should be considered as essential to inspection reports.

Sketches or drawings also have their place in the inspection report. Both can be useful and instructive in cases where ideas or concepts rather than physical objects are being discussed or described.

Guidelines. There is a standard against which inspection reports can be compared. It was developed by the Quality Division of the C. A. Rubio Co. as a training tool for instruction of inspectors. The *Guidelines For Inspection Report Preparation* (Table 1) were later converted into a checklist form which was used to evaluate and grade inspection reports.

The guidelines are composed of 20 points of criteria representing elements of information considered to be essential to the make-up of an effective inspection report. Experience gained through years of interpretation and analysis contributed to the development of the guidelines. They have proven their worth as a standard against which to measure the effectiveness of inspectors.

A rating system used to grade inspection reports was based upon the 20 points of criteria of the guidelines. By allowing 5 percent for each criterion point that is complied with, the following arbitrary rating scale evolved:

100–85 Excellent
84–70 Good
69–50 Average
49–0   Poor

Guidelines for inspection report preparation

1. **Name and address of the company and location where the inspection assignment is conducted.**

   Example: Anonymous Compressor Company
   42934 Commercial Drive
   Bldg. 17, Area 20
   Indianapolis, Indiana 77016

2. **Complete nomenclatural designation of the object of the inspection assignment.**

   Example: ACC Model 429 Three Stage
   Centrifugal Turbine Drive
   Air Compressor Drawing Number 4-2900

3. **Names and titles of supplier/vendor personnel from initial contact through all further stages of the assignment.**

   Example: John Phillips
   Applications Engineer

   Adam Stevenson
   Quality Control Manager

   Phil Stockton
   NDE Supervisor

   Joe Clark
   Testing Technician

   Tom Silver
   Testing Engineer

   Mary Lincoln
   Data Coordinator

4. **Start and finish data of the inspection and approximate time of each sequential aspect or stage encountered.**

   Example: *29th April 1977*
   08:00 Preinspection Conference
   08:45 Welding
   10:20 Pressure Testing
   01:30 Nondestructive Examination
   03:40 Documentation Gathering

   30th April 1977
   08:30 Pretest Meeting
   09:00 Check of Test Set-Up & Calibration
   10:00 Performance Test
   04:00 Tabulation of Test Results
   04:30 Dimension Inspection

   1st May 1977
   08:30 Surface Preparation: Painting
   11:00 Review and Verification of
   Documents
   01:00 Export Crating: Marking

5. **Control numbers of purchaser and supplier/vendor.**

   Example: Nondescript Engineering Co.
   P. O. 528-38-2284
   Anonymous Compressor Company
   Sales Order No. 7-3323-5F
   Anonymous Compressor
   Work Order No. 7-3323-100

6. **Title and number of drawings, specifications, standards codes, procedures and related documents.**

   Example: ACC Assembly Drawing
   No. 4-2900
   N. E. Specification
   12-376
   ASME Boiler and Pressure Vessel Code
   Sections V, VIII and IX
   American Society for Nondestructive
   Testing
   ASNT-TC-1A

7. **Brand name, model and serial number of measuring, testing and welding equipment.**

   Examples: 1. Welding Machines
   2. Measuring Tools (Micrometers, Vernier
   Calipers, Thickness Testers, etc.)

   3. Nondestructive Test Equipment
   4. Measurement Indicators and Instruments (Gages, Thermometers, Manometers, Wattmeters, Tachometers, etc.)
   5. Furnace Recorders

8. **Calibration status and schedule of items listed in item 7 above.**

9. **Personnel qualifications of technical specialists.**

   Example: John Brown
   Welding Operator
   ASME Code Section IX

   Tom Smith
   Radiograph Interpreter
   ASNT-TC-1A Level II

10. **Type of QA/QC System (Manual) and related standard.**

    Example: 1. ASME Code 1, II, V or VII
    2. MIL-T-45208A
    3. MIL-Q-9858A
    4. NHB 5300.4
    5. NRC 10 CFR 50
    6. ANSI N 45.2
    7. Others

11. **Quality program rating assessment and comment.**

    Examples: Good + Explanation
    Avg. + Explanation
    Poor + Explanation

12. **Workmanship rating assessment and comment.**

    Examples: Good + Explanation
    Avg. + Explanation
    Poor + Explanation

13. **Attitude and cooperation rating assessment and comment.**

    Examples: Good + Explanation
    Avg. + Explanation
    Poor + Explanation

14. **Indexed list of supplier/vendor supporting documentation.**

    Examples: 1. Material Test Reports
    2. Pressure Test Reports
    3. Performance Test Reports
    4. NDE Test Reports
    5. Certificates of Compliance
    6. Related Communications
    7. Drawings
    8. Manuals Catalogs etc.

15. **Photographs complete with narrative numbers for easy reference.**

    Example (Figures to appear with Part 2 of this article, March 1978 issue, HP).

16. **List all significant aspects which were *not* witnessed and provided explanation.**

17. **Sketches or illustrations used to enhance or clarify written descriptions.**

    Example (Figures to appear with Part 2 of this article, March 1978 issue, HP).

18. **Opening statement describing purpose of inspection assignment and classification as initial, interim or final report type.**

19. **Body of text containing complete description of each significant sequential aspect or stage of the inspection assignment including adequate elaboration upon each incidence or condition adverse to quality with the resultant resolution by corrective action, rejection or hold status.**

20. **Closing statement covering the inspector's decision to accept, conditionally accept, place on hold or reject the object of the inspection.**

Benefits. Many useful benefits can be derived from a well written inspection report. Review and analysis of these documents can contribute significantly to many related areas of activity.

Information gleaned from inspection reports can add measurably toward a more informed purchasing department. In addition to data dealing specifically with the product being inspected, the report will provide insight relating to the seller's equipment, facilities, quality system, workmanship, efficiency and attitude. Such information can be used to develop an accurate vendor/supplier profile upon which to base future purchasing decisions.

Engineering, operations, maintenance and other personnel can make good use of the functional and performance data from inspection reports, drawings, O & M manuals and various other types of supporting documentation. These all contain valuable technical data in support of the purchased product.

Weights, measurements, design calculations, storage and handling instructions, protective coating removal and others are but a few of the types of information contained within inspection reports. All such information can be of assistance to the purchaser.

Do it right. Companies pay well to have their purchased items inspected. They deserve a satisfactory effort in return. Since the work has to be done in any case, why not do it right? A set of guidelines such as those in this article can serve as a standard of comparison with which to evaluate and improve your inspection reporting system.

An accurate, thorough inspection report can save a purchaser a great deal of money because usually such reports are for *critical* materials or equipment. Often, safety factors are involved in the equipment's operation. An entire plant's operational reliability can be at stake. Sometimes, too, the report is needed as "evidence" in a contractual dispute with the vendor or, for that matter, any other relevant confrontation or "proof" situation. The report shows the care and accuracy with which material or equipment is evaluated. It alone attests to what went on during an inspection.

Three parts. The well conceived and conducted inspection assignment has three elements:

• Preparation
• Execution
• Reporting.

Each element, or phase, is a vital part of the assignment. But only one phase—the report—reflects the *effectiveness* of the other two. For this reason, report preparation should get ample consideration in programs aimed at training of inspectors.

Competent inspectors should be well instructed in the essentials of report preparation, during their training. They should be accomplished inspectors *first*—but the effectiveness of their efforts will be partially measured by their ability to communicate in *report form*.

Quality. The variety and quality of inspection reports differs widely. Clients who contract to have their purchases inspected receive reports which range from hand-written one-liners, through the checklist type form, to many pages of details and verbiage.

Rating. The essence of maintaining reports at a high level of quality is *rating*. Inspectors' reports must be evaluated. The report model, and its grading system as discussed in this series of articles, is based on how thoroughly the report covers material in Fig. 1.

An example. What does a finished report using the system described here look like? How is it rated? To answer these questions, I fabricated an example report (below). It uses fictitious equipment and fictitious companies. But otherwise, it is true to form in incorporating the elements of a good report.

This mock report was graded. It got 78 percent (good). The figure was determined by combining percentages for each criterion point complied with, according to the following breakdown:

1. −5%	11. −5%
2. −5	12. −5
3. −3	13. −5
4. −5	14. −5
5. −2	15. −0
6. −5	16. −0
7. −5	17. −0
8. −3	18. −5
9. −5	19. −5
10. −5	20. −5

Report's format. The report should be prepared on a form similiar to the one condensed (in size) in Fig. 2. The contents, typed on that form, would unfold as in the following make-believe example. An actual report, however, would be embellished with ample photographs, diagrams and other support materials. This is in line with the trite but true maxim that "a picture is worth a thousand words."

Inspection Report Rating Checklist

Inspector_____   Location_____

Inspection Report No _____   Client_____

Supplier_____   Date_____

(1) Name, address, & location where the inspection assignment is conducted. %	(12) Workmanship rating assessment & comment. %
(2) Complete nomenclatural designation of the object of the inspection assignment. %	(13) Attitude & cooperation rating assessment & comment. %
	(14) Indexed list of supplier/vendor supporting documentation. %
(3) Names & titles of supplier/vendor personnel from initial contact through all further stages of the assignment. %	(15) Photographs complete with narrative numbered for easy reference. %
(4) Start & finish date of inspection & approximate time of each sequential aspect of stage encountered. %	(16) List all significant aspects which were *not* witnessed & provide explanation. %
(5) Control numbers of purchaser & supplier/vendor. %	(17) Sketches or illustrations used to enhance or clarify written descriptions. %
(6) Title, number, & revision of drawings, specifications, standards, codes procedures & related documents. %	(18) Opening statement describing purpose of inspection assignment & classification as initial interim or final report type. %
(7) Brand name, model & serial number of measuring, testing, & welding equipment. %	(19) Body of text contains complete description of each significant sequential aspect or stage of the inspection assignment including adequate elaboration upon each incidence or condition adverse to quality with resultant resolution by corrective action, rejection, or holding status. %
(8) Calibration status & schedule of items listed in item #7 above. %	
(9) Personnel qualifications of technical specialists. %	
(10) Type of QA/QC system (manual) & related standard. %	(20) Closing statement covering the inspector's decision to accept, conditionally accept, place on hold, or reject the object of the inspection. %
(11) Quality program rating assessment & comment. %	
Total %	Total %

Signature_____   Date_____

Figure 1—This form abbreviates items that appeared in the guidelines for inspection report preparation. It is used to record a report's grade.

Inspection Report

Supplier:	Date:	
Location:	Job no.:	Shop no.:
Individual contacted:	Item:	

Inspector's signature	Date	Supervisor	Date	Client	Date

Figure 2—This form, usually on an 8½ × 11-inch format, is used for the report. Material should be neatly typed. For an example of contents of this form, see the heading "Inspection Report" in the text.

INSPECTION REPORT

Supplier: HCP Valve Co.
Client: Hydrocar
Location: 2600 So. Industrial Drive
P.O. No. 28-4176-42D
Houston, Texas 77099
Item: 3-1276-1 Relief Valves

DEC. 3, 1977

- **Objective of this assignment** is to perform the inspection function (initial and final) upon four (4) safety relief valves manufactured and tested by the HCP Valve Co. in Houston and purchased by our client, Hydrocar, on Purchase Order 28-4176-42D. The items are flanged, high pressure, metal seated, 1 inch × 2 inches, ammonia service, relief valves according to HCP Drawing 3-1276-1.
- **08:20—Pre-inspection meeting** was held in the quality assurance manager's office to become acquainted, clarify the current status of the valve parts and discuss testing schedule sequence. At this time, I provided the Q. A. manager, Mr. Adams, with a list of documents to be in my possession prior to release for shipment of the valves.
  The following persons attended:
  1. J. P. Jones—Guardian Inspection Representative
  2. Sam Adams—HCP Valve Co. Q.A. Manager
  3. T. Paine—HCP Valve Co. Testing Supervisor.
- **10:20—The welding process,** as practiced at HCP, is well directed. Proficiency of welding personnel together with the correctness of the documentation shows they have effective management.
  Work areas are clean and well lighted.
  Equipment, including the electrode stabilizing ovens, is maintained and punctually calibrated.
  Welder and weld procedure qualifications (ASME Code Section IX) are in order. Material test reports for the body (3-2103-1), flange (1″—1500#RTJ) and weld metal (3/32 ER 309) were checked against ASME Code Section II for verfication of chemical and mechanical requirements of the material specification.
  The requirements of HPC welding procedure 2-2104 B approved by Guardian on 11/1/77 were systematically complied with. This was via sequence beginning with a preweld inspection of cleanliness and edge preparation, to welding with the MIG process, slow cooling to ambient temperature, then finally to weld area surface cleaning and preparation for NDE.

- **13:05—Nondestructive examinations** here are conducted in a controlled atmosphere with a cooled and filtered air supply, a deionized water system and fine equipment housed in a highly suitable environment.

The paperwork is well conceived and functional: records are maintained and easily available.

The Level III Examiner has suitably documented qualifications. So do the other NDE personnel. They have all been trained, examined and qualified according to the recommended practice supplements of the American Society for Nondestructive Testing.

- **Verification of testing prerequisites** included:

1. Visual inspection of equipment—magnablitz penetrant unit type ZA-29E, serial number 75020

2. Pre-test run using a control specimen ($3/8''$ × $2''$ × $2''$ aluminum block cracked at cold water quench from 975°F temperature) to check the over-all performance of the penetrant material system

3. Confirm suitable intensity of two (3650 angstrom unit) black lights by use of a zutz light meter (un-calibrated)

4. Review penetrant materials test report for halogen and sulfur content

5. Review deionized water certification for determination of sulfur and halogen content

6. Verify penetrant procedure number, revision and approval status.

All prerequisites for testing have been complied with and testing will commence.

Parts (body weldment #3-2105-G) were allowed to dry and cool to room temperature after withdrawal from the vapor degreaser (trichloroethylene), which was the final action of the cleaning phase.

- **02:00—Penetrant examination was conducted** in accordance with the procedure which called for testing the fluorescent post-emulsifying method. Parts were dipped in ZA-44X penetrant at 68°F and allowed to dwell for 25 minutes. Emulsifier (TB-45X) was applied by dipping method and covered the surface for a three-minute period. A three-minute rinsing was accomplished in the ZA-29-E automatic rotary wash and verified by black light examination. Drying was accomplished in a thermostatically controlled (175°F) recirculating hot air dryer until parts were visually dry. The developer (YZ-48E) dry type was applied to parts with powder gun and allowed to cover surface of the parts for 23 minutes. Examinations conducted by Level II T. Jefferson and I disclosed two nonrelevant indications. Both were easily removed by wire brushing. The parts are considered acceptable. An NDE report to that effect will be prepared and will so state.

- 04:00—The 3-2105-G body weldments, following another cleaning in the degreaser, were moved to the pressure testing area.

HCP's drawing 3-429-34 and our specifications call for pressure testing (hydrostatic) the body weldment at 3,000 psig (1½ times the design pressure) to confirm the structural integrity of the cast body and the weld.

The weldment inlet flange is attached with studs and nuts to a testing flange (1500 #RTJ). It is sealed by means of a ring seated in the ring joints of the weldment and the test flange. At the same time a 300 #RF blind flange was attached to the outlet. The complete arrangement is then screwed onto the test stand. At this time, the object was filled with deionized water (filter warning light was noted). The adjusting screw was installed to plug up the last opening.

Pressure was applied and brought up to 3,000 psig. A Southerland pressure gauge type 4170, serial number 213, was used for the test. It was noted (by information contained on the sticker) to be in the third week of a six-week calibration interval. Pressure was held for the required 10 minutes. No leaks, pressure drops or other adverse conditions occurred. Body weldments were stamped near nameplate boss "Hydro 3000" and "PT" to indicate the test was successful.

A test report will be prepared for the signatures of the test technician and myself.

DEC. 4, 1977

- 08:30—Body weldments were united with the internal parts and assembled in a combined assembly and testing section. Assembly techniques were routine except for the careful handling of the metal seats. These have a lapped finish on the seating area of one lightband. All mating, moving or threaded parts were articulated and observed.
- 09:40—Functional testing began as the fully assembled valves (3-1276-1) were provided with inlet testing flanges (1500 #RTJ) and mounted on the function test stand. Type 4170 Southerland pressure gauge, serial number 167, (calibrated last week) was used.

Functional testing was conducted in accordance with HCP procedure, 2-2118 for functional testing of metal seated safety relief valves.

Nameplates were attached to the valves prior to final visual and dimensional inspection.

Outline dimensions were recorded and flange faces were checked for possible damage during testing prior to attachment of protective flange covers.

- 02:00—In accordance with the requirement of our purchase order packaging procedure, the valves were heat sealed in polyethylene sheet, after dessicant and humidity indicators were enclosed. They were then wrapped in polyurethane foam secured by filament tape. Each valve is packed between three layers of quilted paper. Each is cradled and braced inside individually constructed boxes of 1″ No. 1 white pine.

Marking instructions were complied with and verified. Three copies of the data package shall be included inside one of the four crates.

- **03:30—Final data** were collected for the required documentation package and verified against the various references such as the ASME code. ASTM standards, AWS handbook, ASNT supplements, ANSI and various others. The following items of data were verified and listed as exhibits with this report:

  1. Foundry material test report for cast (CF8M) bodies—Exhibit A
  2. Material test report for forged stainless inlet flanges—Exhibit B
  3. Material test report for weld filler metal—Exhibit C
  4. NDE report—Exhibit D
  5. Hydrostatic test report — Exhibit E
  6. Function test report—Exhibit F
  7. Assembly or as-build drawing—Exhibit G
  8. Certificate of compliance—Exhibit H
  9. Spare parts list—Exhibit I
  10. Quality assurance manual—Exhibit J.

  The quality assurance program at HCP is really excellent, probably because they have an N-stamp (ASME Section III Nuclear). The quality system manual indicates a program equal to or surpassing the level of control or ASME Section I or VIII, or MIL-9858A.

  Workmanship rating ranges from good to excellent. They have a lot of fine equipment here. Skilled technicians—within the framework of a topnotch quality system—turn out a good product.

  The people at HCP were friendly and cooperative. Their morale seems to be high. This may be due to a higher than usual sense of pride in their work.

- **04:00—Determination complete.** The four 3-1276-1 safety relief valves have been manufactured and tested in accordance with specifications and requirements of the purchase order. They are therefore acceptable and shall be released for shipment to the site.

An inspection report such as the one simulated above really depicts the inspector who prepared it and the organization he represents. In some ways it can reflect an example of the inspector's character and competence by indicating how much importance he attaches to his work. The degree of detail with which he records his efforts is a measure of this importance.

Index